The Decaying American Dream

"Are we ready to accept a permanent condition of inadequate educational facilities and congested housing while we watch a once beautiful America being transformed into a demented wasteland? Are we content with roads upon roads upon roads that go nowhere—because there is no place to go? Do we glory in wading in wastes? Do we want increasing noise and din, mountains of junk on our horizons in place of mountains and trees? Do human dignity and privacy mean nothing to us . . ."

HAVE WE BECOME A NATION OF PEOPLE WHO WOULD SELL THE SUNSET IF SOMEONE WOULD PUT A PRICE ON IT?

These are the searching questions the Rienows pose in this angry, shocking book. MOMENT IN THE SUN is their item-by-item presentation of the ways in which we have ignored ecological principles and abused our environment under the pressures of overpopulation and a creed of exploitation. The results of our greed are all around us: the prehistoric redwoods are being sacrificed to fence tiny housing development yards, Lake Erie is a gummy morass, the Hudson is a sewer, our wildlife is vanishing, our air is noxious, and we suffer from hostilities induced by noise and overcrowding.

No longer c   of A MOMENT I   ot only guarante   ry now—*but for*

D1081741

Rave Reviews
"Moment in the Sun"

Moment in the Sun

Robert Rienow and
Leona Train Rienow

*A Report on the Deteriorating Quality
of the American Environment*

BALLANTINE BOOKS   •   NEW YORK

This edition published by arrangement with
The Dial Press

Designed by Slavomir Dratewka

First Printing: September, 1969
Second Printing: February, 1970
Third Printing: March, 1970
Fourth Printing: March, 1970
Fifth Printing: April, 1970
Sixth Printing: May, 1970

Printed in the United States of America

Ballantine Books, Inc.
101 Fifth Avenue, New York, New York 10003
An Intext Publisher

A Word from the Authors

After nearly thirty years of non-professional but deep interest in conservation issues we offer our first volume on the subject. After participation in projects from California to New York, the publishing of seven ecology-oriented texts for colleges and high schools, conservation articles in magazines and encyclopedias, and lecturing in between on local platforms, television, and radio, we have produced a symposium of observations not suddenly or frivolously arrived at.

We come from new enough frontiers (Wisconsin-Minnesota) to have witnessed one of the final reenactments of the entire drama of American exploitation from virgin forest right on down to the dubious present. From a small piece entitled "No Voice Crying for the Wilderness" in an *Izaak Walton Magazine* way back somewhere in the late 1930's, we have managed to become involved in most conservation and humanitarian conflicts.

We cannot claim many grand victories. During the years between 1943 and 1946, while one of us was engaged somewhere in the Southwest Pacific, the other was able to spark a campaign in northern Minnesota that rescued (in a last dramatic moment of a session of the state legislature) an incomparably lovely stand of virgin white and Norway pines between two white sand lakes, a place now known as the McCarthy Beach State Park. Following a pioneer piece on the coming water shortage in *Harper's Magazine* of October, 1958, the late Senator Robert Kerr wrote us that we had inspired the setting up of his Senate Committee on National Water

Resources whose exhaustive report, issued in 1960, became the backbone of the new national policy on water resources.

In 1958 we received a first prize in the international contest of the Committee on Economic Development with the essay "Water: Key to America's Economic Future"; and there is some heart-warming evidence that the teachings of resource husbandry and "reverence for all life," both of which we have incorporated into the Rienow textbooks for young people, have taken root in fresh soil here and there over the nation.

But because of the hard obligation of earning a living plus professional and continuing military demands, our contribution has been peripheral indeed compared to the great conservationists who dot our land and whose selfless sweat, labor, and often blood have preserved for us what natural beauties now remain. We bow low before such men and women of vision and good will, whether they be naturalists, scientists, industrialists, teachers, governors, lawmakers, or Presidents. They are the salvation of America.

With all their effort it is with sadness that we look out today upon a tired and beat-up countryside, a land with scrub woodlands, a marching inner desert, shrinking natural resources and sinking water tables, a land fouled with man's wastes and pungently interlaced with the world's longest and most notorious sewers. Our industrial fervor has outdistanced our social values—even our common sense. And, underlying it all, our breeding fervor has outdistanced all concern for the future.

We the authors started with thirty feet of files on the subject of our environment. This book was to be an analytical, dispassionate study of what is happening to the America of today. Over a period of four unsubsidized years (one of them a leave from the University) we toured 25,000 miles from coast to coast in all directions. We interviewed hydrologists, local officials, park officials, local health officers, businessmen, naturalists, heads of public works departments, highway commissioners, rangers, influential conservationists, and scientists. We perused congressional hearings and evaluated official reports.

We also read what the President of the United States, various cabinet members, and hundreds of "straight" news reporters and locally attuned editors from coast to coast had to say on the subjects of our interest.

The words of the administration were not dispassionate; they were scathing. The "straight" news reports about the last of the condors and the dying American eagle, the sewage-glutted Potomac and Lake Erie were not "straight"; they were vitriolic and unapologetically purple. The Secretary of the Interior's speeches were not coolly analytical; they were equal parts of enthusiasm and rage. Hydrologists swore in our presence and didn't apologize; health officials used language of descriptive value never heard in classrooms; demographers went into a blue funk, and in the Florida Everglades one or two lovers of wildlife spoke to us through tears.

We surrendered the impossible job of impersonal analysis of a deeply personal matter. We gave up computer thinking on a subject that cannot be computerized, a subject which means your future and ours, the future of the land and the whole American people. We are involved. We are biased for beauty. We are the unblushing partisans of restraint in both exploitation and breeding. We are pluggers for a new, hard look at our misdeeds, for painful self-sacrifice, if need be, to "hold this land" and what is still on it.

The degrees that trail our names are not in the pure sciences but in the humanities and social and political sciences. We do not pretend to the rank of specialists in biology, botany, public health, or even in economics. We frankly envy the scientific jargon of every dendrologist, entomologist, and limnologist we meet. Our notes emanate from the sidewalk and sidestream rather than from the ivory tower or laboratory. Our recognized specialty is public affairs.

Yet our approach is that of the ecologist. Ecology, of course, is the science of the relationship of all living creatures to each other and to their environment. We discuss all public problems in this framework because no problem is an island—all are interwoven and interdependent. And here is the contribution we would make.

But what, after all, is the ecologist in the broadest sense but another word for Stuart Chase's "generalist," with "room in [his mind] for the overall view, especially for relationships and balancing of alternatives"? "To be able to cope with the tough problems ahead of us we should be able to see all the way round them," he writes in *Some Things Worth Knowing.* "Experts and specialists are invaluable but as specialists, they see only the trees, sometimes only the twigs under the trees. . . . We need generalists who do not get lost in the trees." And the late Lord Brain, speaking before the British Association for the Advancement of Science, echoes this thought when he says that what we need today is to relate the sciences to each other, and "we lack the specialists in generalization" to do this.

To all of this Jerome B. Wiesner, delivering his first public address after leaving the post of science adviser to the President of the United States, adds: "What we most desperately need is a group of humanists who comprehend and include scientific and technological knowledge and capabilities in their dreams for the world."

In other words as problem piles upon problem the time has come when we must quickly gain greater awareness of our actions *as they relate to the complete ring of life,* or perish as a great and vital people. Our salvation lies in the embracing of an "ecological conscience" that encompasses all life and its mother, the Earth. All the multifarious activities of man as each group, science, and community drives for its goals, regardless of the effect on other groups or on the earth as a whole—all these conflicting drives, ruthless, unplanned, unrelated—have wrought havoc on a planned, ordered, and closely related ecosystem. The time is at hand when we must stop short and reexamine our surroundings *in toto* if we would preserve our world and life.

Though the stock market goes up and down, its vagaries are like clouds drifting across the face of our sun at its zenith; the sun is still there. And even as the setbacks in our expansion fury do not seriously affect our noontime situation, neither do they alleviate the debauchery of our environment. Because the frantic drain on the land is temporarily eased does not mean that the land is saved.

Indeed economic adversity alone might even aggravate the prostrate condition of our environment, which is now far beyond the point of self-renewal. The public measures of rehabilitation that draw upon the treasury are the first to wilt at any hint of an economic frost. Depression or prosperity, war or peace, our assignment for survival is not only to cease abuse of the land but with assiduous affection to renew it.

There is an editorial from the *Christian Science Monitor* from which we should like to quote:

> One of the warmest and the highest measures of praise is still to say of a man that he is "a man of the Renaissance." By this is meant a person of widely rounded ability, an expert in many things, whose view of the world is never limited to a cramped and narrow corner.
>
> With specialization which has come into almost all fields of human endeavor with the unimaginable explosion of knowledge in modern times, there are fewer and fewer men of the Renaissance about. . . . Yet, we are told, there is a strong swing in industry, government, and even in scholarship away from the narrow expert and toward the man of broad vision and many interests. . . . This is no argument in behalf of the butterfly or the amateur, the man who flits from topic to topic, job to job, mastering none. But . . . although there are many notable exceptions, it is too often true that the so-called expert takes a slightly dehumanized view both of the problems with which he deals and the people likely to be concerned.*

Experts in all fields are indispensable, concludes the editor, but let them "be prepared to look through a telescope as often as . . . through a microscope."

If we would rescue our country now, we shall have to grow beyond our small niches of expertise and specialization (necessary and valuable as they may be) and become in knowledge, words, and deed true "Men of the Renaissance."

Contents

Moment in the Sun

Part One

Perspective

Chapter One

Zenith

Every 8 seconds a new American is born. He is a disarming little thing, but he begins to scream loudly in a voice that can be heard for seventy years. He is screaming for 56,000,000 gallons of water, 21,000 gallons of gasoline, 10,150 pounds of meat, 28,000 pounds of milk and cream, 9,000 pounds of wheat, and great storehouses of all other foods, drinks, and tobaccos. These are his lifetime demands of his country and its economy.

He is requisitioning a private endowment of $5,000 to $8,000 for school building materials, $6,300 worth of clothing, $7,000 worth of furniture—and 210 pounds of peanuts to pass through his hot, grasping little hand. He is yelping for a Paul Bunyan chunk, in his own right, of the nation's pulpwood, paper, steel, zinc, magnesium, aluminum, and tin.

He is heralded as a prodigious consumer in a nation that accounts for one-fifteenth of the earth's people but consumes half of its total product. In one year we use up enough big trees to build a ten-foot boardwalk thirty times around the world at the equator, says Mr. Weyerhaeuser with pride.[1]

Up to the time he has requisitioned his last foot of lumber for his coffin and his three-by-six plot of land (probably arable), he will have been internationally respected for the voraciousness and extensiveness of his appetite, for the zestful way he fulfills his consumptive role in an opulent society.[2] An awe-inspiring amount of the soil's resources (for all things come from the soil) will have passed through him like earth through an earthworm and ended up in the watercourses and in the ever-mounting junk piles of the nation.

The America upon which these demands are made is, as history goes, completely unique. It is not that a few are here living in dazzling grandeur; impoverished societies in all ages have supported an upper crust lavishly. Certainly the affluence of America is highlighted by the merchandising of a floor-length chinchilla peignoir for $14,000. The fact that there is a market for a blue fox blanket at the price of $1,800 to fit a double bed may not be significant. Such items are not generally found even in the best homes. Nor are the matching pillows that sell for $85 very compelling evidence that this is the land of plenty.

It is rather that lavishness has become commonplace. The vast, almost endless assortment of baubles —usually for Christmas-giving—such as gold golf tees at $35 each and a sable lipstick brush in a gold case for $27, comes somewhat closer to distinguishing the United States as an economic wonderland. But mostly it is the mahogany-cased color televisions, the dryers, movie cameras, and such appurtenances of middle-class living that establish our pace. And celebrity homes throughout the nation with their seven or eight baths, numerous fireplaces, and 900-square-foot S-shaped swimming pools are common enough to characterize our affluent society.

As the Sixties rocketed into their second half a prophetic milestone was passed; so fast were we going it was hardly noted. For the first time in the history of the world, which has witnessed innumerable civilizations of dazzling splendor rise and fall, there had emerged a nation in which luxuries superseded economic necessities in sales.[3] In 1875 it took ninety-four cents of each dollar that a family had to spend to provide the basics of food, clothing, shelter, and fuel. But now Americans had reached such affluence that they were spending more than half of the after-taxes dollar for luxuries.

In addition to this awesome fact many former "luxuries" were now labeled as "necessities." Homes were more elaborate, larger, with more baths; food was no longer just baked beans, pie, and cod, or hog and turnip greens; it encompassed anchovies, artichokes, filet mignon, and Persian melon.

Indeed, this screaming newcomer of which we were speaking has something to scream about. His generous expectations are in line with the statistical averages; he need anticipate no undue strain to achieve them. He can reasonably hope, even if we should stand still, to participate in a family income of $7,000 a year. He is inheriting such a claim to creature satisfactions as must make him belch. Collectively, the annual crop of four million (more or less) babies will buy 1,059 million pairs of shoes; they will pull up at filling stations for 91 billion gallons of gasoline; they will line up at the meat counters for 25 billion pounds of beef, and they will demand 200 million pounds of steel, some of which will go into 6.3 million electric refrigerators and the 10.8 million new cars. No wonder that business economists take up their statistical stations at the door of the hospital delivery room as often as at the commodity bourse.

Before each year is out, enough people are added to our country to populate a mammoth new city the size of Los Angeles. The *net* increase of approximately three million persons is roughly equal to the combined populations of Rhode Island, Delaware, Idaho, Nevada, and Montana.

The trade journals gleefully headline this as a "bonanza for industry." Not only do the manufacturers and merchandisers of baby clothes and perambulators applaud the growing queue of customers, but even the steel industry stokes its furnaces in a kind of thanksgiving rite to the Goddess of Fecundity. More cars, more generators, more pipe lines, more construction

steel for more and more people: these are what throw
boards of directors into spasms of delight.

This is, indeed, our moment in the sun as with ingenuity we lift our annual family income by more than
$200 a year while the latecomers to technology drool.
The Asian and African families, stretching a primitive
$100 annual income, are darkly envious. "From where
they squat," says Alexander Campbell,

> the Japanese clerk or industrial worker, with his $720 a
> year, is a rich man. The European working man is a mil-
> lionaire. And the American, with his automobile, his tele-
> vision set, his suburban home, his movie projector and his
> colored shirts (all Americans are still believed to wear
> loud-colored shirts, as affluence symbols) is so incompar-
> ably and beyond normal human experience filthy with
> money that he must be the sort of paunchy Capitalist that
> the Russians say he is. A pig in heaven.[4]

The statistical underpinning for this fabulous and almost unbelievable age is impressive. On the average,
Americans are in clover. According to the Federal Reserve Board,[5] six out of ten own their homes, seven in
ten own automobiles, eight in ten can lay their hands
on a nest egg. In sum, if one strikes up a bookkeeping
balance by taking debts and assets into consideration,
the average net worth for all families is well over
$20,000 and rising.

To be sure, only two in ten own stocks and eight out
of 100 are in hock, but they are balanced by the seven
out of 100 whose net worth is listed at more than
$50,000. Not everybody is buying 18-carat gold mesh
evening bags with a diamond border for $6,000, but
there is enough glitter to rival the finest of the glamorous ancient civilizations.

Little there is that will last. Americans are celebrat-
ing their good fortune by drinking 25 per cent of all
the beer consumed in the world and congratulating
each other over a network of telephones making up 50
per cent of the world's total. Obesity is no longer a
sign of status as it was with the Persians and, indeed,
whole industries direct their ingenuity toward the mar-

keting of foods without nutrition (chain stores report selling 25 per cent more low calorie foods than in 1962), drinks without calories, and gimcrack goods with built-in obsolescence.

The total of services and goods produced (referred to as the gross national product) leaped in the middle Sixties to a sum so incomprehensible that it had to be turned over to a booming computer system. Literally, we had more of everything than we could count!

Automobiles were being built at a fantastic rate. All three major automobile companies announced billion-dollar expansion programs with only a breather imposed upon them by the safety investigation. Heavy machinery was being turned out in record-making quantities—and chemicals and paper; even textiles and food were stretching the tape.

An increased idolatry of production has been sweeping the land, and its icon is the growth chart. The bulk of human effort and most of public policy have been dedicated to the proposition that this free society ought to be judged in history by the way it mobilizes its dwindling natural riches and its talents to the indulgent support of increasing numbers of citizens.[6]

Since World War II the diaper has been flying from the masthead just below the national ensign. In some quarters the pennants were reversed as the national environment—the country the flag stood for—became mauled beyond recognition to accommodate a burgeoning population. Carlyle once said, "You won't have any trouble in your country as long as you have few people and much land, but when you have many people and little land, your trials will begin."

When the famed scientist Sir Charles Darwin, III, visited the United States from England a few years ago, he surveyed the marvels of the age as developed and perfected in the United States and remarked: "This is the absolute golden age of the world." But then he began to observe much more. For one thing, Sir Charles cast a far from beguiled eye on our distressing water situation.

In water famine and in numberless other ways the quality of our physical environment is ebbing. What is of even greater consequence, however, is that the quality of living itself is being chipped at by a thousand small psychic chisels. The strains of Chinafication are beginning to show.

"Meteors are not needed less than mountains; shine, perishing republic," wrote the poet Robinson Jeffers. And Robert Frost, taking this as the text for his lectures, added these words: "Everything shines by perishing, candles, the sun, me. . . . What should we [the United States] do while we're shining—that's the big question. We can't be forever . . . everything shines to perish . . . let's make it big . . . and shining."

But there are those of us who wish that that perishing, however poetic and romantic it may sound in verse, might be delayed.

Chapter Two

Shadows at Noon

Japanese railroad officials are disturbed every time a spell of cold weather strikes the islands; they have found that when people wear overcoats a passenger train carries 20 per cent fewer patrons.

Doubtless our rush hour public conveyances in the United States experience the same cut in revenues when overcoats replace sport shirts and slacks; only we have not yet gotten around to computerizing this angle of the economy. Thermal underwear may be the answer to more and better people-packing on the colder days. At any rate, this is just one—but a fair sample—of the thousands of *critical* issues with which the best brains of American industry will have to concern themselves in the blooming future.

While today's population is about eight times that of 1850, it produces thirty-five times as much, reports a Twentieth Century Fund survey.[1] We are, indeed, at the noontime of production. In our justifiable pride over this accomplishment we ought not to ignore the forces that are at work to make it a fruitless, perhaps a catastrophic, afternoon.

There are three formidable pressures moving in to cast shadows of doubt over our dazzling future. They are: (1) our breath-taking growth in population, (2) the experts' projections of the vast, unplanned economic growth to come, and (3) the ever-mounting demands on us as a nation that a developing world is each day more determinedly pressing.

The obvious menace and the cause of all three threats is, to use James Reston's phrase, "sexual energy." Our population is zooming in a wild curve that leaves demographers of the 1930's speechless. A recent release of the U.S. Census Bureau makes these startling projections:

> 206 to 211 million in 1970
> 248 to 276 million in 1985
> 322 to 438 million in 2010

This latter projection, by the way, was approximately the population of India in 1964. In fact the rate of population growth (not the birth rate) is currently higher in the United States than in India.[2]

Consequently, we are actually all set (even though we are in no other way prepared) for an unprecedented crop of babies. In that baby boom following World War II nature provided a full quota of little girls. These Gigis are now entering the eighteen to thirty-four age group that accounts for 85 per cent of all births. If births increase as fast as women in this age group—a rather safe assumption—the annual number could jump from four million to seven million! In ten years there will be 50 per cent more women in the prime child-bearing ages of eighteen to thirty-four.

For the time being, with the nation at the noontime of its prosperity, there is little to stand in the way of the boom in population other than an awakening. A Russian theory runs: "The more favorable the material circumstances of life, the more the population multiplies." Exultant reports, for instance, came out of Florida as a population expert of the University of Chicago, Dr. Philip Hauser, announced that the current 4,500,000 Floridians would jump to 7,800,000 by 1970. "Florida will make one of the great metropolitan areas in the 1970's. The only word for it is Floridaopolis. This is a new concept—a statewide metropolitan area."

Dr. Hauser, formerly of the U.S. Census Bureau, is not among the exulting, however. In 1958, he said, "I, for one, feel that we are overcrowded already," and he forecast "terrific problems." [3] But almost immediately the Florida Chamber of Commerce translated this projected people boom into retail sales, cash income, sale of life insurance, and hotel occupancy. Proudly the state is hailed to vie with California for the title of "the fastest growing of all the United States."

"Listen!" says the Minneapolis *Star & Tribune* under the photograph of a squalling baby. "You can hear the population explosion in the Twin Cities' suburbs." And they add, "Dad may disagree (especially at 3 a.m.), but to a marketing man a baby's cry is sheer music."

This, then, is the second line of pressure—the increasing expectations of Americans and their commitment to an ever-expanding output and an increasing standard of living. Whenever three statisticians assemble, with or without stimulation, they polish off the old Chamber of Commerce slogans and give them the respectability of scientific terminology. By the year 2000, brashly assuming we can side-step a devastating war, we are assured that the total output of this already fabulous economic system will leap from $504 billion to $2,200 billion. Where each individual now spends $1,830, the amount will jump to $4,000.

Building activity will increase fivefold. The auto-truck output, which now hovers near 10 million, is slated, say these economic prophets, to zoom to 25.9 million per year. The roads will be clogged with 244 million cars. Builders will be erecting, instead of 1.5 million new dwelling units, 4.2 million. Steel production will triple and electric power production will increase by five times. [4]

Mr. D. Lee Stoddard, copublisher of the Elkland, Pennsylvania, *Journal,* had something to tell his fellow publishers about this logic and he said it colorfully. "The purveyors of paradise would have us believe that as long as we keep the stork working overtime, our economy will expand. We are NOT reminded that China has tried this method for years."

He continued:

> I'm certainly not against breeding, but it should be treated as what it is—merely an increase in population and not a panacea for all our present and future economic ills. I don't think it is an oversimplification to say that we make our livings by washing each other's backs. The fact that there will be more backs to scrub and more people to scrub them means only that—just more dirty work, not Utopia.

This is the growth doctrine of America, which is offered always with a fine-print footnote expressing the confident but offhand assumption that the United States will somehow, but assuredly, find the answers to all the resource problems.

But not only have we pressures of our own making; the clamor of the hordes of the world's hungry add to the crisis that confronts us.[5] To these people with the watering mouths we must truly appear to be Alexander Campbell's "pig in heaven." General William H. Draper tells us that in thirty years six to seven billion people will be *fighting to live* on a planet that is not adequately feeding three billion. "The population explosion can shatter *your* world," he adds.

Senator George McGovern, echoing world-famous economists, believes that "major starvation will be the most painful fact on this planet within ten years . . ."[6] and Swedish economist Gunnar Myrdal betters him with the prediction of acute world famine "in five or ten years," adding justifiably, "I am frightened."

In 1964 the State University of New York's Raymond Ewell, vice-president for research at Buffalo, told the American Chemical Society in Chicago that not only will "such a famine . . . be of massive proportions, affecting hundreds of millions, possibly even billions of persons . . . the most colossal catastrophe in history," but it will probably occur "within twenty years."

But a "world famine" doesn't appear out of nowhere like a cyclone on the horizon. No one can put a finger on the moment it began. It creeps up on us until one day it is past ignoring. The United Nations Food and Agricultural Organization tries to impress the world that hunger on a global scale is a growing reality; in 1965 it estimated 10,000 fatalities a day due to malnutrition.

And so fast are conditions and thinking changing that another year after that we find Dr. Robert C. North, professor of Political Science at Stanford University, declaring: "The twin problems of expanding population and contracting resources dwarf all other problems. . . . This awesome time bomb . . . ticks away. . . ."

At the same time, a Senate Government Operations subcommittee was hearing from a handful of Nobel Prize winners on the subjects. From Dr. Albert Szent-Gyorgyi (Marine Biological Laboratory at Woods Hole, Massachusetts): The situation may become such that "men will have to kill and eat one another"; from Dr. Polykarp Kusch (Columbia University physicist): "To postpone action [on population control] now, is to make necessary nearly unthinkable action later on."

Said President Johnson conclusively, we cannot feed the hungry world "unless and until the growth in its resources and the growth of its population come into balance."

In addition to the testimony of noted scientists there are the cold and foreboding facts. From Dr. Earl R. Butz (Purdue Agricultural College): "The man-food ratio around the world, never high enough to be very exciting to two-thirds of the world's population, has actually been in a decline in the last half dozen years." While but three or four nations in Latin America approach adequate diet, the whole underfed continent faces a major emergency: to find food for 385 million *more* people before the end of the century.

Although Latin America leads the world in births, Africa will not, by the year 2000, be far behind. There will be 775 million people in this once disregarded continent. Asia, the remaining underdeveloped part of the world, will, projections say, be saddled with *3.4 billion* people—as many as the whole of the world at the present time.

Thus we find our glowing future shadowed not only by our own abnormal growth and appetite but by the fecundity of people the globe over. "Can the United States be comfortable in a world of agony?" asks population expert Dr. Isaac Asimov. A more vital question might be, "How safe will this food-rich nation be, with the half-starved hordes of the world straining at every boundary? How long will paper treaties contain them?"

Frankly, the problem that threatens to destroy Earth and us with it is of our own conscious (but unthinking) doing. We have interfered just enough in the natural processes of nature to cut down greatly on deaths over the globe while we did nothing about cutting down on births; a policy like this can have but one answer. In 1901 whereas only 770 infants out of a thousand survived their first year in India, medical science today sees to it that 905 survive. About a generation ago Indians had a life expectancy of twenty-three years; now they exist for forty-eight years.

This is the condition everywhere. In the opinion of Dr. Paul Sears, "Honorable men are wondering whether it has been ethical to introduce modern death-control into areas where there is no control of human numbers." [7] A couple of years later Dr. Isaac Asimov, speaking at the Albany, New York, Medical Center, put it more bluntly: Only two solutions exist, he said: "lower the birth rate, or raise the death rate."

So it is that the Western nations stand by wringing their hands while they witness two-thirds of their foreign aid lost down the sinkhole of expanding population demands. Every time your heart beats three more new hearts start to beat and—contrary to all of man's previous history—most of them survive to cut down by just so much your share in the world's products.

India, called by DeGaulle "that dust of people," and by others "the vampire" because it sucks up the blood of civilization, is not the most notorious offender in fecundity today. The Latin American countries (where the per capita output of grain has gone down 16 per cent since 1930) with their birth rate of forty-one per thousand put it in the shade. Egypt is increasing at such a rate that a population figure is grossly outdated before it can be published; it will double its people in fifteen years!

India is so often given as the horrible example because it has gone farthest down the road of no return. Many a public health worker in Latin America, sweating in steamy jungles or traveling the unfriendly pampas to bring help and save lives in the cause of humanity (or just in the cause of the American market perhaps), has lain awake nights wondering "Why?" He is but stretching out their misery.

The population growth in Central America is also greater now than in India—or any other part of the world for that matter. Says columnist James Reston: "The political and social implications of human fertility are only dimly realized." When we stop to think that the first billion of people on the globe took from the dawn of history until 1830 to be produced, the second billion took only a hundred more years, and the third billion but thirty-one years while the fourth billion will require only fifteen years thereafter, we begin to realize what a monstrous thing human fertility has become. Commented Van R. Potter in a letter to the *Saturday Review* some years back: "The problem of self-limitation of growth was solved a long time ago by cells; it had to be before the higher organism could develop. . . . All uncontrolled growths kill the host on which they live."

Congressman Morris K. Udall tells of "a key democratic nation in Asia . . . attempting to rise by its bootstraps [that] recently completed a successful five-year program by increasing its economic output 12 per cent. Are its people better off?" he asks. "No, because in this time its population increased 15 per cent and net living standards are *worse than before.*" [8]

Now, the Tikopians don't have a very sophisticated society and certainly no research groups, but they have come to grips forthrightly with the population problem. Tikopia is one of the British Solomon Islands in the Western Pacific, where it is easy to take in the fact that there is but a limited amount of land of which each family has a certain allotment. Professor Raymond Firth tells us (*We the Tikopia*) that the head of a family, especially not one rich in land, will order the younger males to forego marriage since the children of older brothers will have first call on the food.

Despite the enforced celibacy, sexual satisfaction is not forbidden these males, but conception is rare— side-stepped by the race-old method of *coitus interruptus*. They also resort to abortion and infanticide when pressed. Thinking Americans may question whose arrangements are the more uncivilized, Tikopia's or our own.

"When you are all the way down, there is no place to go but up." Is the reverse also true? Many will doubt that we are at our zenith. But for thoughtful persons who will look about them with a less feverish eye the signs of deterioration in our standard of living, both material and spiritual, due to the three-pronged pressures here considered, are too plain to be shrugged off much longer. From a recognition of what these deteriorations are, and what they are leading to, not even an excess of sun blindness can much longer exempt us.

Chapter Three

The Hidden Price

The cataloguing of our resources (both irreplaceable and so-called renewable) and of the drain currently upon them is not within the province of these pages. Official charts and reports are available, and they clearly show what the three pressures are doing to our raw materials.[1] Conservationists point out the drains and beg for more cautious husbandry.

But now the wizards with the crystal spheres rise up from industrial complexes and campuses, from bureaus and benches, to hypnotize us with dazzling predictions. The soothsayers stoutly assert that "nowhere in the foreseeable future" can they detect any scarcity which would hobble our genius in gadgetry or force us to deny ourselves one single integrated snap-in, snap-out, needs-no-threading AM-Radio-Stereo System in our new town model fastback. No shadow must fall on our production chart or breath of scarcity dampen our consumptive ardor.

Where is the discrepancy between the forecasts of the husbanders and the wizards of expansionism? A keen observer may detect two conjuring tricks which significantly distort the future's image on the glassy globe.

The first is purely a trick of illusion: we gaze into the dark glass and see the great stockpiles of iron ore that will last us for generations. In the poor light we do not discern that these are stockpiles of low-grade taconite for pelleting, where once stood massive mountains of rich red Mesaba hematite—now forever gone. We are shown growth charts to document the claim that the redwoods are growing faster than they are being sawed down; again we do not see clearly enough to recognize that these fascinating statistics are obtained by comparing the growth of suckers from the stumps with the growth of the majestic giants they succeeded! This statistical hoax, which has apparently hoodwinked the masses of American citizenry, pops up again and again in serious studies of "renewable" resources. From the extensive *Resources in America's Future* we quote:

> Finally, the share of sawtimber in annual growth is even smaller than indicated by the inventory figure. It follows then that if the supply outlook for all timber is critical, the prospect of meeting sawtimber demand is still less promising. And since even in the Medium projection the year 2000 shows a large gap between demand and available growth, it follows that the sawtimber outlook is correspondingly dimmer.[2]

But how smugly we relax when U.S. Forest Service bulletins flash across our vision flaunting the 186,000,000 acres of government "forest lands." There is no commentary superimposed to inform us that this extensive acreage (except for a few precious relics, often inaccessible) is not forest at all as American forests went in the olden days. It is in great part miserable land from which the big timber has been brutally stripped and which was then thrown back upon the government in "payment" of delinquent taxes.

Today some of this acreage is charming second-growth woods. Much of it is continually kept cut down to saplings of from six to nine inches in diameter; and some of it is pretty scrubby brush territory which because of climate, water, and soil alterations will always remain so. To eyes that have looked into the dark depths of a virgin forest, to represent these sad stretches of spindly, managed woodlots as "forests" is little less than blasphemy.

The second trick of the wizards of promotion is not illusion but legerdemain. It consists of attracting so much attention to the GNP, the finished product of our industrial genius, that we neglect to observe where more and more of the *raw resources* are coming from to maintain this American superiority in production. We are so mesmerized by the limitless flow of finished goods that we do not think to question our ever increasing dependence on other nations for raw materials or what this trend may some day mean to us.

Natural resources impoverishment, of course, when it reaches a certain critical point, signals our permanent eclipse as the world's first power. We are used to thinking of ourselves as "a surplus nation," and up until 1940 this was roughly so. We produced more raw materials than we consumed. Samuel H. Ordway, Jr., former head of the Conservation Foundation, notes:

> During the forties this position changed. . . . At the beginning of the century the United States produced some 15 per cent more raw materials than it consumed (except for food). By the middle of the century, however, this nation was consuming about 10 per cent more raw materials than it produced.

By 1952 thirty-three separate minerals had entered the "critical" list. "Nor can the United States indefinitely depend on the rest of the world for its mineral needs at present and increasing rate of consumption." [3]

"With only 6 per cent of the world's population, the United States has in the past used enough ore to account for half the world's steel output, and has consumed more than half the world's oil and about nine-tenths of its natural gas," reports the Twentieth Century Fund.[4] Between 1940 and 1961 the consumption of minerals in the United States doubled. Since then the drain on raw materials has been tremendous.

Only a few resources are still sufficient for domestic demands. We can now, however, proceed to exhaust other nations' as we have our own. "For other basic raw materials—petroleum, bauxite, lead, copper, iron ore, potash, and zinc—the nation has turned increasingly to sources outside its borders. These must be added to the list of vital raw materials that the United States has always imported—tin, chromite, manganese, nickel, and rubber." [5] "Basically," says Landsberg, "the country is in a have-not status." Yet it has always been a basic truth that no "have-not" nation which becomes too much dependent on others for its raw sinews of strength can long survive, any more than can the old king lion who has lost his teeth.

"If present trends continue," forecasts Hugo Fisher, administrator of the Resources Agency of California, "the United States within fifteen years will have about 9½ per cent of the world's population. At this time this 9½ per cent will be consuming some 83 per cent of all the raw materials and resources produced by the entire world." [6] Therefore, as the Twentieth Century Fund projects the future, the United States "will have to look elsewhere for many of its raw materials, particularly to the undeveloped areas of Africa, Asia, and South America. Its dependence on imports from every corner of the globe will mount." [7]

Among the ferroalloys domestic reserves, according to *Resources in America's Future,* are adequate only for molybdenum. [8] Tightness will shortly develop in the supply of a variety of raw goods, sulphur among them. If all this situation augured was an increased exchange of goods among nations we might properly applaud the development. But one must consider this in the new context of scarcity and in the framework of inequality.

Here, then, is a nation, the envy of the world, that "is consuming the world's reserves of minerals and fuels at an almost terrifying rate." How far are the advanced countries including the United States "morally justified in using their present economic leadership and power to strip their own and other countries of vital non-renewable resources at rates that may create alarming shortages and severe economic difficulties within the lifetime of people already born?" asks a Population and Economic Planning report.[9]

Here, then, is the United States, where every person consumes 1,455 pounds of food a year. This is the country where obesity is such a constant threat that we pay millions a year for reducing pills to combat over-eating. Indeed, 30 per cent of the women from the poorest levels of American society are grossly over-weight, and the degenerative conditions in army draft-ees are frightening.

Only the minuscule Kingdom of Kuwait, sitting on its fabulous pool of oil, can rival the United States for highest per capita income in the world. By contrast the people of eighty-four countries (in Latin America, Africa, the Middle East, as well as the Far East and Southeast Asia) exist in the squalor that less than $200 a person a year income supports. Of the most basic commodity the Statistical Reporting Service of the U.S. Department of Agriculture has this to say:

> Distributing present food supplies in India as far as they could go at the rate of 2,300 calories per person per day (minimum adequate level) would mean that a tenth of that country's 480 million people would have nothing at all to eat. If this food were distributed at the U.S. consumption rate (3,190 calories per person per day), 153 million Indians would starve.[10]

The cruel fact is that of these eighty-four countries, thirty-seven have per capita incomes of less than $100. Rather sinisterly the Chinese Minister of Defense, Marshall Lin Piao, reminds us that these deprived and envious people of the globe now comprise the over-whelming majority of the world's population.

California's Hugo Fisher believes that the bitter fighting over the Colorado River's waters will be child's scuffling compared to the scrap coming up when the emerging nations wake up to the manner in which we are consuming their—and the globe's—raw resources. And Dr. Paul Sears of Yale wryly comments: "I have not yet heard them justify the continuance of suspicion and the multiplication of armaments with the double objective of keeping industry prosperous and eventually reducing global population, but this may be a short step. I hope not."

While Americans each year are profligately consuming 450 pounds of pulpwood in paper per person and using enough lumber to build the touted ten-foot boardwalk thirty times around the equator, normal housing for the underprivileged around the world is a grass or mud shack or, as in Hong Kong, a room for four just big enough to accommodate a single bunk bed! It is from this world of privation and disillusionment that we must hope to import mountains of raw materials without resentment and political objection.

"Unless a favorable balance of population and resources is achieved with a minimum of delay, there is in prospect a Dark Age of human misery, famine, under-education and unrest which could generate growing panic, exploding into wars fought to appropriate the dwindling means of survival," reads the formal statement issued by thirty-eight Nobel Prize winners advocating population control and led by Sir Julian Huxley and Cass Canfield.

"In our long look ahead at demand and supply of resources," concludes Landsberg *et al.*,

> we do not see any general running out; instead we see the prospect of sustained economic growth supported by an adequacy of resource materials, *provided* technologic advances and economic adaptation of them continue, *provided* foreign sources of raw materials remain open through maintenance of a viable world trading and investing system, and *provided* government resource policies and private management of resource enterprises improve in farsightedness, flexibility, and consistency.[11]

Here are some big "provideds." Our entire resource base, then, depends upon three probabilities, the second of which is reasonably shaky and the third of which, judging by all past indications, is downright questionable. (We shall discuss the technological-economic advances in Chapter XX.) The Population and

Economic Planning report fairly describes our historic stance in resource development thus: "It has been pointed out that many natural resources can be developed only in the somewhat far-fetched sense that a small boy raiding his mother's larder can be said to be 'developing' the supply of jam."

For most of the past, "developing" a resource has simply meant the opening up of new means and activities to increase the drain upon that resource without plan for replacement. "Husbanding" of the non-renewables and "enhancement" of the so-called renewables might be, under the circumstances, more desirable goals.

To all who dare stop in this dizzy race to think, it is clear that with both unrest and awareness among the have-nots growing day by day the situation is explosive. But far short of holocaust or a general uprising, many exigencies may cut us off from necessary and depended-upon supplies. A wave of nationalistic resentment, a rash of Castros or Sukarnos, communistic conquest, or even natural catastrophes may cause economic repercussions that may send our soaring production into a tailspin.

We have made ourselves vulnerable in a thousand ways. Thus, we must nurture and placate those foreign sources of raw goods on which our production so heavily leans. What this appears to mean is that to maintain our material living standards, we must henceforth commit our own technology in increasing ratio to the struggle to accommodate great numbers of people on this earth—whether we want them or not. The price is higher than we think.

Chapter Four

Stoking Stomachs

GOAL OF THE GREAT NEW AGE

Food to stave off starvation is the grim and primary demand of a misery-ridden world. Does it seem a little irrational that, while we can't even keep 3 billion fed today, we cheerfully plan to keep 6 to 7 billion "adequately fed" tomorrow? We should understand now that to raise the minimum of food for all the world's starving, we need not only the prospective increase of Canadian and American exports of 20 million additional tons of grain by 1980; we shall need by the year 2000 not the pittance we and Canada can spare, but *an additional amount of food production equal to the entire present production of the world.*

And if all this seems fantastic for 7 billion, double it again in thirty years; then quadruple it in fifteen—just to keep abreast (minimally) of global hunger.

With these cold facts in mind, let us examine the munificent dream of many uninformed Americans about our "feeding the world." First, our much bewailed "surpluses" in grains are, almost overnight, no more.[1] Wheat, at a peak of 1.5 billion bushels in 1960, is now at the near normal reserve of 800 million bushels—a reserve that we maintain as emergency security. Corn, which peaked at 2.1 billion bushels in 1961, is also down near normal reserves. Butter reserves, which totaled 521 billion pounds in 1954, are all but wiped

24

out, as is cheese, and we are ready to step onto the world market to *buy* dried milk for export to the hungry. Only cotton and tobacco, which people cannot eat, still cram our storehouses.

On February 7, 1966, *U.S. News & World Report* published a rather thorough study of our world-feeding potentials, drawn up by its staff of economic experts. Suppose all holds were barred, all land available put under cultivation and mined to the limit, and every facet of American technological genius employed. Could we, even for a short period, feed the hungry of the entire world? [2] Far from it. We could feed a little more than half of it. [3] However, with these exhaustive efforts (and lucky harvests) we could easily feed the hungry of the *free* world—*for the very short time it would take for their surging populations to catch up with our limited efforts.*

Yes, we could, full throttle, wipe out the shortages of the free world temporarily, taking into consideration four big "if's."

First, who is going to pay the initial $4 billion it will take—which is in addition to the $2 billion already being expended for Food for Peace? *Second,* where will we find the "bottoms" to carry the mountains of grain (32 million metric tons) to the starving lands? (For wheat alone it will require the equivalent of 300,000 freight cars to move one year's supply to shipside for transportation overseas—a freight train 2,055 miles long.) *Third,* how can we revolutionize the eating habits of these confirmed rice-eaters toward the grains that we can grow—wheat, corn, and soybeans?

Fourth, and most important, since the world raises its food production 1 to 1½ per cent a year while stubbornly raising its population 2 per cent, it is evident that even feeding the hungry free nations is but a miserable stopgap.

Speaking of the world's undernourished, "We don't have enough capacity to feed all these people," said Secretary of Agriculture Orville L. Freeman. "Unless they learn to feed themselves, there will be world famine." He then explains: "The estimated increased needs between now and 1980 are in the neighborhood of 300 million tons. The potential reserve productive capacity of this country is 50 million to 55 million tons more. There is a 250-million-ton gap here that only the underdeveloped nations themselves can fill." [4]

So we must surrender fond dreams of rescuing humanity from itself and rely on encouragement and know-how for the unfortunates. With plenty of stars in our eyes and cash in our pocket we can try to push a world-wide agricultural revolution, but it will be like trying to shove an elephant.

The paper prognosticators who would help the undeveloped nations raise their own food skip over such tedia and pitfalls as the cost of 30 to 50 million more tons of fertilizer, a $5 billion investment for new fertilizer plants, the transportation involved, the added legions of experts, Peace Corps and other personnel to start things rolling, and the imposition of a revolutionary new program of education in agricultural methods upon primitive societies (who resent us to begin with), all the while fighting taboos and tribal prejudices ingrained for centuries. They also overlook the American taxpayer.

Yet for humanity's sake if not for the GNP the elephant must be pushed. It is not that these nations have not steadily been bettering their production of food, for, slowly, some of them have. The hopeless part of it is that they have been bettering their baby crop even more and with far greater zest.

But the American scientists who endlessly debate the world's production potentials for the sustenance of animal life in six or eight billion stomachs have bigger plans even than these. They are quite nonplussed at having witnessed the deflation of those economists and others who have so long declared our surpluses could feed the world. They have, therefore, redoubled their way-out fantasies, and now look up from their slide rules and computers with faces flushed with triumph. Recipes for food meal combining atrocious fodder such as sawdust, ants, fish heads and innards, seaweeds, slimes, mosses, even powdered granite—souped up with synthetic vitamins to relieve the conscience of the steak-eating perpetrator—pour out of the laboratories. "I can't think of anything worse than to ask them (the inventors) to live on it," remarked a critic of one such formula.

Some years ago Drs. S. Harrison Brown, James F. Bonner, and John B. Weir, three California Institute of Technology scientists, outlined a program for American industrial leaders. They reported that systems of processing ordinary rock into atomic energy, into metals and minerals, must gain our attention if we would have the equipment to support the seven billion people that will greet the twenty-first century. Sea pigs, a kind of vegetarian beast, will be developed to graze the ocean!

We have corps of high-caliber brains researching day and night for a "breakthrough"—the magic solution in which all true Americans believe. "Breakthroughs are anticipated with new research tools using radioactive isotopes, high capacity calculators, and highly specialized tools," reports the Center for Agricultural and Economic Adjustment.

Important breakthroughs in genetics could have significant effect on multiplying production, thus temporarily lessening world hunger Yet while the scientists feverishly seek their happy strikes, and the Western World zooms ahead, betting its entire future on the longest shot in history, Thomas M. Ware, head of the Freedom From Hunger Foundation, testified before a Senate subcommittee: "Very few grasp the magnitude of the danger that confronts us. . . . The catastrophe is not something that may happen; on the contrary, it is a *mathematical certainty that it will happen.*" (Our emphasis.)

There is much more mouth-watering fantasy in the realm of manufacturing belly-filling pap from algae, but the ardor of this experiment was somewhat dampened when scores of soldiers who had volunteered for the guinea pig job of tasting the cakes, bread, and cereals containing the meal retched violently and turned yellow with nausea.

But suppose we were able by some miraculous serendipity to dole out sufficient sustenance (of whatever kind) to keep the undeveloped nations docile and sufficient fairy stories to keep them in a hopeful attitude of some day inheriting our own standard of living. Suppose we were able to attain some sort of world-feeding program so that we might continue to exploit the earth's resources and hang onto our moment in the sun.

We should not hold onto it, even then.

Because in the world of the future, as it is headed today, our major dedication must be to procreation and appetite.[5] Our great minds, our national goal, must be devoted to the kind of shameful research indicated above. The very computation is degrading. It is an answer to not much more than bestial existence.

It is no longer difficult to see where we, the rich Americans, fit in the crush of the future: it is with our backs to the wall. What was once a pleasant, humanitarian crusade has become a political necessity, an accepted obligation to billions of mouths over whose skyrocketing numbers we have no control. The more we feed, the more they breed. It has been quite a jolt to wake up to the fact that the annual surpluses that have been so long bewailed and that have for decades caused so much concern and head-scratching in every administration are, after all, in the words of the Department of Agriculture's Lester R. Brown, "but a crumb on the table of the world."

Our only hope of permanent help, our only hope of averting world-wide famine and panic, as the President himself has come to see, is to make a mighty and immediate effort to curb the roaring expansion, to tame the spiraling human curve within some decent bounds. But this is not easy when we ourselves are overbreeding, and how can we fervently urge birth limitations on other people when we legally outlaw them in the supposedly most advanced nation on earth? What kind of hypocrite is it who can smile approvingly as Japan promotes abortion to hold the line in population, while we refuse a raped twelve-year-old child the mercy of such relief?

No matter. We shall pay well for such stubbornness, and it need have little to do with the GNP, for there are scarcities other than goods in a Chinafied world. There are consequences that are less measurable but far more soul crushing.

What is the worth of these other things? Remarked one disgusted planner, "Nothing, apparently, to those who would sell the sunset if someone would put a price on it." There are elements without which (although we turn stone into steel and plankton into the bread of life) we are clods, numbers on a machine, our eyes forever vacant of dreams. Their loss will truly make us less than men.

How much are we willing to pay in the coin of soul and mind for our own indulgence in overbreeding and our condoning of it in the rest of the world? Will we pay with loss of choice, with queuing jostling, elbowing, with yet unimagined traffic snarls, a tragic increase in cripples and defectives, a vaulting incidence in mental illnesses and crime, a new tax burden to support the more than 50 per cent juvenile population, a strangling of culture while the stark necessities of existence absorb our energies?

Said the late Editor-emeritus Edward Meeman of the Memphis *Press-Scimitar,* "To live rich, thrilling, joyous life, not hardly-worth-living existence, *we need space*." Are we, then, ready to accept a permanent condition of inadequate educational facilities and congested housing while we watch a once beautiful America being transformed into a demented wasteland? Are we content with roads upon roads upon roads that go nowhere—because there is no place to go? Do we glory in wading in wastes and sitting on stoops of houses that grow every year more conformist, shoddy, and makeshift? Do we want increasing noise and din, mountains of junk on our horizons in place of mountains of trees? Do human dignity and privacy mean nothing to us? How much are we willing to pay for our support of quantity instead of quality? [6]

Americans have never known the misery of having nowhere to turn, no place to go, just to be alone and to breathe freely. Yet since we do not believe in mass immolation or sacrificial massacre the only escape from such misery is its prevention. All measures must be taken *before* the exigency; once here, there is nothing to do but endure it.

Professor Bruce Welch of William and Mary College deplores the passive acceptance of population expansion while we devise frantic means to provide for its demands. "Simple arithmetic should suffice to show that this approach is madness and folly," says the noted biologist in *National Parks Magazine*. "Animals are not simply machines for the consumption of food. Each kind, including man, has behavioral and physiological limitations of one sort or another." [7] Then he adds: "Far short of the population density that will tax potential food supply there will be a limit to human tolerance, the advent of social and cultural stagnation, the disappearance of freedom—and compassion—and sensible morality, the reign of an artificially tranquilized and emotionless sub-animal existence."

One of the revered myths of the race has been that people bring strength to a nation. When small phalanxes of armed men faced each other in deadly battle on the plains of medieval Europe, people were the king's only strength.[8] King Alfred, striding on foot into battle at the head of his little band of faithful house carls, knew how precious each loyal arm was to the defense of Wessex and his Anglo-Saxon England. When the farmers faced the British redcoats at Concord Bridge, every brave heart and every battered musket counted for more than its weight in gold.

But the corner has long been turned. Great masses of people today in excess of the necessary uniformed minority mean weakness for the nation; they are a liability to be defended, an impossible burden to care for in an atomic visitation. When a nation frankly admits that it cannot under any circumstances marshal even enough blood plasma to treat one-twentieth of its probable casualties in the event of atomic war, it would seem that the corner had been turned a good while back.

Summing up, although scientists and sorcerers may succeed, for a time, in demonstrating what Edgar Ansel Mowrer calls their "appalling inhumanity" by producing enough Multiple Protein Factor or whatever "to fill ever more billions of bellies," it may be properly asked, *to what end?* The most acute misery of tomorrow—the unbearable for Americans—will not consist of giving up steaks for a paste of chaff and entrails, although this is an unspeakable possibility. It will be in the adjusting of our present comfortable, free-wheeling, and luxurious style of living, the finest man has ever known, to the degradations and regimentations that a teeming populace cannot avoid bringing.

Underlying everything is an inexorable and inglorious truth the three pressures we have noted above are altering the whole course of our national future in a way that is debasing, even subhuman Not only are they foreclosing on our assets, energies, and enjoyment of living all in a cause that, in the face of present trends, can only be futile and insane—they are foreclosing on our aspirations and creativity, our hopes of a worthy contribution to civilization. They are casting all possibilities of greatness to the dogs of appetite.

> When goods increase, they are increased that eat them: And what good is there to the owners thereof, saving the beholding of them with their eyes?
>
> Eccles. 5:11

Long before the stomach dies, the man will die.

Part Two

The Devouring of
Our Environment

Chapter Five

Ecology—the Relentless Science

Basic to an understanding of what a crowded and crumbling environment can do to man is an understanding of ecology, the science of "the mutual relationship between organisms and their environment." It is the science of man's relationship to all living things and to the very earth itself.

Supreme Court Justice Abe Fortas, in accepting the Albert Schweitzer medal from the Animal Welfare Institute in November, 1965, had this to say: "Life is a seamless web. It connects us not merely with one another, but with all that is sentient—with all that shares its miracle of birth and feeling and death." And Fairfield Osborn, in his small masterpiece *Our Plundered Planet,* declared as a "flat statement" that "in a world devoid of other living creatures, man himself would die."

Thoreau so identified himself with his beloved fields, woods, and lake that he became an integral part of them in mood, in pulse, in sensation. Almost every great or thoughtful mind has involved itself deeply with nature and earthy things, with all other forms of life.[1] It is well known that both Presidents Washington and Jefferson loved their acres and the natural beauty that grew on them to the point of obsession.

But it is not so well known how closely Lincoln associated himself with nature, how attuned he was to other forms of life. Historian Coyle in *The Ordeal of the Presidency* [2] tells a moving story about this unfathomable man.

> After the fall of Richmond, a young French diplomat, the Marquis de Chambrun, was riding through Petersburg in a carriage with Lincoln, when he stopped the carriage to look at a noble white oak with gnarled wide-reaching arms. Chambrun was deeply impressed by Lincoln's feeling for the tree and recorded that "he talked as if he might be some kind of a tree himself."

Thoreau's most famous quotation is "In wildness is the preservation of the world," and he believed that artificiality brings decay of virility and then death. True or not, it is an indisputable and proven fact that we cannot beat up our environment without beating up ourselves. This law is relentless. Though the consequences may be delayed, be forestalled, even masked, they will always strike and often to kill.

In the old days when the lovely Schoharie Valley in upstate New York was a garden of hops, skunks were honored. It was said that natives "would shoot anybody who shot a skunk." The reason was both ecological and economic: the skunk was, in nature's plan, the enemy of the hop grubs and in that role the defender of the Valley's enterprise.

The insight of these settlers is rare; men and civilizations, past and present, have been blind to the proper place of fellow creatures and lesser life forms in the pattern of existence. From the Head Office of the Royal Bank of Canada in May of 1960 came a monthly newsletter profoundly concerned about our neglect of our environment. Said the letter:

> The forces set in motion by every act of every animal and bacterium, by every inch added to the growth of plant or tree, affect the lives of other creatures. The principles which govern these interrelationships are embraced in the science called ecology, a word coming from the

Greek for "home" or "estate." Ecology is the study of how the household of nature is kept in order.

Why are the salmon gone from Lake Ontario and the bison from the plains, the deep three-foot layers of humus washed to the sea, and the climate altered? Professor A. F. Coventry, speaking to the Toronto Field Naturalists' Club, warns, "We have for a long time been breaking the little laws, and the big laws are beginning to catch up with us."

Great civilizations have dwindled to mediocrity or collapsed like a rotten gourd for violation of the big laws of ecology.[3] Professor Raymond Bouillenne, director of the Botanical Institute, University of Liège, who knows the African scene intimately, traces this sorrowful trend.[4] Where are Cyrenaica's gardens of Berenice, once so famed in Rome? The Libyan Desert hides the ruins of great cities such as Thysdrus, whose sport stadium once held 60,000 men. Beneath thick layers of Sahara sand the French explorer August Chevalier found traces of dense forests that existed less than 2,000 years ago. What happened to the fabled glory of Arabia, Babylon, and Tibet? In Morocco alone, since the Roman period, "12½ million acres of forests have disappeared as a result of fire and overgrazing by sheep and goats."

Egypt of the golden tombs, whose rich fields once spread far over the land, now shrinks and starves within the valley of the Nile. China, once lush with forests and the fruits of vine and twig, has watched her deserts march in, driving her too fecund people before them into the last refuges of the valleys of the Blue and Yellow Rivers.

Was it only a million years ago that the first man stood upright? Was it only eight thousand years ago that man began to till? In the now classic volume *This Is the American Earth,* which Nancy Newhall scripted and Ansel Adams photographed, fact after shocking fact hits the reader in the face as it traces the history of man's destruction of Earth down through the millennia.

It was thousands of years ago that men devastated, with the help of uncontrolled seas of sheep, the rich, lake-dotted lands of northern Mongolia—now despised wasteland whose very name repels. Can we believe that Greece was once an Eden of forests and waters; that Palestine was brought from overflowing richness to famine, drought, pestilence; that in Europe wilderness was wiped out by men before the fifteenth century? [5]

When the avid human tide swept over North America it laid waste not only to the level forest lands but reached up the mountains as well. "Thank God," cried Thoreau, "they cannot cut down the clouds!" Most of the mammoth kills of bighorn sheep, buffalo, elk, caribou, moose, bears, and antelope were for boasting; the pioneers massacred buffalo to take out the tongue and left the rest to rot. In the Midwest dynamite thrown into the thousands of teeming lakes destroyed forever the ecological colonies that had been building up since the recession of the last glacier.

But all ecological sins come home to roost, and bitterly indeed have the once richly endowed civilizations of the past paid for their rape of nature. In America the long overdue account of our disregard for ecological laws is only now beginning to be presented. The payments must be made, if not in cash, then in blood.

The essence of technological, if not civilized, pursuits is the constant clashing with ecological principle. A wheat field or an apple orchard is, by itself, an invitation to ecological breakdown. They offer no defenses in depth to the attack of pests or diseases.

On the other hand, Professor Samuel Graham cites the protective qualities of naturally mixed stands of trees, for instance, "In the North, where you have the familiar mixture of beech, birch, maple, hemlock, and pine, you seldom find damage done to the hemlock. But where the species exists in pure stands it may be destroyed in a single season by the hemlock looper." [6]

The pest's commuting distance is shortened. He has been spread a feast, and joyfully he multiplies. When, as in New Brunswick, a spray program for control of the spruce budworm is launched on the headwaters of the Miramichi River, no thought is given to the river's salmon; shock follows when we find the river clotted with the bodies of 90 per cent of the one- and two-year-old fish.

We let the great cats in our western forests claw open the landscape on the upper reaches of waterways and are stunned when nature reacts with a violent and choked flood. At Christmastime of 1964 the west coast of California, where unrestricted redwood and Douglas fir logging is carried on, was the tragic scene of very damaging floods.

But in the very heart of the area a miracle took place. It happens that Nature Conservancy owns and protects in its natural state the whole of the watershed of Elder Creek in Humboldt County. The report on the Northern California Coast Range Preserve said: "Elder Creek, as an uncut watershed, ran clear even though extremely high. Observers from airplanes reported that it stood out as an exception among the roiled waters of the other streams in the region."

Still these destructive trends continue unabated over the entire world. Bouillenne terms the regression of the forest massif of Central Africa "disastrous." He notes that in the Congo, where the cover is just too delicate to withstand clearing for hunting and cultivation, 30,000 square kilometers of soil have been destroyed in six years.

In Madagascar, the drama has been played out over a period of 60 years. This island was once covered with splendid forests; today 70 per cent of its area is occupied by an ocean of tough grasses, ravaged by fire and unsuitable even for the feeding of herds. In short, we are in the throes of an apparently irreversible progressive *reduction* of the surface of cultivable lands.[7]

What happened to the great oak forests of the Hittite Empire, where the conqueror Tamerlane hid his herd of elephants? Where are the groves of cypress and palms that once made lush the desolate plains of Iraq? Why is there no trace of the vanished forests of Phoenicia, whose stout timbers long ago raised this people to greatness as a naval power? When the 35,000 men of Tyre cut Lebanon cedar for the Temple of Solomon, how is it that this thriving tree community never reseeded and recovered from the shock? And why has the Sahara Desert been moving southward— for the last 500 years—at the rate of at least a mile a year on a wide front of some 1,800 miles (the estimate of K. H. Oedekoven, forestry researcher for the U. N. Food and Agriculture Organization)?

The answer is, of course, that when man scalps the land he outrages the ecology; he destroys the humus, evaporates the water, erodes the soil, alters the climate, and so shocks the environment that never again can the conditions that brought these choice climax forests into being prevail.

Here, then, is a brief sampling of ecological relationships. Put in the words of Phillip Keller the lesson is: "We make our greatest mistake when we believe that the world belongs to us. It does not—we belong to it!"

Much of our small sinning against the laws of ecology is through ignorance. We have an inbred passion for killing snakes—even the harmless and ecologically precious black snake, which can slither its way into rodents' holes and attack them in their very retreats. California farmers, understanding that they would be overrun with rodents were it not for this valuable ally, accost the museum collectors out gathering snake specimens with the stern bag limit of one snake per farm.

Then there is the common bluejay, whom most people resent because of the manner in which it gulps whole sunflower seeds by the pound. But the bluejay pays back society in a unique way; foresters have discovered it is nature's most ardent "reforester." The jay not only places the seed of trees in the ground with great care, but it also covers the spot with leaves and pine needles as a protection from the weather. Taking a cue from the bluejay, at least one state of the Union supplies each hunting license buyer with a package of pine seeds to be scattered in waste areas on his hunting expeditions, an idea that Theodore Roosevelt would have considered "bully, indeed!" And although Mother Nature invented poison berries and seeds, she created sixty-three kinds of birds with a consuming appetite for the baneful things, which foresight probably saved humanity in the form of *Pithecanthropus erectus* from an early extinction!

Often the account of the interrelation of living forms is steeped in drama. Thus it happened that one year the citizens of Cattaraugus, Erie, Wyoming, and Allegheny Counties in New York State were witnessing with horror an army of inchworms avidly devouring their forests. Ten thousand more acres were in the path of the marching worms when without bugle calls and seemingly from nowhere a counterforce of birds, field mice, shrews, and the Calasona beetle was suddenly mustered. Within days the infestation was over.

The intricacies of the world we live in are underlined by the report of three Cornell researchers—Thomas Eisner, Rosalind Alsop, and George Ettershank—who studied the webs of orb-weaving spiders. Designed as a special trap for flying insects, these webs have a framework of ordinary threads interlaced with adhesive strands of a very sticky quality—a device that should have doomed the unwary insect without hope of disentanglement.

But what did the researchers find? That some moths have been provided with detachable scales on their wings and bodies. Merely by leaving a few excess scales behind on a sticky strand they can thwart the hungry expectant spider. Other moths are covered with a powder with which they can coat the sticky drops and so make their Houdini-like escape.

Thus not only is the minor world of insects and spiders complex, but it maintains a fair balance. Spiders have, over the millennia, trapped insects. "But over the many millions of years insects have been preyed upon by spiders, the insects have developed equally 'ingenious' evasions." [8]

This intricacy of relationships in nature bestows benefits of which man is too often totally ignorant. Speaking of a hated and harassed bird, the Red Tail hawk, ornithologist Alexander Sprunt, Jr., says this:

> The food of the Red Tail is mainly small mammals and not poultry as it is often believed. Birds constitute no more than 10 per cent of its food, while an examination of 562 stomachs showed remains of mammals (principally meadow mice) in 409. Reptiles, insects, and crawfish are also taken. [9]

During the breeding season a single Red Tail will bring 1,000 mice to its nest to feed its ravenous young. Without its appetite and that of other hawks and birds of prey the world would be ankle-deep in rodents, and women would have to live on top of stepladders.

But perhaps one of the finest examples of the competence of nature and the bungling of man is the story of southern Oregon's pine country, where there has been a serious population explosion of porcupines. The porcupine, which delights in girdling a young pine just as the tree is entering its best growing stage, has a place in nature and undoubtedly even a right to its share of pine trees. But it was not intended that porcupines should preempt the Northwest any more than that man should monopolize the globe. Why, then, was this happening?

Then old foresters recalled that once the porcupine had a fierce and insatiable enemy, a sleek big cousin of the mink, who had roamed these forests with a special purpose of harassing the prickly rodent. This was the fisher, who, of all animals who might have a taste for juicy fat porky flesh, had also the rare ability to leap from one tree top to another, stalk his quarry, and dispatch it without being needled painfully in the process. It was a very special art. But if the fisher relished porky, man relished the fisher's silky fur even more.

Thoughtlessly, he trapped the species out of the forests, and then wailed to watch his forests destroyed.

It is not always so direct a disturbance of nature's plan that causes trouble. Most often man upsets the habitat to which a creature is highly attuned. Consider the giant California condor—the "Thunderbird" of Indian lore—whose dark bulk once soared lazily over many parts of the Western sky. The condor must have cliffs for nests, where he is provided with just the right air currents to bear his heavy body aloft in his search for carrion. Brooking no violation of his privacy, he will abandon a nest should human traffic come within earshot.

Because he demands a tiny but inviolate corner of this world for himself, the condor seems doomed. Poisoned and hunted elsewhere, the forty remaining birds have retreated to the Sespe Wildlife Refuge of 53,000 acres, which man reluctantly assigned them in 1951. Even here he is being threatened. There are those who think we need another impoundment of water on the Sespe River more than we need the condor. In this case we cannot claim that we did not know the ecology of the species; we are simply—and callously—ignoring it.[10]

We can put in our dam and create still another undistinguished development and drive the condor to extinction. For some unfathomable reason we think this makes us richer than the Indian who stood in silent awe as the Thunderbird soared far overhead, then floated, with its weird and Harpy grace, into the canyon's swirling mists.

Ecosystems need not be as big or as dramatic as that of the fisher-porcupine-pine tree relationship. They need not cover the thousands of acres of a refuge edged with misted cliffs. The drama of the life chain can be excitingly enacted within the environs of a dead tree. In the design of nature, where nothing is ever lost or wasted, it is imperative that the tree, which removed chemicals and other materials from the soil, return them so that they can be used over again.

Thus, in the little world of a dead tree, shelf fungi first spring up to speed the decomposition with the enzymes they secrete. Then they, in turn, provide wastes that green plants can feed upon. Now insects join in the attack; carpenter ants and wood-boring beetles invade, channeling out vast cities of tunnels, and opening thousands of doors to the weather and to bacteria. Then woodpeckers in pursuit of the insects industriously peck out larger and larger cavities.

Ultimately the rotting tree falls to the ground, creating in its shelter a home and food supply for a whole new host of creatures. In move the armies of slugs, mice, and snails, squirming larvae, worms, and hibernating beetles, to chaw and dig and speed the breakdown of the log. Soon come their camp followers, toads, frogs, snakes, and moles, who sidle in to live happily on this woodland smörgasbord. Even the beautiful mourning cloak butterfly comes there to hibernate—a delicious morsel. The fallen log is palpitatingly alive as it crumbles into humus. In this wondrous, complicated way the tree's "life-giving elements are returned to the earth that gave it birth. A chain of life is ready to begin again." [11]

A scientific team of botany, biology, and zoology professors sought to discover why the giant cactus of the Sonoran Desert, the saguaro, is in trouble. Why, despite its 200-odd fruit, each harboring 200,000 seeds, is this handsome plant failing to hold its own? Again, man was found in the picture. He brought in cattle in the 1880's in such numbers that the low plants, which provide cover for the small saguaro, were eaten away. With sparse plant cover erosion followed, channels were cut, and the scarce water supply drained away.

All this is a common enough ecological chain. But man added new complications for the majestic saguaro. Man hates the coyote, whose regular food consists of desert rodents, notably the ground squirrel, wood rat, and rabbit. The ground squirrel and wood rat feed on the saguaro as much for water as for food.

Since, however, it became official government policy to exterminate the coyote by all means (including the frightful 1080 poison), the rodent population has multiplied astronomically. There are now fears that the Saguaro National Monument may not survive.[12] We will have exchanged an eternal wonder for a beefsteak; we will have lost a nesting site for desert birds such as the woodpeckers and elf owls; we will have fostered death and cheated life; we will have taken another edge off the quality of man's experience.

Centuries ago Leonardo da Vinci, in a combination of science and intuition, mused: "In nature is the answer to everything." Alan Devoe, over a decade ago, explained: "All creatures are in a common brotherhood . . . interconnected with everything else. Not only is there a basic brotherhood between [all men] but there is a bond between a man and a mouse, or a tree and a fox, or a frog and a raccoon." And he added: "We are one small ingredient in a whole of unimaginable Vastness . . . a part of a general and embracing interdependence. . . . We are supported by starfish. An owl props us. Earthworms minister to hold us upright." [13]

As early as 1939 Hamilton Basso in *Days Before Lent* put a speech in the mouth of old Dr. Gomez, a Central American revolutionist exiled from his country:

> Do they not understand that as man subdues nature he subdues himself—that man, being an animal, is as dependent upon the operation of natural laws as an amoeba or a frog? . . . Let the balance necessary to man's existence be destroyed, and it is quite possible that he will go the way of the wild horse and the white-tailed gnu.[14]

The many years of senseless attack on the coyote with the indiscriminate poison sodium fluoracetate (commonly known as 1080, already mentioned) set up a terrifying sequence of tragedy. The initial target kill is gruesome enough: one ounce mixed with 1,500 pounds of horsemeat makes a lethal bait even if only two ounces of it are consumed by a coyote. An investigative lick may be enough.

The evil of the bait runs through a whole chain of innocent victims. A mouse samples a grain and dies. The fox or bobcat that eats the mouse retches and dies. A bird that consumes the grain droppings will also expire. The poisonous vomit falling upon the grass sickens and kills the animals who graze upon it. And, of course, the buzzards, eagles, crows, and jays or any carnivorous animals that eat the poisoned carrion are doomed. There is a kernel of irony in the fact that a dove, quail, duck, or pheasant that may have consumed the man-placed bait 1080 just before being shot may become a deadly repast on the table of man himself.

Thus, we see that we have ecological "chains of death" as well as "chains of life." A shattering thesis has just been verified by three professors of chemistry, reported at the 1965 meeting of the American Chemical Society at Atlantic City, New Jersey, on September 16. The professors, Donald E. H. Frear, Ralph O. Mumma, and William B. Wheeler, of Pennsylvania State University, and the fact they reported —stoutly ridiculed by scientists and government officials alike for many years—is that forage crops can and do take up insecticides from the soil *through their root systems* and pass it into grazing cattle, thence into man.

The Penn State report, says the Pennsylvania *Game News,* December, 1965, showed that even though a crop *has not been sprayed* in the year of harvest, pesticide residues that were still present in the soil from preceding years were absorbed in the new and quite unsprayed crops through the plants' roots. The scientists grew a number of forage crops in sand and soil permeated with "radioactively tagged" dieldrin, DDT, and other insecticides. Then they watched each insecticide through radioautography as it rose into and distributed itself through the plants!

Can the familiar story of Mao Tse Tung and the sparrows be true? Some years ago the Chinese dictator was led to believe that the sparrows were eating too much of China's precious grain. On his order, so the fantastic tale runs, "millions of Chinese, young, old, and crippled, took poles, bamboo, and brooms and waved them at the sparrows. The frightened birds fluttered into the air and kept flying until they dropped to earth dead of exhaustion."

Whether the birds were frightened to death by a seemingly endless sea of humanity gone suddenly insane, or whether the Chinese actually beat the birds to death, the ecological point was made. The insects that the sparrows had been feasting upon increased so disastrously that the fruit crop was almost ruined. The battle of the sparrows was called off.

In somewhat like manner fishermen in northwest Missouri, ignoring the thrill that the annual migrations of the fresh-water white pelicans gave the observers, and resentful of having to share fish with them, organized raids on the birds' island nests and decimated the population. Today the white pelicans are on the critical list for survival.

But so are the game fish, unfortunately. It so happens that the diet of the pelican is largely rough fish; with the pelican all but wiped out, the rough fish are increasing and crowding out the game fish, ruining the fishermen's sport.

Sir Francis Bacon once said, "To learn to dominate Nature we must first learn to obey her." And to understand her laws, it might be added, "Men are running wild through the biological world like some malignant agent," warns Dr. Marston Bates, the renowned naturalist of the University of Michigan. "Everything man touches turns to garbage." Or to corpses.

The Committee on National Resources of the National Academy of Sciences puts man's role in more dignified but no less condemning terms:

> Man is altering the balance of a relatively stable system by his pollution of the atmosphere with smoke . . . , alteration of the energy and water balance . . . , over-grazing, reduction of evapotranspiration, irrigation, drainage . . . , building of cities and highways; by his

clearing forests and alterations of plant surface cover, changing the reflectivity of the earth's surface and soil structures; by his land-filling, construction of building and seawalls, and pollution, bringing about radical changes in the ecology of estuarine areas; by the changes he effects in the biologic balance . . . , the erection of dams and channel works; and by the increasing quantities of carbon dioxide an industrial society released to the atmosphere.

It is hard to tell whose indictment is the harshest. Aldous Huxley, famed English author, has accused: "Committing that sin of overweening bumptiousness, which the Greeks called *hubris,* we behave as though we were not members of the earth's ecological community, as though we were privileged and in some sort, supernatural beings and could throw our weight around like gods." All of which seems to substantiate Leonardo da Vinci's no-nonsense damning of glorious *Homo sapiens*: "Perfidious Man! Cursed is the day you left the cave."

Undoubtedly Da Vinci had had a bad morning; perhaps somebody had sat down on his palette. It was inevitable that man would alter his environment to increase his convenience. It is less excusable that he has been both so callous and cruel in his alterations that all life must now pay dearly.

Perhaps if man nurtured greater understanding of the role of each of his fellow creatures on earth he might act more cautiously in the destruction of any life. When he picks the despised stinkbug off the berry cane to crush, does he realize its value as a repellent of lice and other pests? When he shoots a brown thrasher in his garden does he know that this bird accounts for nearly 6,000 bugs a day? What kind of double talk is it, asks nature writer Ferris Weddle, to exult in the killing of a cougar because "it saves a dozen deer" and in the next breath to bewail the "overpopulation" of deer causing starvation from lack of browse? Do California taxpayers (whom, says Fish and Game Director Walt Shannon, it costs $629 per lion in costs and bounties for the killing campaign) still see no inconsistency here? [15]

One hundred and twenty years ago Michigan placed a bounty on timber wolves and all but exterminated them; there are only about forty left in the entire state. But twenty of these live safely on Isle Royale. As a consequence, the moose on Isle Royale, far from being diminished by the wolves, are developing into a beautiful superbreed. The wolves have served nature's purpose of eliminating the runts, the old and diseased.

In a less direct fashion we have the now classic story of the boy who set out to trap the skunks in the vicinity of his duck pond. After awhile his ducks began to vanish mysteriously, one by one. It took an old woodsman who understood the web of life to explain to the boy that skunks eat snapping turtle eggs, and that when the skunks are killed off the turtles increase and quietly pick off the ducks. Akin to this ecological ring is the grasshopper-prairie dog chain, described recently by zoology Professor George M. Sutton of Oklahoma University. Burrowing owls feast on grasshoppers and similar pests. But they use the burrows of prairie dogs for their nests. When ranchers, seeing the prairie dogs nibbling at their pastures, persuaded federal agents to start a full-scale chemical warfare against the prairie dogs, the burrowing owl population decreased. Soon armies of grasshoppers and other insects began to take over and the end is not yet come. It will be interesting to follow what happens.

But ecological thinking is new, and there are few indeed who take any heed of end results when they decide to tamper with their environment. "The utilitarians," notes naturalist and Professor Dan McKinley of Lake Erie College, Ohio, "aim [at] as many people as possible, all carefully regulated as to hours of labor, leisure, and lechery. As they quibble, unique organisms . . . such as bogs, deserts, and islands are carelessly lost and haphazardly succeeded by the stability of ragweeds, starlings, barn rats, and eroded soils."

Were it not for predators such as owls this continent would be covered with two and a half inches of mice from coast to coast within a year, say the statisticians.

Senator Gaylord Nelson tells of a bird watchers' paradise—a little island covered with sooty terns. Someone released a few rats on that island which multiplied and cleaned up all the terns without much ado. Rats are almost as destructive as men.

Botanist Kenneth W. King of Antioch College recommends that we adopt Rachel Carson's "biocentric concept" for our own well-being. And Aldo Leopold long ago pleaded for the "ecological conscience" that would place man in a less arrogant but truer spot in the Creator's scheme of things. Charles A. Lindbergh came to grips with his relationship to his environment in the jungles of Africa, far from the distractions of civilization. "Lying under an acacia tree with the sounds of the dawn around . . . I became more aware of the basic miracle of life," he wrote. "Not life as applied humanly to man alone, but life as diversified by God on earth with superhuman wisdom—forms evolved by several million centuries of selection and environment. . . . I realized that if I had to choose, I would rather have birds than airplanes. . . ." [16]

But perhaps ecological awareness is growing at last. The high party official in China who instigated the bird-extermination idea has been dispatched to become foreman of a land-clearing project in remote, icy, seldom-come-back-from, northwestern China. And in Russia a strange edict has been issued. Dolphins, it seems, enjoy a very elaborate sound communication system, which some scientists call "delphinese." (According to a news item: "It is of interest to note that while some dolphins are reported to have learned up to fifty words in English—used in correct context—no human has been reported to have learned delphinese.") The Soviet Government announced in March of 1966 that henceforth the catching and killing of dolphins was banned because "their brains are strikingly close to our own."

In a more serious vein we are now told that 1080 has at last been discredited in the West. And in the prairie states, notably North Dakota, natives are beginning to understand the ecology of trees and soil from the great shelterbelt planting of the 1930's. Luxuriating now in "beautiful lanes of verdure, holding down the soil, conserving snow moisture, reducing fuel bills, and giving beauty to the landscape," they are again planting 11,000 acres a year in seventy-three soil conservation districts, writes State University Extension Service forester John Zaylskie.

Former Governor Karl F. Rolvaag of Minnesota, a leader among governors, rescinded the bounty on timber wolves.[17] On the side of industry Parke, Davis (for but one example) collects soil samples and isolates 34,000 cultures of microorganisms a year in the hope of making the exciting discovery of a new cure for some still unconquered disease. And one of the many other endeavors is that of scientist A.W. Kuchler, who is leading a vast mapping of the nation's vegetation to give us insight into the patterns of existence, a needed inventory of our heritage of life forms and their relationship to man.[18]

"Less than a century divides the era when America was looked upon as a Garden of Eden or savage wilderness and the time when it took first place as the world's industrial giant," historian Arthur A. Ekirch, Jr., reminds us. "Probably no people have ever so quickly subdued their natural environment. . . ."[19] They have, moreover, subdued it with a brutality and lack of foresight that have left the world gasping. Yet most scholars still pretend an abiding faith in our American future.

However, it is almost without exception a faith in man working with nature, not in his ability to continue the pitiless and pitiful fight against her. The great engineer-designer Richard Buckminster Fuller, who launched the International Union of Architects' ten-year plan of "world redesign," says: "The universe is so successful, I simply want to learn its principles and apply them rather than to exploit it blindly and fear for survival."

"Man," says natural scientist F. Raymond Fosberg,

director of Nature Conservancy, "is doomed to extinction if he cannot be persuaded of his dependence on an intricate life process and his need to respect and protect that process at every step in order to deserve its respect and protection." Where only a few years ago popular naturalists like Bernard de Voto and "Ding" Darling stood almost alone, ecologists are today buttressed by the biggest brains in publishing, industry, and government. Department of the Interior's old and hated Bureau of Predator and Rodent Control has been rebaptized the Division of Wildlife Service, and its approach greatly broadened in the public interest.

We do not live to ourselves; man was not meant to live to himself.

When Dr. Alfred G. Etter, western representative of Defenders of Wildlife, lost his dog to strychnine set out by a State Fish and Game agent "to kill a few magpies to save a few pears," he wrote a touching memorial. Some of it went as follows:

> It is strange how unimportant each of us may seem in the great fairy ring of life, yet how good it feels to touch a dog, to hug her big head, to feel the beating tail against your leg. In the great range of time and earth, it is good to know the feel of other life, to wipe away the loneliness of being man.

> For that which befalleth the sons of men befalleth the beast; even one thing befalleth them: as the one dieth, so dieth the other; yea, they have all one breath; so that a man hath no preeminence above a beast; for all is vanity.
> Eccles. 3:19

Chapter Six

Space and Sprawl

News Item: "It takes six times as much land to feed people a steak diet as it does to feed them cereal." Former Secretary of Agriculture Ezra Benson, 1957.

News Item: "California alone can expect three million acres of open land to disappear by 1980 under the searing progress of growth."
Population Reference Bureau, June, 1964.

News Item: In spite of "substantial qualitative improvement" in agriculture, there will be "a rise between 1980 and 2000 of over 30 million acres in cropland needs. . . . The estimated demand for forest products is so much larger than the foreseeable domestic supply that something like 300 million acres would have to be added to the existing 484 million acres of commercial forest land in order to meet the Medium projection in the year 2000."
Resources for the Future Foundation Report, 1963.[1]

News Item: "Our calculations show a land 'deficit' of 50 million acres in the Medium projection for 2000 even assuming that every foot of mountain, desert, and swampland has found a use in one of the categories of demand. Eliminating even as little as 60 million acres as not suitable for any of the projected uses, the indicated deficit rises to 110 million acres. . . ."

Resources for the Future Foundation Report, 1963.[2]

News Item: "By 1975 . . . unless more land is found to put in use for crops than now appears likely, that will mean a per capita acreage of only 2.25 assuming the *minimum* population figure. When that level is reached, Americans must use their land much more intensively than at present or begin to think in terms of more cereals and less meat in their national diet."

T.S. Buie, U.S. Soil Conservation Service,
North Carolina.[3]

Thus ends the Great Steak Era, and the drop toward an Asiatic diet begins.

But this is not the whole story. The Foundation's report makes no allowance for any rise in recreational needs for the crowded millions between 1980 and 2000. "The myth [is]," says Harold Gillian, in the *Sierra Club Bulletin,* "that the need for park and wilderness areas increases at the same rate as the population." Then he quotes Lincoln H. Day of Harvard: "Actually it increases about four times as fast as the population owing to increased leisure, higher incomes, and the growing popularity of outdoor recreation." [4] Also, it might be added, owing to the growing percentage of youngsters in the total population.

News Item: "Developer predicts twenty-five big new cities in thirty-five years . . . a new city boom is almost upon us—one not so different from the industrialization process that mushroomed scores of cities through the western half of the nation between 1840 and 1900."

UPI release, November, 1965.

News Item: "Given full play, all of the identified demands for land by the year 2000 add up to more than the 1,900 million acres *total area* of the forty-eight contiguous states."

Resources for the Future Foundation Report, 1963.
Where will the missing 110 million acres come

from? Where will the acreage for the twenty-five new major cities throughout the country be found? Whereas the population growth rate of the world is set by United Nations Demographers at 2 per cent, the growth rate of towns is set at 4 per cent, and many big cities are expanding at the phenomenal rate of 5 to 8 per cent.

Where will the great masses of Americans of the years to come find recreation, nature, enjoyment? The earth is limited, as Charlotte E. Mauk reminds us: "There can be only so many sleeping bags laid down, only so many campfires built, only so many pairs of feet walking across before the damage exceeds the annual restoration." [5]

Thus ends the Great American Wilderness Era, and the Cement Desert Era begins.

What does a cement-coated world do to humans whose feet for a million years have loved to tread the springy forest soil and sand? We do not know; we only know what it does to pigs. Let us quote from a recent clipping at hand:

> Pigs raised by rancher Bill Silveira of Tipton, California, became neurotic and developed ulcers because they couldn't act like pigs. . . . The trouble lay with the concrete pens in which Mr. Silveira kept them. "Nature designed the pig to root for his own living," he explained to the Council of California Growers. "When you keep him on washed-down concrete, where he cannot root for food, he can become frustrated into an ulcer case."

Basically, the space competition is between men and their cars; [6] either one of these exploding phenomenon can smother the continent.

Travelers rhapsodize about Venice possibly more than about any other Old World city because, in large part, it has not and cannot succumb to the automobile. In that city of over 350,000 everybody is a pedestrian or a *vaporetto* passenger. Nobody risks his life dashing across streets or breathing poisonous fumes; traffic noises and confusion are forgotten.

What a contrast to Los Angeles, the city that supinely capitulated to the automobile and is now strangled by its freeways and their foul breath like a man in a tank of boa constrictors. Washington, D.C., is bidding for such a fate, dispersed as are its workers and shoppers far and wide over the landscape because of the automobile. Few cities indeed which enjoy Chicago's advantage of being situated along an extensive shoreline have adapted the shoreline to a lovely drive that siphons off travel without bisecting the city. Many visiting foreigners from less favored lands agree with Russell Baker's ironic evaluation in the *New York Times:* "America—it's a wonderful place to drive, but I wouldn't want to stop there."

For the next decade the American scene that will experience a population growth of 58 million will shudder under a disproportionate avalanche of 50 million space-consuming cars. "Already," comments Edward C. Crafts of the Bureau of Outdoor Recreation, "automobiles occupy more space in America than do people." A four-lane highway consumes up to fifty acres of land per mile, preferably of the most level and strategically located.

The car is not only a monstrous land-eater itself, but it abets that insatiable land-eater—endless, strung-out suburbanization, commented the *Architectural Forum* back in 1956. "Our old way of figuring density of so many persons per square mile has now become irrelevant. The crucial figure for United States planning is now density of cars." [7]

Even in disuse and old age the car is crowding man out of his environment. A technological explosion in the steel industry which calls for richer raw materials has reduced the demand for scrap metal. Although feverish research is now going on to find some profitable way to utilize the blight of automobile graveyards, the profit has gone out of scrapping, and eyesores of acres upon acres of rusted hulks scar our landscape wherever we turn.

It costs $8.00 to tow away one auto. Yet three of

them compressed into a compact bundle after all the extras and paint have been removed bring just $8.00 —if a buyer can be found. No wonder that Boston is plagued by derelict autos abandoned on its streets—at least one every day. Chicago has gone into the junk business and as a public service accepts old cars. However, with the passing of the highway beautification bill, hopes are high that improvements will not be too long delayed.

Everywhere the battle for open space is bitter, the competition mounting. The most profitable uses—however unsightly, ill-considered, or shortsighted—have been crowding out less lucrative but more aesthetic uses. "A new highway, a new facility, a new development, each tends to go where resistance is weakest, and this is usually an existing park or some unspoiled open space," writes Joseph J. Shomon in *Audubon Magazine*.[8]

Atlanta has cannibalized more than 60 per cent of its park land. Over cries of outrage the historic Morningside Park in Manhattan is giving way to a school. In Milwaukee and Portland, Oregon, the pressures have built up concern and rancor. New schoolhouses, as in Albany, New York, frequently elbow their way into parks and recreational land.

Richmond, Virginia, with its approximately 300,000 population, is often cited as a forlorn example of park consumption. The director of the city's park and recreation department, Jesse Reynolds, has had to sacrifice land in exorbitant amounts to highways and development. Complains this expert: "Already, Richmond misses the desirable goal of having ten acres of open recreation area for every 10,000 citizens. We've only 50 per cent of that now." Richmond, like so many other cities, is the victim of a turnpike that cost most of one park and an interstate highway that will eat up another. A third park, Maymont, is in the process of sacrificial slicing.

A UPI release from Danvers, Massachusetts, tells of a seventeen-mile stretch of Interstate 95, a ten-year-old superhighway, which has already become outmoded and unable to handle the traffic and must now "be replaced by an even more super highway . . . at a cost of more than $14 million." But the real irony of all this spending is that man is always a few decades too late in his projects. The spatial demands and death-dealing fumes of today's automobile will (unless drastic changes take place in its design) almost surely ban it from the hearts of all cities within a dozen years. The automobile has made itself so obnoxious in close quarters that the trend to bar it from the city rather than invite it more easily in, seems inevitable. Henceforth, these costly highway monstrosities that have choked, decimated, and paralyzed movement in so many metropolitan regions will remain, to deface and restrict living room forever.[9]

Economically, parks are far more sound than are residential developments. Suggests Hugo Fisher, Administrator of the Resources Agency of California:

> The next time someone rises in your council meeting to say, "Why certainly a park would be nice, but we can't afford it—we need the land on the tax rolls," you ask him to show you the long-term figures. I say to you, here and now, that the land in parks is almost always more profitable in a community than that same land would be on the tax rolls. Most urban land on the tax rolls goes into residential developments. Does your city *really* make a tax profit from residential developments?

He continues:

> Before accepting the tax roll argument, I suggest we add up the costs of the new schools, the new streets, the police and fire protection, the sewage facilities, and all the other services necessary to any housing development. Then . . . contrast this with the increased values in areas surrounding land dedicated as parks or open space. Why is the highest priced land often around parks and golf courses? [10]

Recently, the director of the New York State Health Department's Bureau of General Engineering and Sanitation Services, Joseph Salvato, stunned a hundred local officials at a professional meeting. In this state of 50,000 square miles he asserted there is a critical scarcity of land for the disposal of refuse. By 1970 the average daily per capita waste per household from this consumer-centered society of ours will amount to 4.8 pounds, a real challenge to those responsible for finding holes to bury the refuse in.

It is a mammoth problem, this question of space. So many misuses of land are irreversible. The fertile cropland once hard-topped, the wilderness once chainsawed, the river bank once scarred by factory sites, the mountain top once skinned, these are decisions you don't unmake. Appreciation of this fact is difficult for Americans to come by.[11]

In the year 1800 there were 104.2 acres for every man, woman, and child in the United States. Even in 1870 with the population almost 40 million there were 48 acres for each individual in the country. By 1900 the figure had been lowered to 25 acres per person, a lot of elbow room and hardly a favorable environment in which to raise questions about battering and mauling the landscape or wearing out farms.

By 1930 there were many more people but no more land. The average had dropped by 40 per cent to 15 acres a person. Much of this land had limited use; only 3.91 acres per capita were suitable for cultivated crops.

Today, counting all the inhospitable deserts, mountains, and swamps there are but 10.6 acres for each person in the nation. The cropland so abused over the years has now shrunk to but 2.6 acres per person. As we have seen, the U.S. Soil Conservation Service expert, T. S. Buie, predicts 2.25 acres per person as the danger point—a figure probably to be realized by 1975.

No wonder, too, that the Population Reference Bureau in 1964 prophesied that within six years it might be necessary for vacationers to make reservation for the national parks two to three years in advance. "If we continue our population numbers game, eventually no one can win the right to freedom and solitude by the sea or in the forest—regardless of how much time or money he may have. The stakes are dwindling all the time."

On October 20, 1965, the Department of the Interior's Assistant Director for Planning and Research, Daniel M. Ogden, Jr., reported that while there were but 3 million visitors to the national parks in 1930, there were 73 million in 1960, and "this year 110 million are expected." He adds: "There were 187 National Park areas in 1961. We have added 23 new ones in four years."

Why, then, many may ask, does the National Park Service keep on encouraging more and more visitors? Paul Tilden, in *National Parks Magazine,* recently made the caustic comment: "There is no easy answer to [the] overcrowding . . . but we are sure of one thing: the answer does not lie in actively soliciting more park visitation. And that is exactly what the Interior Department is doing with its current program for more airports in or adjacent to National Parks." The airports would be improvements to serve heavily visited units of the national park system, say Park Service officials. "Presumably such units would then be even more heavily visited. What kind of reasoning is this?" asks Tilden disgustedly.

William R. Catton has recorded in moving words what it means for a father of three young boys to have the thrilling adventure of park experience still available.[12] Determinedly, he had prodded little Phillip, four years old, with encouraging pushes, wheedling, and promises of candy for two long, steep miles up Gobbler's Knob at Mt. Rainier to the fire lookout.

"The view from there is magnificent . . . there are few places . . . where one can get such an exhilarating sense of freedom and of being in tune with the world," he writes. "This feeling was especially strong on the afternoon we were up there, as there was a layer of scattered clouds just below us in the valley between Gobbler's Knob and the Big Mountain. Truly we stood on Heaven's threshold."

Not much was said. The youngster sturdily negotiated the two miles back down the mountain. But when they reached the bottom and just as they emerged from the woods, young Phillip turned and solemnly shook his father's hand. "Thank you, Daddy, for bringing me here," he said. Adds Mr. Catton: "What more could a father want?"

That mystical moment on top of the mountain, alone with nature, will never be erased from Phillip's mind. But moments of aloneness with the virgin beauty of forest, seacoast, or mountain, which lift the heart in a thrill that no civilized experience can equal, may soon be erased forever. "National Parks are created for people. But people—as their numbers increase—are a threat to national parks," continues the author.

"What does it matter if we have four children instead of three?" parents may ask.

"Unless we expect our children to show more reproductive forebearance than we were willing to," replies the author,

here are the implications of simple arithmetic: if we stop with three children, and each of them emulates us and has three children, etc., we will have nine grandchildren and twenty-seven great grandchildren; if we have four children who each have four, etc., we will have sixteen grandchildren, and presumably sixty-four great grandchildren. Erosion along the Wonderland Trail two generations from now can be greatly hastened by the difference between twenty-seven sets of footsteps and sixty-four. And the ratio gets even larger in the next generation, and the next.

National polls show 96 per cent of Americans want something done about saving land—and want it now. It is no enjoyment to wait in long lines at park entrances only to be turned away, to scrounge desperately at nightfall to find a place to park a car or pitch a tent, crowded in like animals in a stockpen, or forced to pick up other people's garbage before you can set out your lunch.

But more important than polls are indexes of action. A private non-profit organization, Nature Conservancy, has with individual and foundation support set aside 200 small tracts throughout the nation. These tracts are notable for their uniqueness as "living museums." It has a backlog of hundreds of projects, land areas that local groups find attractive and valuable and wish to remove from the path of the devouring bulldozer.

With the passage of the Wilderness Act signed on September 3, 1964, Congress has regularized the actions of administrators in preserving tracts of unusually beautiful wild land for future Americans. It now remains for public demand to back the Wilderness Society, the Sierra Club, the National Parks Association, and other public-minded organizations, as they strike out to establish, within the remaining six or seven years allotted them, an inviolate wilderness sanctuary for a future world that will surely, sorely, need it.

But wilderness is fragile and vanishes when outdoor toilets, roads, motors, and great swarms of people invade it. Its hiking trails beckon the wilderness lover of every age; horses and canoes it welcomes to its heart, but the "facility-minded" has no more place in that majestic solitude than he has appreciation of it.

Therefore, a special Bureau of Outdoor Recreation has been set up in the Department of the Interior for the outdoors lover who, though forgoing the experience of complete wilderness, longs for the open streams, beaches, lakes, picnic- and campgrounds, swimming facilities, less ambitious trails, or just for the solace of being surrounded with nature.[13]

Now state governments have launched long-range plans for outdoor recreation programs. New York State began the action in 1960 with a $75 million appropriation for open spaces and parks; New Jersey followed with a "Green Acres" project that was endorsed by the electorate three to two.

In 1961 Wisconsin Governor Gaylord Nelson (now U.S. Senator) spearheaded a $50 million investment program in open lands over the head of legislative opposition and with the whole-hearted blessing of the voting public. Minnesota in the same year worked out an open-space program of major proportions. Ohio, Florida, Connecticut, and Pennsylvania followed suit. Today recreational waysides, scenic easements, artificial lakes, wetlands, wildlife refuges, and recreational trails such as Wisconsin pioneered are an accepted activity of almost all the states. All these are admirable "holding actions," and all require utmost public support lest they fizzle out like a shooting star.[14]

But more important, perhaps, than the creation of new parks is the rationing of the old. Practical officials forecast a hefty admission price system for all parks, state and national, in the years just ahead. Already a fee of $7.00 for admission (for one whole family) during one calendar year to all national forests, parks, and monuments, has been instituted. This is "Project Golden Eagle Passport," a pocket card all automobile owners are urged to purchase, the receipts of which go into the vitally important Land and Water Conservation fund for the purchase of more parks and recreation lands.[15] But the Golden Eagle Passport is nonetheless the biggest bargain in America today.

Rationing in the years ahead will be something else again. Soon, getting into a national park will be considerably more difficult than obtaining tickets for the biggest Broadway hit; it will be a case of waiting until your number comes up on a list—perhaps years from when you want your vacation.

As the demand for more and more park space spirals with each passing year, the overflow of park rejectees—from twelve to fifteen million Americans—hopefully pack their tarpaulins and mosquito dope to invade the national forests for their vacations. Staunchly the forest rangers man their watchtowers, all the while building 8,000 to 10,000 new picnic and camping units and repairing 10,000 battered ones each year.

But even the national forests are becoming overcrowded, and new ones are hard to come by these days. And since, despite Secretary Freeman's more exalted directions, forest rangers are still being drilled in the 1890 creed that gives first priority to the forest's cash potential rather than to its human values, recreation among the stumps and within earshot of a buzz saw may sometimes prove disheartening.

In an attempt to stretch our limited recreation lands, the theory of "multiple use" is advanced, which properly means that lands intended for timber may also pinch-hit as recreational lands of various kinds. This is a valuable concept in commercial forests, where farsighted industries are beginning to provide facilities for great numbers of park-rejects to camp and vacation. But the danger with the glib use of the term "multiple use" is the tendency to reverse the coin and introduce the ax into lands intended for primitive recreational enjoyment alone—an incompatible switch.

For wilderness is so fragile that if forced to accommodate disturbance in the slightest degree it will vanish before our eyes, robbing all Americans of tomorrow of the true wilderness experience that our forefathers knew. Rare indeed is the nation still blessed with the irreplaceable treasure of true wilderness—and it is ours only because the white man has so recently taken over this vast continent that he has not yet been able to tame every corner of it. Scientists emphasize that the uniqueness of the American wilderness is in itself sufficient excuse for its vigilant protection against "multiple use" invasion.

Secretary of the Interior Udall has recently gone a step further. "Some lands," he remarked in September, 1966, "must be saved even though they will not be used, will not, perhaps, even be seen by people this year or next. They must be saved because they are an irreplaceable part of the American inheritance." To which Wallace Stegner adds: "We simply need that wild country available to us, even if we never do more than drive to its edge and look in. For it can be a means of reassuring ourselves of our sanity as creatures, a part of the geography of hope."

Americans, bred to wide unimpeded horizons, find themselves acutely annoyed by the crowded conditions when they sally forth for a presumably restful outing. Caught in a frightful crush they take the traffic jam as just a temporary stroke of bad luck, not the warning sign of an inexorable future. Motorists held up in bumper-to-bumper traffic in and around parks howl loudly for more roads. But every road that we can build, though the engineers work day and night without ceasing, will be filled as soon as the concrete is dry!

More and more roads simply destroy what the traveler has come to see, and in themselves call for more cars and more congestion. In many places all that more roads and facilities accomplish is defacement (such as is now occurring in the Great Smokies, for example) without relieving congestion in any noticeable degree. When the seats in the coliseum are sold out, they do not build another tier in front of the already-seated customers, which would not only block their view but would leave no floor space for the show; instead and without apology, they snap down the box office curtain.

Before many years have elapsed an individual or corporation or political subdivision proposing the destruction of land for a particular use, however economically profitable, will have to clear its proposal with public authorities, who will weigh it on more sensitive scales. It will be considered not only presumptuous but intolerable for an individual to foreclose for all time a historic application of land to the welfare of man.

There are many costly, desperate, and far-out propositions being formulated for alleviating our open-space crisis. But, like all our efforts so far toward rehabilitation, they are cures of symptoms, not of the disease. They all strive toward accommodating the agglomerating masses, toward fending off consequences now long overdue. Few are the valiant who dare attack the cause of the complaint. Our "cures" for congestion thus far are all aspirin for the headaches, while the disease spreads in the nation's body untreated. Aspirin is not to be discounted; it is needed so that the mind is relieved to concentrate on the real cure. But it should never be set forth as the cure.

Queries Secretary of the Interior Stewart Udall politely: "Is it not time to ask whether man, as part of nature, is subject to the laws that govern other species, particularly the law that for every species in a particular environment there is an optimum population?" And if, because of weak wills and weaker minds, we are some day forced by federal ukase to resort to a pill to solve this problem of space shortage, it certainly won't be aspirin.

Chapter Seven

The Great American Thirst

Water, the water of earth's rivers and lakes, has been the nursemaid of mankind. From the days of our first true ancestor, Cro-Magnon, man has loved rivers above all other dwelling places.

It is believed that this Man of the Old Stone Age, a refugee from Asia's glacial cold, first looked out upon the ivy-draped banks of the Dordogne River in France some 25,000 years ago and knew that he had found his home at last. The river answered his every need. After the blizzard-swept plains of Asia this friendly valley of sparkling water, where the warm sun pressed back the glacier, and berries, nuts, and toothsome bulbs abounded in the moist soil of the banks, must have seemed like a caveman's version of heaven.

First, water sculptured out man's caves and furnished shelter, drink, food, and protection. Then water offered a protective moat from the enemy, fostered agriculture, transportation, trade, power, and manufacture. With few exceptions every great metropolis, every great civilization that the world has ever known, has built on some body of water, usually at the mouth or on the banks of a principal river.

Today it happens that man, using water in infinitely more ways than he has ever used it before, has made himself more dependent on it than ever in history. And the United States, leading the world in water consumption as in the consumption of all resources, faces an anomalous situation: pinched and worried as we now are while using 360 billion gallons of water a day, what are we going to do in 1980, when we shall be using (or think we shall be using) 600 billion gallons a day? Since water is the primary resource, the condition of the water supply is the most vital physical index of a nation's well-being. Gauging by this index, we have in the past decade suffered a very sharp decline in the quality of our living standards.

Not only have our arid West and Southwest, which have been harnessing their rivers and pumping up their fossil water for many years, taken alarm as they run out of rivers and see their water table sink. Even the water-lush East, whose wastage of this first resource (now officially linked by court decree with oil, gold, and marble) shocked investigating Secretary of the Interior Udall, has suffered a traumatic awakening.

The cause, as is always the case, was an emergency situation resulting from a five-year drought that so lowered the Hudson, Potomac, and other rivers that the raw sewage on the river bottom churned up in the motorboat's wake, and the foul waters were blanketed with the bellies of dead fish. Americans are notoriously addicted to ice water, but of late, when it is no longer served in a restaurant, the Easterner has learned to shrug it off with the air of the true Continental. When, however, he is forbidden water to wash his car, he is frankly miserable.

Actually, it was not the forty-five-inch deficit in rain over the drought period that caused the water crisis in the East; the drought only brought a long developing situation to a head. Most of the time when the crisis was mounting over the past several decades the normal thirty to forty annual inches of rain kept falling, and the natural cycle from sea to clouds to rain never faltered. The Earth, however, has only so much water; we have never had a drop more, and we shall never have a drop less. The fresh water that we use is indestructible, but it is also finite, measured. In contrast, people are an uncontrolled eruption.

Let us repeat the staggering statistics: if the seas' waters were spread equally over all the Earth's surface the entire globe would be inundated nearly 9,000 feet deep; there are some 314,000,000 cubic miles of water in all the oceans (compared to 3,000 cubic miles of fresh water in Lake Superior); there are nearly 6,000,000 cubic miles of fresh water sealed in the polar caps; 1,000,000 cubic miles, roughly, are contained in the earth's upper crust (to a depth of 2,500 feet), and probably two or three times that amount exists in the deepest aquifer (to a depth of 15,000 feet). Earth's fresh-water lakes and seas hold another 30,000 cubic miles of water—and we in North America are the lucky holders of one-fourth of this amount.

Associate Chief Hydrologic Engineer of the U.S. Geological Survey Roy L. Nace, who presented these concise estimates to a meeting of scientists of the American Association for the Advancement of Science, went on to tell them that there are perhaps only 3,000 cubic miles of water in the topsoil, approximately the same amount in the atmosphere at any one time, and still another 75 cubic miles in all Earth's rivers and streams. Truly, the inhabitants of a world with this awesomely bountiful, intricate water system will never run out of water. What we are running out of is usable, reachable, potable water—and this, after all, is all that counts or will ever count to us.

Why, since we are richly endowed beyond conception, can't we make use of it, make more of the unusable salt water usable, more of the unreachable water reachable, transform the soiled water into potable, and renew our heritage? Briefly, we are in a technological bind, because our people and uses of water are exploding so fast. When the late Senator Robert Kerr's Select Committee on National Water Resources issued its two-year report [1] a few years ago on the water situation, Senators Engle, Hart, McGee, and Moss were so disturbed by the findings that they warned: "Stripped bare of jargon, the facts are tough . . . , shocking . . . , frightening. . . . They will be soft-pedaled only at the nation's peril."

Hopefully for the future, the so-called Clean Waters Act which the Johnson Administration pushed through in 1965—if properly buttressed with funds and not strangled to death, bit by bit, in courts—has set goals for cleansing our watercourses, source of much of our water supply. But we have turned a historic corner. Never again shall we wallow in water.[2]

Our living standards, therefore, in regard to our most precious physical resource, water, have deteriorated, and in two directions. *First,* we are pinched because our available water per capita has shrunk phenomenally; *second,* the water that we are now using is greatly inferior in quality to anything Americans have ever known (or tolerated) before. And so great is the lag, so lingering the public apathy, so miserly the rehabilitory measures thus far,[3] that our plight will worsen seriously before any measures can improve it.

Considering the first half of this murky picture, the U.S. Geological Survey tells us that "every part of the United States has at least one type of major water problem . . . becoming more acute and widespread as population and industry grow." In 1965 we used 359 billion gallons of water a day, says the Department of the Interior, which amounts to some 1,900 gallons per capita per day for all uses. We use 145 gallons per capita per day domestically. Congressman John Blatnick of Minnesota, who has long sponsored remedial water legislation, says that we each use more than 12 gallons for a shower and that leaking taps and pipes dribble away an estimated 300 million gallons a day in New York City alone. Researchers C. K. Kline and R. D. Fox of Michigan State University have discovered that faucets leaking 150-degree hot water at the rate of but 30 drops a minute will waste 54 gallons a month. At 60 drops the waste is 113 gallons, and at 120 drops, 237 gallons. When the dribble is a half inch long the wasted water amounts to 1,014 gallons per month! For this profligacy we pay for 13, 28, 58, and

248 *extra* kwh. per month, so the wastage is two-pronged.

There was considerable mirth in New York City when, during a temporary water shortage a few years ago, dry Texas sent up a truckload of the liquid labeled: "Have a drink on Texas." That amusement was short-lived.

Texas has little to laugh about. In its high plains the citizens are drawing 7 million acre feet from the water table that nature is recharging at the rate of only 50,000 acre feet per year. In one 25,000-square-mile area in New Mexico and Texas, natives have been pumping it out 140 times as fast as it is trickling in.

The Mississippi basin wells are 400 feet deeper on an average than they were ten years ago. Nebraska has dug 27,000 wells since World War II, sucked down its fossil water table more than 15 feet, and will run completely dry in from 50 to 100 years. Alarmed, a special legislative committee has been formed. It doesn't take the world's best banker to draw up the balance sheet on this kind of withdrawals.

Washington, D.C., will try to pre-empt by 1970 a daily allotment of 1,200 million gallons from the Potomac, which happens to be 200 million gallons *more* than its average midsummer flow in normal years— 400 million gallons more than its flow in dry years! "They aren't looking for engineers," remarked one hydrologist drily. "What they need are legerdemain artists with a good background in black magic." It is scarcely to wonder that Carl G. Paulsen, former chief hydrologic engineer for the U.S. Geological Survey, said with some disgust, "Americans have become a nation of water gluttons."

But profligate as American households and cities are, agriculture and industry gulp water in quantities that make the meters and water officials' heads swim.[4] Examples without number have been cited in press and pamphlet about the industrial water hogs. Suffice it to recall here that one modern paper mill takes more water each day than do the people of a city of 50,000.

And as for agriculture, it takes, under present methods, 40 gallons of water to grow the feed for one egg; you may brood over that at breakfast. Every ton of corn rations 350,000 gallons; this you might also ponder at breakfast while munching your corn-fed bacon.

Irrigated agriculture *consumes* 60 per cent of the water it draws; industries, such as iron and steel (mammoth users) and chemical, pulp and paper, food and aluminum, suck up billions of gallons of water but turn back all but 2 per cent of it—hot, poisoned, and not fit to use, however.

We hardly dare look into the projected future. The water projections have an element of unreality, of fantasy, that questions the sanity of the projectors. Six hundred billion gallons a day in 1980 and 900 billion in the year 2000?

Surely the St. Thomas native who, with no water for toilets, furtively places his night soil outside his door for collection may envy the uncounted gallons of water thoughtlessly run down our drains here in America for washing a handful of carrots. In parts of Mexico women walk fourteen miles a day with a jug to and from the nearest well. In jam-packed Hong Kong the traveler learns to save his slop from washing teeth and sponge bathing to flush the hotel toilet; in homes and apartments spigots are open for a short period *once every four days*. Of late in our largest city, water inspectors have begun to snoop about in private apartments and homes seeking to discover a dribbling spigot, a leaky toilet. Does no one yet see a hint of the regimentation to come?

With all this coming competition for water there is evolving some high-pressure politicking. The water engineers fill their professional journals with pleas to run our water systems on a business basis, to judge and allocate water intelligently, to meter, to slash waste. But local politicians don't read these journals. Nor do they mend fences any more. They caulk water pipes.

An administrative official in Charlotte Amalie, St. Thomas Island, lowered his voice as he confided to us:

"The eleven senators just won't let water pay its own way. Low-priced water is a vote-getting issue." In the States mayors and governors alike avoid dampening their constituents' ardor with water restrictions. The Romans had their bread and circuses; the modern politico has his shower bath.

"Because water is the central material problem of mankind," according to the *Monthly Letter* of the Royal Bank of Canada (which has become a potent force of conservation in the Northeast), "the nations of the world have banded together to study it over the next ten years. They call this operation "The International Hydrologic Decade.'" Unless we can quickly marshal research and institute a completely new approach, we "are heading for more and bigger problems . . . and for eventual extinction."

What is being done, and what have been proposed as solutions? [5]

Big dams are a temporary expedient for local retention of water; but they are victims of diminishing returns.[6] The storage capacity of a reservoir may have to be increased four times to double the dependable flow; evaporation often outruns the advantage of the added storage capacity (Lake Mead gives up the top seven feet of its storage to the action of the sun annually), and dams always silt up. It is only a question of years before they are useless monuments to ugliness.

Compared to the storage qualities of nature's aquifers, the biggest man-made dams are puny things indeed. In our present primitive hydrological state, big dams offer potent control of floods, hydroelectricity, and limited water supply, but most of our important interstate rivers have already "been damned to death"; and if atomic power develops as predicted, their principal excuse for being (hydroelectric production) will become obsolete within twenty years.

Other expedients to save water abound. Industries are urged to recycle their waste water after cooling it, to be used again and again; a movement to poison phraetophytes (water-loving plants and trees) is under way along the watercourses. Cloud-seeding has not been abandoned as a means of inducing rain, although the experts honestly assure communities that no cloud-seeding should be counted on to furnish much more than a 25 per cent increase from rain clouds that are already overhead.[7]

Another gallant attempt to add to our water bank is the recharging of the aquifers. Long Island storm water basins have been in operation for twelve years; today Nassau County has 400 or more of them. California has also pioneered, but the vanguard in this truly hopeful approach is pitiful indeed. To recharge the aquifer with our effluents seems to be to defeat everything, to willfully plunge us into the irrevocable predicament of a completely septic environment.

There are many grandiose schemes that have recently been submitted to relieve our acute pain of water deprivation. Some geniuses at big (and covetous) thinking suggest a wholesale diversion of Alaska's plentiful water via a great ditch straight down the continent, a rape of ecological relationships that would probably drain the western half of the continent dry, leaving nothing but desolation and deserts. There are scores of plans for sucking out the Great Lakes with pipes splaying southward in all directions. Sadly for this horrendous possibility, the Great Lakes are already down by so many shore feet that docks and lake cabins are stranded far up beach, and Lake Erie is "dying" in a morass of repulsive slime.

One or two unwitting wagsters have proposed towing down from the North Pole gigantic icebergs of pure unsalted water and melting them in the harbors of our great cities, piping the water into the skyscrapers where, it is assumed, ice coolers may be eliminated.

There is also desalinization. Many desalinization plants are building, and the hope is high that the cost of such water, many times too expensive now, may be made practical.[8] Industry tries to hold water costs down to $.10 or $.15 a thousand gallons; smaller water users pays a public utility between $.12 and $.28

a thousand. Water is now being desalted for about $1.00 a thousand, far out of reach for most uses.[9]

No major breakthrough is yet in sight. Freezing, and electrodialysis now being tried in Israel, are two more expedients, but the day is near when water will demand its own price. Atomic energy seems the best bet for cheaper-than-a-dollar-a-thousand water, but this would require mammoth plants producing mountains of unwanted salt, in addition to the dumping of loads of boiling hot brine into our bays and streams. This is not to mention the quantities of deadly radioactive wastes that would have to be disposed of—somehow.

After being bombarded with the idea that water desalting (once it can be made economically feasible) will solve all water problems of the future, it is discomforting to probe into the cold statistics. "The 200 or so desalting plants around the world produce only some 50 million gallons daily. By contrast, New York generally uses over 1 billion gallons a day and at a cost of only 20 cents per thousand gallons," says David R. Francis, business and financial expert.[10]

But let us look ahead and credit all the rosy predictions of the big business prophets. "Westinghouse talks about a 20 billion gallon daily *world* desalting capacity by 1984," says Francis. However, it is a cold douche to read next that by the same date, 1984, the Department of the Interior projects the water needs of this nation alone (not of the world) as 600 *billion* gallons!

Moreover, all water desalting, which would necessarily take place near the ocean, would create the expensive problem of pumping the water *up* and, after treatment, pumping it thousands of miles inland to where it is most needed. This last difficulty bothered investigating scientist Sir Charles Darwin, III, so much that he concluded it was a fatuous dream. Desalting is being energetically pursued not only by Westinghouse but by American Machine & Foundry Company, Baldwin-Lima Hamilton Corporation, Chicago Bridge & Iron Company, Aerojet-General Corporation, Dow Chemical Company, Bechtol Corporation, Fluor Corporation, Ralph M. Parsons Company, Foster-Wheeler Corporation, Badget Company, E. I. Du Pont de Nemours & Company, and Monsanto Chemicals. Even so, a gigantic water deficit looms ahead. Price hikes are inevitable, but by 1984 price will long have ceased to be of importance. We shall be desperate.

The most sensible, and productive of most generous results over the long run, are the measures that work with, not contrary to, nature. Nobody has ever discovered a more competent way to hold water from running away to the sea than nature's original plan. America's primeval forest soils contained 137,000 pounds of humus per acre, and one pound of humus will store two pounds of rainwater in a wet spring, releasing it gently to the streams as it is needed in the dry season. Today, after stripping our forests and eroding off the humus, we find our once-forested soils contain only between 20,000 and 70,000 pounds of humus per acre, and sometimes almost none at all.

To rebuild our water-giving, life-giving humus, we must again clothe our watersheds with trees and native foliage plants. But stripped land has other long-term damaging, although less obvious, effects. Civil engineer Frank D. Steiner of California has published a pamphlet encompassing a lifetime of serious study concerning the effects of "careless men and voracious animals" on once fertile, flowering land. "When a watershed is subjected . . . to paving, draining, and urban sprawl, excessive terrestrial heat plays havoc with established climates," he writes.[11] Terrestrial heat engenders atmospheric dryness, which in turn causes *failure in the rain cycle*. A Senate document published in 1936 shows that the precipitation curve in California between 1850 and 1934 underwent "a downward trend of eight inches . . . during the eighty-five year period. In other words, the annual average precipitation in California dropped one tenth of an inch each year. The downward trend did not stop in 1934. . . ."

Steiner continues:

The loss of cloud-borne water from 1850 to 1960 on 75 million acres of California's land area (minus 25 million acres barren land and deserts) amounts to 412 million acre-feet which represent the accumulated losses of precipitation on the basis of 1/10 inch per year. The average annual precipitation in 1850 was estimated at 33 inches. In 1960 there were only the equivalent of 22 inches recorded.

To curb the onslaught of the deserts world-wide, Mr. Steiner advocates "bio-technological means, i.e., all the means modern technology can offer plus massive forest shelterbelts." [12]

We are now in such a condition of crisis that we shall undoubtedly have to resort, sooner or later, to myriads of mammoth, grotesque technological complexes all along the seacoasts to manufacture needed water. They are, however, desperate expedients, offering comparatively meager supplementation at best. They can be more disastrous than helpful in the end if we accept them as "the cure." Let our salt palaces and salt mountains not lull us into the belief that we can get by without strenuous watershed rehabilitation of a nationwide order.[13]

In Brandywine Valley of Pennsylvania a small band of farmers, devastated by the disastrous flood of 1942, got busy contouring, strip farming, tree farming, water holding, and planning guided runoff with the result that in 1955 (only thirteen years later), when thirteen inches of rain fell in ten days: "the damage was negligible, the flood waters almost clear, and the meadows were ready for grazing the next day. . . . Most every factory in the valley was saved," related farmer J. W. Hershey.

Hydrologist Dr. Norman Curtis of Cobleskill, New York, found that an eighty-year-old maple woods stored 12 inches of rain the first day, tapering down to 4½ inches on the eighth day, while open land held but 3½ inches the first day, depleting to less than 1¾ inches on the eighth day. In Utah conservation methods applied to the watershed doubled the available water for irrigation.

The nationally famous (and fought over) Adirondack-Catskill Forest Preserve in New York State was established as a 2.5-million-acre "forever wild" preserve back in 1894 *not* primarily for recreation (as is the mistaken notion today) but primarily as a water preserve—a vast watershed to supply future New Yorkers with the water the Board of Trade wisely foresaw they would need.[14] It has worked in a miraculous fashion to do just that, furnishing New Yorkers with eleven rivers, swamps, and thousands of lakes, and maintaining the ground water levels, without which New York State would long ago have shriveled into non-productiveness. Those who, either thoughtlessly or in greed, would now abandon the "forever wild" clause in the Constitution, which has thus far insured our life-giving waters, and who would further "open up the locked-up forest" to recreation that pollutes and to lumbering that destroys humus, water, and cover, might well ponder this irrefutable fact. Can we today afford to reduce the water retention of even one square mile of our limited watershed?

As for the value to our water supply of the national forests, Michael Frome [15] writes as follows:

> Many rivers are born of snows and glaciers and rain within the National Forests. On this sonorous roll call of beloved American streams are the Yellowstone, Platte, Rio Grande, and Colorado; the Green, Salmon, and Snake; the Klamath and Trinity; the Wisconsin, Current and Au Sable; the Allegheny, Potomac, and James. . . . The National Forests protect water supplies of hundreds of cities and towns, and furnish irrigation water, flood protection and hydroelectric power.

And Abel Wolman Associates, Johns Hopkins University, concluded in research conducted for the Select Committee on National Water Resources of the Senate that "Possibly the greatest public benefit of these areas . . . *is for their watershed value and not for grazing, timber, wildlife, or recreation.*" (Emphasis is ours.)

Other efforts of great value in keeping the continent from drying up are those that seek to save and encourage the swampland. Swamps are the cheapest kind of surface reservoir we have—where we are lucky enough to have them. Florida, which spent $100 million to cure its problems of "too much water" by drainage, found its wildlife dying off, fires sweeping great areas of muckland, and salt water busily seeping into the depleted water table. Now they have to spend $400 million more in a first effort "to cure the problems created by the first $100 million."

The prevention of fouling what good water we have with out wastes is, of course, the immediate need. It goes far beyond more intensified treatment of wastes; it now demands a complete overhaul of all our disposal methods. It involves revolutionary methods of waste reduction, transformation, and re-use of which we have never dared to dream.[16]

The first step is the separation of the storm sewers from the domestic sewers. In the hearings on the Water Pollution Control bill in the House, water officials told how in a storm the plants simply could not begin to handle all the flow of combined sewage and storm runoff, and so they "just skipped the whole thing," and the rivers suffered.

Metering of all water is around the corner; it is logical and inevitable. Metered water may greatly widen the social gap between the Washed and the Great Unwashed. "We are without doubt the last generation to enjoy luxuriant use and a luxuriant attitude toward water," as a member of the League of Women Voters put it. The League of Women Voters and the Izaak Walton League have been among the first to recognize the coming water famine. A 900 per cent increase in the price of water, as predicted in *Nation's Business,* can indeed change some pins on the graph of the gross national product.

Lewis Herber [17] predicts a 100-billion-gallon-a-day shortage by 1980, and it appears now that this is no misty dream. The seriousness of the outlook is revealed most clearly by the heresy of the proposed cures, one of which in John Bardach's words is: "It may be that the impending pressure on rivers, streams, and lakes, not less than upon the land itself, will force a decision to regulate the rate of increase in population." [18] This, the most bizarre solution of all, is the only permanent answer to this whole truly desperate problem.

Once there dwelt a King in a tiny but very fruitful kingdom, bordered all round about by cruel and barren lands. But the King was sick unto death. Brought to his bed by all manner of self-indulgence he groaned in his suffering and irritably bid his court physicians to heal him. Now, the leeches (as the physicians were yclept) had long known the true remedy for the King's malady, but it was an unpleasant one—so unpleasant they feared the King's ire should they apply it.

So they quickly applied expedients—pain-killing drugs and unctuous reassurances. But while these dulled the King's misery for an hour, they soon left him feeling more wretched than before. Then the leeches resorted to opium, but this, while it furnished the ailing King with periods of blissful fantasy, also passed away, leaving him worse off in stomach and temper than ever.

Then the wisest of the leeches said, "The King is our Protector. Without him we are destroyed. We must bravely abandon expedients; we must concoct the ancient herbal remedy and forthrightly puke and purge the King; it is our only chance." So this they did, and the King, now deathly sick, was surprisingly unresisting.

Within seven days the King began to improve. Finally, he rose from his bed feeling like new. But as soon as he felt recovered, the King, in his ignorance, returned to the unrestrained dining and carousing, as was his wont, and the tumefaction returned upon him worse than before.

Now, what all these sycophants—leeches and wise men—at the King's bedside knew well was this: that

no cleansing herbs or remedies ever devised could restore lasting health to their ruler unless he ceased glutting himself and reduced his swollen girth. But who
would tell the King what to do? Frightenedly, they
conferred together and wrung their hands, but not one
among them could muster the hardiness to tell his Sire
the blunt and unwelcome truth, or seek to curb him.
And so, for risk of offending the royal temper, they
cravenly let him die.

The world today is a sick world, drained of its life-
giving waters and toxic with the wastes of too many
people crowded into too many congested areas. All the
river dredging, diversion of streams, poisoning of
phraetotypes, the cloud-seeding, much of the dam
building, the re-use of waste water and sewage—all the
frenetic busy work of a foolhardy civilization whose
water resources are on a permanent decline but which
refuses to admit it—are merely the treatment of symptoms. They are temporary pain-killers—the aspirin of
science.

The "water pipe dreams," which would slice through
a continent to drain down Alaska's water to feed our
insatiable economy, which would suck out the hearts
of the already shrinking Great Lakes, which would
lasso the icebergs—even those that would, hopefully,
desalt enough water from the oceans to fill our endless
unrationed demands—these are like the opium fed the
King: they give moments of blissful fantasy, hallucina-
tions of well-being. They can, however, but postpone
the moment of truth.

There are, then, the true remedies: the replanting of
watersheds, the anchoring of topsoil, ecological upper-
stream treatment with small reservoirs and small dams,
the saving and restoring of rivers and swamps, the
cleansing of the watercourses, the husbanding of water
by universal metering. These are the ancient but effective natural remedies for the world's water problem
today.

But, as with the King, how can even such medicine
sustain the world in health indefinitely unless the *cause*

of the sickness is removed? Is John Bardach prophetic? Will it, as he suggests, be the grave lack of water that will at last force upon us regulation of population increase? Is it a choice between excessive breeding—and the water necessary to human life? If so, who will tell the Queen?

Chapter Eight

Ravished Wonders

President Lyndon B. Johnson, playing the lead part in his own production, the signing ceremony for Assateague Island Seashore National Park, stepped downstage to ally himself with Theodore Roosevelt as a defender of our heritage. Said he:

> Conservation has been in eclipse in this country ever since Theodore Roosevelt's day. Members of the House will listen with care because conservation had barely gotten off the ground when Uncle Joe Cannon, the Speaker of the House in those days, issued one of his many ultimatums, and he said: "Not one cent for scenery."
>
> Well, those days are gone and forgotten, and we are going to start repealing Cannon's Law here today.

Really repealing Cannon's law calls for more than additional legislation, the President has insisted. The pressure of population for sources of energy, for municipal water, for lumber, for irrigation, is forcing us to the most cruel and irrevocable of choices.

We are following in the steps of the Egyptians, who also once proudly ruled the world. Today their fecundity has forced them to a major desecration in the building of Aswan Dam. That the ancient awesome temple of Abu Simbel, a sculptural wonder located above the dam, will be forever inundated, becomes an irrelevancy as the Egyptian population gnaws at the vitals of the countryside. As the frantic race for food accelerates, the free choice of the society is gone, and the temple of beauty gives way to the dam of utility.

For generations we spared the Rainbow Bridge that nature sculptured. But suddenly under the impact of economic progress and the claims of a growing population it, like Abu Simbel, had to give way. Today the shifting waters of Lake Powell lap about the natural wonder that we, as a nation, in all our presumed affluence could not afford to keep inviolate.

The oil and gas interests press heavily on the Kenai Moose Range of Alaska and demand development of the Katmi National Monument. Although there are twelve existing ski areas on national forest land within a one-day round trip of Los Angeles and fourteen more good sites (some already developed) within two and one-half hours' drive of the city, the skiing interests are now attacking the San Gorgonio Wilderness Area. The dam builders threaten the Bob Marshall Wilderness Area of Montana with the Sun Butte dam.

And, says Editor Michael Nadel of *The Living Wilderness* (winter, 1965–1966 issue), out of nowhere the Olympic National Park, Washington, a region conservationists believed they had saved after a long-drawn-out controversy, has been assailed by a *one-man* study team. Mr. Fred Overly, Regional Director of the Bureau of Outdoor Recreation, proposes a 69,000 acre slice from this unmatchable rain forest to be handed, say conservationists, as a "timber grab" to the lumber interests. Strange indeed that one man should be given the prestige to place so outrageous a proposal before the February 11, 1966, hearing held by the Senate Commitee on Interior and Insular Affairs and to force its consideration. There is one pregnant difference: while Egypt bows to the destruction of its ancient beauty in deference to food, we are doing so merely for additional profit in an already glutted economy.

Yet for all our dollar worship, who in any past era would have proposed the slightest desecration of the incomparable Grand Canyon of the Colorado! Yet for

an unbelievable moment the Secretary of the Interior
approved the construction of the Bridge Canyon dam
below that National Park and the Marble Gorge dam
above it. The first would have backed water into the
park for thirteen miles, and the latter would have held
back the river's water within the Canyon and wiped
out, as a geological force, the "river flowing" that has
created the Grand Canyon.[1]

It was Theodore Roosevelt who stood on the Canyon's rim on May 8, 1903, and warned:

> In the Grand Canyon, Arizona has a natural wonder
> which, so far as I know, is in kind absolutely
> unparalleled. . . . I want to ask you to . . . leave it as it
> is. You cannot improve on it. The ages have been at work
> on it, and man can only mar it.

Despite a courageous renunciation of the proposal by
the Administration, the Bureau of Reclamation and its
allies are trying to keep it very much alive.[2]

What the Grand Canyon and the Olympic National
Park proposals signify is the breakdown of the national
park system,[3] a confession that we can no longer afford
these aesthetic islands, that the tides of economic avarice must inundate them. All this at the very moment
when the Administration is endeavoring to rouse the
consciousness of natural beauty in the American mind
and heart.

It is less than a decade ago that the projected Echo
Park Dam in Dinosaur National Monument on the
Utah-Colorado border was barely defeated by an
aroused body of conservationists. Though the battle on
behalf of the park system was won at that time, the
scouting forays of the dam builders revealed a vulnerability in the defenders. It was this: their lines were too
thin to hold by themselves, and the mobilization of the
general public was hampered by a dazed disbelief—a
disbelief that such sheer effrontery could ever be advanced. The fact is, there is today no national wonder
that is any longer "safe."

So here we are dazedly struggling to stop the instal-

lation of a hydroelectric power plant that menaces the
Grand Canyon, heritage of breath-taking beauty for all
Americans. We are condoning by our silence the leveling of 69,000 acres of already preserved Douglas fir
and Sitka spruce in the Olympics to beggar our heritage further. Some call this the age of affluence; others
the "era of ravished wonders."

Dr. Alfred Etter, former professor of biology at
Michigan State University, comments:

> Not long ago a proud note in a Las Vegas, Nevada, news-
> paper declared that a giant new electric sign had been put
> up on a new hotel. Seven thousand light bulbs and several
> miles of neon would keep three men occupied full time on
> repairs and maintenance The "peak" electricity from
> Bridge Canyon would subsidize *this* kind of candle power
> —though candle is scarcely an appropriate term any
> longer. *Why darken the grandest canyon in the world to
> light such ephemeral and frothy development on our des-
> erts?* Is this the "developing" America that we must bow
> down before and worship? [4]

Next door to Stanford University on the attractive
Palo Alto Peninsula forty miles south of San Francisco is the proud little town of Woodside. It is pleasant and attractive. And what is more its citizens love
the town as a retreat from the commercial ugliness that
scars so much of the face of America. And it is these
aroused citizens of Woodside who but lately won the
national spotlight and made their community a symbol
of the frustration the preservers of beauty everywhere
seem to experience. Quite gallantly this handful of citizens dueled with great utilities, government bureaucracies, and educational behemoths in a losing battle to
avoid the defacement of a network of high-voltage
overhead transmission lines cutting across their little
town.

Briefly, the Atomic Energy Commission drew up
plans for a 5.3-mile-long 220-kilowatt transmission
line to join up its new $125 million Stanford Linear
Accelerator Center at Stanford University to the
Monte Vista-Jefferson power line of the Pacific Gas &

Electric Company. Woodside, in the path of the marching steel stilts, not only passed an ordinance to compel the builders of the lines to go underground; its City Council voted a boost in the local tax to cover its share of the cost of burying the lines.

After a number of court victories which ordered federal agencies to obey scenic ordinances, the AEC, well-entrenched in congressional circles as well as corridors because it is permanently pregnant with patronage, rallied its congressional friends to the passage of a special law exempting the AEC from such ordinances. Keeping a research program on schedule and a research team intact—these indexes of progress could not be sacrificed to aesthetics nor even to the rights of the citizenry to have its local laws respected. The fact, too, that a $1 million overhead transmission line would cost $2.5 million if put underground was economically unsettling, particularly since it might create a precedent for all the high-tension lines of the booming future.

The point is that, all our new resolutions of knocking the dollar from its throne to the contrary, when the individual decision comes up, we have not been strong enough to "kick" our profit addiction. We continue in the obscene old routine as, bit by bit, our environment shrinks and is further scarred under the rapacity of our primitive greed.

The California coastal redwoods, equaled nowhere else on earth, trees which antedate Caesar and the birth of Christ, are no more able to withstand our avarice than are the little Woodsides of the nation. Let us examine the tragedy that is happening to them as we pictured it in some of our 1966 writings.[5]

Each new morning now there is a great ugly gap in the skyline where only the day before massive 2,000-year-old coastal Redwoods towered. Yet while the chain saws moan day and night seven days a week, feverishly converting a great American heritage into grapevine stakes and lawn funiture, a strange and eerie quiet grips Washing officialdom. The end of all hope for a National Redwood Park—the only hope to save this beauty resource from its destroyers, the lumbermen, floods, and highways—is in sight.

Yet but two years ago, spurred by public outcries and pricking conscience, the National Park Service collaborated with the National Geographic Society in a thorough study of the Redwoods and came up with plans for a wonderful park on Redwood and Prairie Creeks, a park of 90,000 acres (even this is small as national parks go). It would include Prairie Creek State Park plus 33,000 acres of the best of the remaining untouched stands. Within its boundaries would be eighteen miles of rare coastline where roam the last of the Roosevelt elk. It would save the world's tallest trees.

Said President Johnson at the time: "It is possible to reclaim a river like the Potomac from the carelessness of man. But we cannot restore—once it is lost—the majesty of a forest whose trees soared upward 2,000 years ago!"

At once Representative Jeffrey Cohelan in the House and Lee Metcalf in the Senate introduced this bill into the Congress. Fifty Senators and Congressmen rose to sponsor it. Generously, the President set aside $10 million to start it off. . . . Hopes soared. . . .

Then strange things happened.

It would be enlightening indeed to discover what went on behind scenes in the Interior and Insular Affairs Committee as the wealthy lumbermen (just three) brought their pressures to bear on the government of all the people sitting in this committee. The pleas of thousands of letters, telegrams, and telephone calls from the rank and file could not force the people's representatives to consent to a hearing.

Finally, the silence broke. The Secretary of the Interior came forth with a brand new bill, completely surrendering his former proposal. It is a pitiful substitute indeed. Centering on Mill Creek in Del Norte County, the proposed park of the Administration would take in 43,800 acres—hardly big enough for a redwood to lie down in. Worse yet, one third of the area outlined is already a part of two State Parks—the Jedediah Smith and Del Norte Coast. All Udall's proposal amounts to is the link-up of these two State Parks with but 7,800 acres of virgin redwood forest, and the purchase of an upland watershed already 75 per cent cut over!

Should this pinchgut substitute come to pass and should we be brought to these sad straits, we suggest a modest delegation of bureaucrats make a pilgrimage to the so-called park and tack up an appropriate sign lettered "THINK LITTLE."

How can this fiasco be forestalled? Enough public outcry can yet salve a respectable Redwood National Park. The original proposal based on the National Geographic Society's two-year survey can be pushed. This is the Cohelan-Metcalf measure, backed not only by the National Park Association, the Izaak Walton League, Wilderness Society, Audubon Society, Wildlife Management Institute, Citizens for a Redwood National Park, Federation of Western Outdoor Clubs, Trout Unlimited, Public Affairs Institute, *New York Times*, Nature Conservancy, *Washington Post*, Cleveland *Plain Dealer*, *Chicago's American*, and editors and scientists all over the nation—not to mention thousands of garden and service organizations and millions of just plain people who love trees. It would cost us $140 million—which comes to about seventy-five cents per American.

In the meantime the "vindictive logging" that was launched to devastate the proposed park acreage before either park could be created finally aroused with its arrogance the ire of President, Congress, and people. Under Presidential pressure a year's moratorium on lumbering in the proposed park areas was agreed to while this nation made up its money-oriented mind on the question: "Can we afford to set aside a park large enough to insure survival of the redwoods?" [6]

In the face of our surfeited economy a billion board feet of these surpassingly beautiful giants are annually being chopped up to the very edges of the proposed park for a host of mundane products that find themselves in the trash heap in a few years. Concerning the possible cutting of the newly discovered world's tallest trees in the Arcada Company's tract, the *New York Times* remarks editorially: "To cut these trees for lumber would be like dismantling the Statue of Liberty for its salvage value in scrap metal." Yet just about the time the tubs and lawn chairs and garden fences have found their way to the dump yard, all these peerless, unprotected old stands of virgin redwoods will be gone.[7]

As for the straggly 50,000 acres of state parks and memorial groves clustered here and there like small beads on the highway string, they will, because they are not in solid chunks or complete watersheds and therefore violate the hydrological cycle, be doomed to eventual destruction by wind and floods. This is not to mention their decimation through the whimsies of state road builders. These most spectacular living things on earth will have been blotted out in one generation for temporary economic gain *for a small handful of people*. The report of the California Redwoods Association tells us that the redwoods have survived in California for 30 million years. Think of it! What is the word, then, for one passing arrogant little generation that is preparing, as of this writing, to destroy them for all time?

Across the continent another natural wonder is fighting to survive under the blows of expanding demands. In 1966 we drove down to discover for ourselves what was happening to it. "In the late 1800's," Assistant Superintendent Carroll Burroughs of Everglades National Park told us, "you could paddle a canoe from Miami to the other side of Florida. Where before there were twenty alligators there now is one." The Everglades of southern Florida, a 1.4-million-acre ecological unit of subtropical wilderness, is an exotic haven for a collection of birds, animals, and vegetation not matched in this hemisphere.

We saw the strangulation of the Everglades. Its once clear, moving waters were shrunken to shallow pools and to muck, its wildlife expiring, because of a vast engineering work to the north which arbitrarily and alternately holds back its life-giving waters or drowns out the Everglades at the pleasure of the northern counties. The spill-over of flood water from Lake Okeechobee has for thousands of years seeped and drifted slowly down for long distances to the sea, feeding the rare life of the Everglades. Then, reaching the salty tidewaters, it has mingled and fused with them to form and nurture a multitude of estuarine life which, say the naturalists, is "a thousand times more productive than that of the surrounding waters."

But man, in the form of the Corps of Engineers, interfered with a long barrier dike. This dike, reports naturalist Peter Farb who studied the situation for the Audubon Society, "is really a vast land-reclamation project (involving) more land than all the irrigated acres in the famed Western big-dam projects." Built, charges Mr. Farb, "for the benefit of a few land-owners and real-estate developers," it is nonetheless paid for by the nation's taxpayers.[8] Ironically enough, these taxpayers are actually being taxed for the destruction of a national wonder that presumably belongs not to Florida fast-buck artists but to the American people.[9]

Naturalists all over the nation, and principally at the University of Florida, have roused to battle, since not only does the peculiar fresh-salt water environment provide for the multimillion-dollar-a-year shrimp fishery and $775 million per year income to the state of Florida, but these estuaries are literally "one of the richest breeding grounds for fish and marine life on the continent."

As a national park the Everglades is a strong tourist attraction which accommodated over 977,600 persons in 1965 and an estimated million plus in 1966. But a visit there now is truly a disheartening experience. Unless Florida can respect and protect the balance of the Everglades quickly, tourism will dissipate. In 1966, after years of disastrous drought, the sluice gates were cavalierly opened to divert hurricane floods from the north and the once-parched area was deluged, drowning the wildlife. Thus, under man's management the water level has been gyrating from extreme to extreme, decimating flora and fauna. As with the coastal redwoods, nobody wants to visit a graveyard, whether it be of beheaded sequoias or of decaying tropical wild-life.

Then, there is what we have done to one of the original "Seven Wonders of America"—Niagara Falls. We cannot afford to permit water to flow unused over the Falls merely to look at. We pretend a cultural interest while a delegation from the International Conference of Composers huddles around Sir Ernest MacMillan blowing a pitch pipe on the note "C" in their effort to detect the tones in the water's roar. We are pleased when Kucharski, the Soviet composer, reports the sounds exciting and seeks to translate them into music. But we are not at all incensed at greater and greater diversions of the waters of the Niagara River to the hydroelectric turbines.

The Niagara River is only thirty-six miles long, but it is one of the most powerful, tempestuous, and spirit-stirring rivers in the world. It flows from Lake Erie into Lake Ontario, thus draining four of the five Great Lakes. In its short course it drops 300 feet, including the 160 feet of Niagara Falls. Undisturbed by man, the Niagara River spills 200,000 cubic feet a second over the brink of the Falls.

But with the installation of hydroelectric plants that seek to provide the equivalent power needs of a city of 3,500,000 persons, more and more of that water is being diverted. Mayor Franklin Miller of Niagara Falls, Ontario, observed that "if any more water is taken from the river for power purposes we won't need the new international bridge, because people will be able to walk across the upper river."

Under treaty between Canada and the United States 100,000 cubic feet a second *must* flow over the Falls during the day in the tourist season; even so, there are some slide rule specialists who wonder whether the tourist spends enough to warrant such wanton waste of commercial energy. There is strong pressure from the power interests to cut back the summertime flow to 70,000 cubic feet a second.

Of course, during the night and during winter a feeble 50,000 cubic feet escape to splash over the brink. Disappointed off-season honeymooners resort to comparing the picture postcards they had dug out of their grandmothers' trunks with the tamed and jaded spectacle of today. No more does the pleasant shock of cold mist in the face assail the tourist who leans too close. At night even the sharp ears of the United Kingdom Composers Association would have difficulty detecting all twelve tones they heard in the roar.[10] At least six go to light the lamps of what's becoming China.

In Arkansas there flows a mountain stream so rare, so beautiful that it has been nominated a national river by the National Park Service. A movement to set it aside as such has gained momentum. But while the defenders of the Buffalo River exult over its beauties and exclaim over its natural charm, others have marketplace measuring sticks. The United States Army Corps of Engineers has determined that flooding forty-five miles of the middle section of the river and destroying its wild and untrammeled character is "economically justifiable."

Can the Ozark Society, created to preserve the beauty of the Ozarks, defend the Buffalo for its pleasure-giving qualities, the distinctive charm which is the real worth? No, the Society is compelled to argue the case down in the countinghouse where one challenges an impoundment by the salability of the Kilowatts.[11] It is like arguing whether a nation should make a harlot of its beauty queen on an estimate of the fees she would earn. That is exactly what we are doing as we prostitute the Buffalo River and our other natural beauties of primeval forests, lakes, and canyons and permit the raping of our wonders for the dollars they will bring.

With what swelling pride American geographers once taught school children about the unmatchable Great Lakes! These were the largest freshwater lakes in all the world. They were invaluable, envied by all nations. Americans of a former day played in them and around them, used them for pleasure boating and excursions, grew rich on their commercial fishing, and exulted openly that these mighty reservoirs were a positive insurance from midwestern water shortage for all time.

Then we proceeded to destroy them.[12] The cities on the shores piped their offal, ships and industries spilled their effluents into the waters that had once been as clean as fresh rain. Green Michigan, and cold blue Superior to a lesser degree, turned gray, and what had been a nation's pride became a nation's problem.

Then suddenly a lake got sick. Lake Erie, which stretches for 250 miles from Detroit to Buffalo and has long choked on the industrial refuse of parts of Michigan, Ohio, Pennsylvania, New York, and Ontario, went into the first spasms of approaching death. Besides the acids and oils, wood pulp, and pesticides, Lake Erie now suffered from the seepage of ordinarily constructive elements of man-made chemicals, nitrogen, and phosphorous. These artificial fertilizers have the cancerous effect of accelerating the aging of the lake. The fourth and shallowest Great Lake is dying faster than any other well-known body of water in the world.[13]

"In Lake Erie," says Wisconsin's Senator Gaylord Nelson, "the percentage of chlorides—which closely reflects municipal sewage pollution—is 230 per cent higher than in 1900. The water also shows an amazing concentration of calcium, sodium, potassium, and sulfate compounds. It is no longer simply water. It is a chemical tank."

Lake Erie produced 75 million pounds of good fish as late as 1955; a great lake that has been there for uncounted millenia dies slowly. The last count some years back tallied but 38 million pounds of rough fish. It is inconceivable that anyone would want to eat the flesh of these forlorn polluted creatures. Some believe that this lake has probably gone beyond the point of no return.

"But don't feel too badly," urges Senator Nelson with a deft touch. "American optimism is equal to a defeat of such a magnitude. It turns out that the Corps of Engineers is now planning to build a whole new lake—even bigger than Lake Erie—*in Alaska.*"

Chapter Nine

Flight into Eternity

But the Alaskan Rampart Dam, which would create for us a new American lake of expansive beauty to console us in our loss of Lake Erie, has a less beautiful side to it.

Continues Senator Gaylord Nelson: "Nowhere in the history of water development in North America have the fish and wildlife losses anticipated to result from a single project been so overwhelming." The federal Fish and Wildlife Service reports: "The $1,300,000,000 cost to taxpayers is nothing compared to the loss of salmon, ducks, moose, and fur animals." (The cost to the Eskimos is something else again.)

Dr. Howard Bradley, honorary vice-president of the Sierra Club, who has spent some time on the scene paddling up the winding channels of the mighty Yukon where the salmon now run, and evaluating the Yukon Flats that would be lost, declares this piece of land "unique for all North America for its richness as a breeding and rearing area for water fowl and for its moose, caribou, grizzly bear, mink, fox, beaver, and other fur-bearing animals that thrive among its thousands of lakes and ponds."

Scholars on the subject, such as Howard Kuhns at the University of Alaska, have conducted research showing that this towering structure, which would flood 11,000 square miles of prime American wilderness, would also be a gross economic blunder.

The industries it would (happily) attract would have to buck very high costs of labor and very high costs of transportation for the minerals and raw materials, most of which would need to be imported. The great Pacific Northwest, to which the Rampartites propose to sell "all surplus power" already has (according to its own Bonneville Power Authority) plenty of surplus power of its own, comments Dan Swift in a recent *Defenders of Wildlife News*.[1] Felix Steyckmans of *Isaak Walton Magazine* adds the acid comment: "Bear in mind that the Ranpart Dam plan calls for a reservoir so large it will require twenty years just to fill it after the dam is built."[2]

Izaak Walton Magazine also documents the fact that "there are coal deposits (in Alaska) which could . . . produce power at a cost of about 4 mills." Quite generally (but cavalierly ignoring the oceans of radioactive waste to be produced) economists forecast that atomic power will make such a hydroelectric dam obsolete within twenty years. "But," said a biologist with a shrug, "the boys with the bombs are looking for some excitement out of it." Their moment of joy will not, however, return to us the rich wildlife heritage it will indisputably annihilate.

Back in 1935 Edward A. Preble deplored "the will to destroy, which is still dominant" in the American character. Our love of wholesale slaughter, he said, is historic, and it is not a proud record.

> About 1870 [he wrote] as many as 1500 ducks (principally canvasbacks and redheads) were frequently killed on Chesapeake Bay in a single day; one man killed 187 canvasbacks in a day and 7000 in a season. Somewhere 118 ducks were killed at one shot, and two men killed 1500 in one day. Four men killed 400 teal in one day. One discharge of a Mexican armada (several barrels united and shot together) yielded nearly 4700 ducks at one discharge.[3]

Such accounts make most hunters today shudder. But we still have sub-humans among us to sicken the most dauntless sportsman. In June, 1965, some of this sort approached Santa Barbara Island in California, set aside by President Franklin D. Roosevelt in 1938 as a refuge for all wildlife, and senselessly fired into herds of big clumsy sea lions sunning themselves on the rocks.

Let the *Los Angeles Times* continue with the story:

> Riddled with bullets, dozens of dead and dying sea lion, a few sea cows and at least one sea elephant littered the beaches, rocks, and tidal pools, some still moaning in agony. The senseless carnage evidently was the work of one or more riflemen who circled the island in a boat.[4]

The perpetrators of this cruel slaughter probably did it "for the sport of it"—not merely to cause suffering. But it is of interest to note here other subterfuges used to mask predation or just the killing instinct. When non-lovers of pigeons want to exterminate the birds they inform the press that they have found neoformans in their droppings—a fungus that may be found everywhere in air, soil and in the droppings of many other animals (man not excluded), as well as in the juice of fermented peaches! [5] Likewise, when some comrades thirst for a good fox hunt, they suddenly discover a rabid fox chasing an infant around his playpen. And it was a few yarn-spinning gunmen who loved to watch a winged eagle topple from its dizzy heights, not the old wives, who invented the heart-rending tales of eagles snatching newborn babies from the midwives' helpless arms. Man is indeed ingenious when he wants an excuse for blood-letting.

In the process of the copious slaughter that has marked American history over the centuries, we are told that there are now seventy-eight species of mammals, birds, reptiles, and fish in danger of imminent extinction.[6] For all of these Secretary Udall is entreating greater protective legislation. In the world at large, says Mr. Peter Scott, son of the hero of South Pole fame, and president of the International World Wildlife Fund, "since the last dodo bird died in 1681, on Mauritius, more than 100 other species have become extinct

. . . today 1,000 more species are threatened." The International World Wildlife Fund is incorporating all this in *The Red Book,* at once dubbed the "Doomsday Book."

In 1869, 11,000,000 passenger pigeons were shipped from Michigan in forty days, says the naturalist W. J. Schoonmaker, from *one town!* To enumerate and describe the demises of those species unfortunate enough to be occupying Earth at the same time as *Homo sapiens* and forced to pay for it with their lives is to repeat a tale told many times and falls in the category of spilt milk. States a release of the Department of the Interior,[7] "In less than 150 years, nearly forty birds and mammals have disappeared from the American scene, about half of them since 1900." We are really speeding it up.

We can do nothing now for the passenger pigeon, the ivorybilled woodpecker, the heath hen (which we drove into its last stand on Martha's vineyard and then released an army of house cats to polish off).

It is bootless now to consider the passing of the Gull Island meadow mouse or to retell how great earth-moving machinery graded the island for a fortification and heartlessly buried them all alive. The Merriam elk of Arizona and New Mexico, the bighorn sheep of the Dakotas, the great plains wolf are gone—through shot and shell and ignorant disregard—although the plains wolf clung to life until 1930. The showy green and yellow plumage of the Carolina paroquet was last glimpsed by human eye in 1935, and the tattered remnants of the Cape Sable sparrow of southwestern Florida were snuffed out in the hurricane of 1937. All, all have vanished into the everlasting night by the ukase of mighty man. Said Charles William Beebe, the great American naturalist, "when the last individual of a race of living things breathes no more, another heaven and earth must pass before such a one can be again."[8]

What we can and must consider now are the fellow creatures whose hearts still beat—at least, a few of them—but who as a species are in real peril: the blackfooted ferret, the grizzly bear, the kit fox, elephant seal, mangrove fox squirrel, southern sea otter, Heerman's gull, the roseate spoonbill, the blue-crested elegant tern, Franklin's grouse, the great white heron, Florida's Everglades kite, the American crocodile, the green sea turtle, the Great Lakes sturgeon, grayling, and others.[9]

Biologists mourn for the great auk—big, awkward, lovable—whose passing, after ordeals of bloody slaughter, was abetted by the scientific collectors, as is so often the case. In Allan W. Eckert's best-selling book *The Great Auk* he graphically describes "the terrible tune of 'swish–thump' that marks the onslaught of profiteering hunters with their murderous clubs" and calls it the "greatest shame of all." We cringe today to recall the tangling acres of nets that our grandfathers set out in baited fields to capture and club to death the great swarms of sleek, dovelike passenger pigeons. (How wondrously competent they were! Of the estimated three billion pigeons they managed to exterminate every last one.) No longer do the pioneers of northern Minnesota dynamite the lakes and skim the thousands of pike, bass, sturgeon, and pickerel into their boats to pose proudly in hardware store windows with strings twenty or thirty feet long.

We have evolved a great deal in our attitudes and civilization since Henry Bergh had animal entrails thrown at the back of his head (no one dared throw them into his face) as he strode about the markets in New York in his efforts to enforce humane treatment of dumb creatures. But we still have a long way to go before we can be truly called a cultured society. The long list of our harried and nearly gone wildlife gives us the rich opportunity to prove our humanity as a people before the last hour has struck. These tortured species offer us a chance for redemption, and today many thousands of remorseful Americans have united in small groups to save this endangered animal, or that dwindling bird species.

"Atwater's prairie chicken, once common on the

Gulf Coast, has diminished to about 1,000 birds as civilization has encroached on its native prairie habitat," says a pamphlet issued by the Nature Conservancy, a non-profit organization of influential conservationists, who make a specialty of beating the bulldozer to some choice habitat. Texas Nature Conservancy and the World Wildlife Fund are cooperating in raising $365,000 to buy 3,400 acres of wild Texas prairie in the prairie chicken's last-ditch struggle.

Victor H. Cahalane, author, and assistant director of the New York State Museum at Albany, tells us that the population of the grizzly bear in the United States has been cut down to about 600—which maintain life only by huddling in and around Yellowstone and Glacier National Parks.[10] Adds this authority on North American mammals, "South of the Canadian boundary, the gray or timber wolf is down to 500 to 850 animals in Michigan-Wisconsin-Minnesota and Montana; these numbers are declining." As for the red wolf, he may be in even more severe straits: existing only in Louisiana, southwestern Arkansas, and Texas, he appears to be on the verge of extinction.

The whooping crane has attained more fame than any other vanishing species and elicted the most noble response from the scientists and the wildlife officials —who have gone to much expense and pains to protect its habitat and flight—to the cooperating journalists who have popularized it, making the progress of its rescue from oblivion as exciting as a horse race. Many Americans await the report on how many whoopers finally check in at the Arkansas Refuge by January of each year almost as breathlessly as they wait the culmination of the World Series. Surely this is a good sign, and the methods used to bring this beautiful specimen back from a handful of about seventeen birds in the 1930's to a current figure in the forties might well be utilized to make known and win the nation's help in saving other of our companions living on the edge of doom.

Certainly the whooper race is far from won; the new idea being pushed by some officials of robbing the nests of these oversensitive birds in order to raise more young ones in captivity may check their slow advance, even cause abandonment of their nests, and thus doom them.[11] If to some ornithologists a whooper is interesting only as a rare specimen study of *Grus Americana* in a zoo, to others of aesthetic appreciation the glorious quality of the whooping crane is his defiant scorn of adaptation to a lesser world than he knew. It is his gallantry while facing oblivion, his persistence in tirelessly tracing and retracing fall and spring the age-old patterns of his kind, refusing to be limited or tamed, that has tugged at American hearts and won him so passionate a cheering section.

In the sky *Grus Americana* becomes a symbol of all the exhilarating wildness America has known. In a zoo he becomes just a skinny, crestfallen crane with sheared and droopy wings.

There is a small but persevering band in California, sparked by Mrs. Beula Edmiston, which calls itself the Committee for the Preservation of the Tule Elk.[12] The dwindling herd of this shy but exceedingly handsome elk has retreated before the onslaughts of man to its last refuge, the Owens Valley, and even here it is being cut to pieces by hunters.

The Tule elk, they tell us, "tops the Department of Interior's list of America's threatened mammals," and the International Union for the Conservation of Nature is adding it to its list of the world's most rare species. The Committee's chairman, Walter Dow, hopes that "some day the people of Los Angeles will realize that they own the most unique natural park in the world and will set it aside as such." But whether this occurs before the heads of all these hapless creatures adorn the knotty-pine-and-chrome game rooms of a lot of second-class sportsmen, only the next few years can tell.

Then there is the plight of the big black manatee, or sea cow, which Allan Eckert describes as "a large, harmless, and rather comical-appearing vegetarian mammal which spends its life [and is now losing it] in the coastal salt water . . . of southern Florida." [13] The clownish manatee, which boasts a mustache of tentacles that push the food into its mouth in a most hilarious fashion, will not be here long to delight youngsters and old alike. So vicious has been its slaughter, because its flesh tastes like good beef, that even now with heavy protection there are but a handful of sea cows left to continue the uneven struggle to escape the dark wave of oblivion. Lawbreaking non-sportsmen covertly continue to pick them off with their guns, one by one. How high, would you say, should the fine be for the extermination from the face of the earth of so harmless, pleasurable, and unusual a form of life, which has been hanging around almost since biological time began?[14]

Akin to the Tule elk of California are the tiny, delightful Key deer of Florida. On a research trip to the Keys we enjoyed the pleasure and privilege of meeting a pair of these exquisite creatures. The ranger had picked the male out of the bay and nursed the female, who had been hit by a car, back to health. There they stood in the door of their small shelter, three feet in length and only two feet tall at the shoulder, chewing their cud and surveying us with mild brown eyes that showed no trace of rancor or of fear.

"By 1947," says the study the ranger furnished us, "this diminutive deer had almost reached the vanishing point, through over-hunting, poaching, and conversion of habitat to residential developments. The plight of the Key deer . . . resulted in the establishment of a Federal refuge on leased lands in 1954. . . . As of 1965, 6,745 acres were included in the refuge." After a patrolman was assigned to the area, the number of deer rose from less than 50 animals to about 300 eleven years later.

But the human pressure swells, pressing the deer on straits already far too narrow (nineteen are killed on the highway annually) into a corridor between the two relentless tides of men and sea. The Department of the Interior's attractive brochure *Refuges of the Florida*

Keys engenders complacency by telling not quite the whole story (as all these departmental back-slapping brochures incline to do for obvious reasons). These "refuges" of the Keys for both the Key deer and the great white heron (also diminishing) are in great part temporary leases that may be revoked at any moment. We postpone buying this land at $1,000 an acre, although we know full well it will be worth $2,000 or more tomorrow. When the pressure becomes great enough, both deer and heron will be quietly sacrificed. Perhaps that is what we are waiting for.

If extermination by indifference is to be the fate of the Key deer and the great white heron, the extermination of the American bison was much more colorful and exciting. Of the 50 million or more bison that once roamed the Western plains, no single wild specimen remains alive today. We have all read how train after train of boxcars loaded with hunters drove through their panicking ranks, the men hooting and shooting wildly. By 1890 the once-surging droves that had blanketed the plains had been reduced to less than 500 exhausted and terrified beasts. We content ourselves now with a few domesticated, managed herds, the thunder gone from their hooves and the wild light from their eyes. But we saved them from the endless night.

It is shocking to hear that there are now but nine to fourteen Florida kites in existence. The Everglades kite, which resembles a marsh hawk, feeds almost entirely on one species of fresh-water snail. As Floridian developers, draining marsh after marsh, paraphrased Uncle Joe Cannon with their slogan "Not one cent for snails," the Everglades kite retreated to a corner of the Loxahatchee National Wildlife Refuge[15] southeast of Palm Beach, where it is now all but extinct.

Florida developers are also prime agents (along with poisons and illegal shooting) in the extermination of the nation's symbol of majesty and strength, the American bald eagle. When we consider that a bald eagle, if he luckily escapes the illegal hunter, may live for thirty years, we understand the significance of the steady year-by-year decrease that worries Audubon officials so much. It means that we keep counting the surviving oldsters from whose ranks some members drop off annually, while few juvenals come to fill their places. "Nest success" is falling each year. As human population densifies, success drops. Around Chesapeake Bay, historic haunt of these giant birds, a recent tally showed nest success at but 13 per cent; the highest percentage—51—occurred in the middle of the Florida Everglades, miles away from human habitation.

The eagle eats carrion—principally dead fish—and many of these have been poisoned by insecticides (DDT has been found in every unhatched egg).[16] The bald eagle is making its last stand in Florida and Alaska. With the tall nesting trees to which it has been accustomed to return year after year razed, with insecticides gnawing at its vitals and making sterile its eggs, there seems little chance of our national emblem's survival. It is an agonizing ordeal for both ornithologists and patriots to watch.

So fades the scream of the lordly American Eagle, the scream that resounded from American coast to coast for uncounted millennia and was heard nowhere else in the entire world. So authentically American is this proud bird that we have placed it upon our coins and Great Seal and enshrined it in literature, legend, and history. Its demise, too, is authentically American: pushed out of existence by a people who could afford it neither respect for its nesting sites, protection from poisons and guns, nor even room.

Following less swiftly, but ineluctably, the path of its cousin, the golden eagle, target of the Western ranchmen, is also losing its fight for life. With a wingspread of seven feet and a speed of 120 miles per hour, the golden eagle is rather a splendid example of the Master Hand. A weak law to protect the golden eagle has been passed; the practice of shooting eagles from light airplanes with machine-mounted shotguns, which former Senator Keating denounced on the Senate floor as "barbaric, shameful slaughter," is no longer a popular sport. (One bounty hunter in Alpine, Texas, took 12,000 birds in twenty years, says Dr. Walter Spofford of the State University of New York.)

But loopholes in the Act still authorize the Secretary of the Interior to issue permits to kill eagles on one ranchman's unsupported claim that he is losing lambs. Considering the vivid imaginations of some (not all) sheep- and cattlemen in the past and their reputation for trumped-up charges, how long will the last 4,000 golden birds be suffered to exist? But perhaps no animal who averages less than one young every four years can compete with human fecundity for very long.

The airplane has been the vantage spot for the slaughter of numerous forms of wildlife, which, of course, have no chance against it. It is death raining from a heretofore benevolent heaven, and this they are not equipped to anticipate. A small news item in a local paper reads: "Polar bears have become easy targets for hunters giving chase in airplanes and armed with high-powered automatic rifles. Polar bear rugs are now in vogue and magnificent white pelts bring high prices." A weekly newspaper supplement mentions under its "interesting items" column "wall-to-wall polar bear carpeting." We are back in the buffalo age again. Polar bears are rare; the coward is a flourishing breed.[17]

Then there is the new North American sporting thrill, in description of which all adjectives falter. It was revealed with quiet anger by Art Smith in the New York *Herald Tribune*.[18]

If you have a spare $350 and can measure up to the Canadian National Railways' idea of a "Sportsman," there is a defenseless white whale waiting for you in Hudson's Bay out of Churchill, Manitoba, and he may be legally taken by the most hideous method known to man. This, the Canadian National would have you know, is a brand new "sport." This Canadian province, sings the railroad's agent, "has just come up with the final answer for the sportsman who has everything"—whale hunting!

What does an American "sport" want with a fourteen-foot-long white whale? All he wants is the jawbone; whom he will wield it against is a mystery, since he is no Samson. "Peddling the lives of white whales, whose carcasses and hides are to be sold for fertilizer, dog food, and ladies' handbags may be a cute maneuver to trap tourists into supporting Manitoba's Indians and Eskimos but . . . even a pickerel fisherman wouldn't call it a 'sport,' " concludes Mr. Smith.

Universally, the whale species is taking a beating. The great blue whales, whose 90- to 100-foot length makes them the largest animals in the world, are virtually extinct. Highly intelligent, these family-loving, slow-breeding mammals fell before the world's greed for their oil. Although Japanese, Soviet, and Norwegian whalers have led the chase in the past few years, and according to a spokesman for the International Whaling Commission, "are expected to stay on and fight for the last whale," we in the United States cannot sit on the sidelines piously pointing fingers. The whole northern portion of the Atlantic coast is one long monument to our dedicated over-killing of this mammal of the deep. How far have we come since those days? Only the white whale will discover.

In August, 1965, fifty zoologists from three continents traveled to Madison, Wisconsin, at the behest of Professor Joseph J. Hickey and sponsored by the American Museum of Natural History and the National Audubon Society. What called this emergency meeting of all those noted ornithologists, field zoologists, falconers, and professors from centers of learning on the other side of the world? It was the impending fate of the peregrine falcon—bird of prey, vassal, and companion of kings and nobles for centuries ("A courageous and swift falcon of almost cosmopolitan distribution," says *Webster's*)—that was the sole matter of concern.

The Hawk Mountain Sanctuary publication says that the peregrine is, in real peril. "The conference," it continues,

> explored the status of the Peregrine in Europe and North America, revealing its unprecedented disappearance in eastern American south of the St. Lawrence, virtually within a decade. . . . The die-off was most apparent in a loss of nesting success and failure of eggs to hatch, followed in a few years by loss of one or both members of a pair, and without replacement.

In Ontario fifty pairs traced through the years had dwindled to but three. The bird was in distress in Great Britain, the Baltic, France, Germany, and Finland as well.

For four days (and nights) the learned men discoursed on pesticides, pathogens, human encroachment. During this time Dr. Derek Ratcliffe, an Englishman, presented an impressive, documented study that traced the decline of the peregrine to the increase of chlorinated hydrocarbons in agriculture, a study which seemed to seal the case.[19] So it is that the peregrine's payment for its long and loyal service to the kings of men is in a shameful coin.

The other doomed (or seemingly doomed) bird is that giant scavenger with a wing span up to nine and one-half feet, a weight of twenty-five pounds, and a thirty-year lifespan, the California condor, of whose plight we have spoken in Chapter V, and which we shall not discuss here. "The California condor is living geology," write Dick Smith and Robert Easton in their small book (*The California Condor*). "When he is around we have a link of life to the saber-toothed tiger and the primitive past." [20]

Suffice it to ask: Are we ready to snuff out 100,000 million years of evolution and sacrifice this spectacular performer who soars 20,000 feet into the heavens, "this national treasure, one worthy of protection, respect, and understanding by all the American people"? Here, indeed, is a true test of our measure as responsible masters of all we survey. Professor Robert S. Brodey of the University of Pennsylvania calls our self-centered and callous toying around with the condor's life "an example of 'brinkmanship' in the field of wildlife management [that] is intolerable." [21] Hopefully, comments ornithologist Alden H. Miller, who has completed a twenty-four-month survey of the condor,[22] "one-third of the surviving [forty] condors are young birds."

But if the whooping crane and the California condor continue their flight into eternity in spite of all the efforts of the most noble of men to retain them, they will have accomplished one thing. They will have helped, through all the publicity of their martyrdom, to make Americans realize that it is easier and far less expensive in the long run to take advance steps to keep a species from the brink of eternity than it is to keep it from toppling over once we have prodded it to that brink. Consider our far from extinct but progressively shrinking waterfowl.

In 1962 we established a record low in duck breeding population. From a 1956 peak of some 36 million, it plummeted through years of drought (to which we apparently did not adjust our bag limits sufficiently) by 47 per cent! The estimated kill declined from about 12.8 million in 1957 to about 3 million in 1962—a 75 per cent decrease. Then in 1965 "large kills in Canada and the United States . . . reduced the duck breeding population to the lowest levels since reliable surveys were started in 1947." [23]

In March, 1966, a survey showed not only "fluctuating censuses" in all the flyways of waterfowl, but presented such a shock that Director John Gottschalk of the Department of the Interior could scarcely credit it. "The most surprising part of the survey," said the release, "was an apparent drop in the total goose population in the Pacific flyway. Birds numbering only about half of last year's count were tallied. State and Federal wildlife officials believe such a reduction unrealistic and additional surveys are being conducted to try and locate (sic) the approximately 572,000 missing geese."

The rains of 1966 plus the 1965 and 1966 additions of important waterfowl habitat (an accelerating program involving 222,000 acres and 235,000 acres in the respective years) gave the ducks a "shot in the wing" of another order. They began a modest comeback. Thereupon and immediately, shooting hours were increased to a half hour *before* sunrise on all flyways, bag limits for the day and in possession were raised, the bag limit on the flagging mallard "still at a relatively low level" was doubled, pintails lost their special protection. The State of Utah happily declared an open season even for the rare whistling swan. (Said Milwaukee ornithologist Owen Gromme: "It is like shooting an angel.") Although "the breeding population is still below the average for the last eleven years," all is back to normal on the shooting range—all, that is, except the 572,000 missing geese who never did come out of the reeds where they were hiding.

If the waterfowl population continues to decrease by 8 per cent per year and the hunter population increases geometrically, it will take a gigantic effort by the reasoning sportsmen who favor restraint to rescue this resource from accelerating decimation. Record kills of Canada geese prior to 1966 had already thinned the great wedges that are a joy to the eyes of millions of Americans as the graceful formations sweep north in the spring and south in the fall. When that far-off honking ceases in some fateful year to come, one of the most thrilling of nature's sounds will have left the world.

We are still living in the age of almost unrestrained killing. Wildlife is defenseless, its only advocate the better inner nature of man. Death is so final. And extermination of a species is playing God, but it is God without wisdom and God without scruple. For in crowding and exploiting a species into extermination we not only tear asunder the interdependent web of life of which we are a part, but we obliterate some of the wonder of creation and rob ourselves of a joy of coexistence that is priceless.

Natural scientists plead for more inviolate refuges. And while there is yet time to forestall many more bird tragedies, must our television towers be 1,000 and more feet high? As Charles A. Kemper comments in *Audubon Magazine*: [24]

> There is plenty of evidence that any tower over 500 feet is a threat to bird migrants. . . . A 1,000 foot structure is a real killer. I shudder to think what a 1,500 or 2,000 foot structure will do—especially when it is night in the middle of the Mississippi flyway.
>
> If humans can send rockets to the moon, transplant kidneys, and achieve all sorts of fantastic technical wonders certainly they can solve such a relatively simple problem as this, if they want to—that is.

The management of the Empire State Building in New York City have acceded to a plea from the Audubon Society to extinguish the lights on its top thirty floors during foggy or rainy nights because so many birds have been attracted by the illumination, have slammed against the building and been killed.

Are animals nothing more than "crops"? asks biologist Alfred G. Etter of the Defenders of Wildlife. "In these days when bookkeepers decide the fate of our landscape and thus our wildlife, we cannot afford to sell miracles at discount prices."

There is a poem so attuned to this chapter that we have asked permission to include it here.[25]

Sound of Wings

Ghost wings down corridors of time
Unseen where countless millions flew.
Now all one sees is empty sky.
No wingbeats shimmer morning dew.

Where myriads had flown to roost
The moonlight gleams on empty bough.
Plume hunters passed with eager guns;
Dead bodies float in silent slough.

No more is heard the curlew's cry
Wild, echoing, through moonlit night.
Birds long extinct, in ghostly flight.
They have gone to join the vanished bands.

Tomorrow will the condor soar?
Will eagles, symbol of our land?
Or will they too, on silent wings,
Forever join that specter band?

—Paul F. Long

Man, when he turns humane and concerned, can often save a species almost gone. He did it with the American white egret in a wonderful way. He is bringing back the glorious trumpeter swan—our largest waterfowl—which has begun to nest east of the Rockies in a remote part of LaCreek National Wildlife Refuge, South Dakota, for the first time in eighty years. "Four healthy trumpeters!" exults a Department of Interior release, "nesting on a muskrat house!" An inviolable refuge established in time, severely enforced protection, plus publicity to elicit public concern, saved them; there are now 600.

For all of human history man has dreamed of other men on other planets, his companions in our great solar system, and longed for some communication with them to help solve the agonizing, unsearchable mystery of life. In our generation he has been rudely brought face to face with the searing truth: There is no one else. Space probes have mocked all hopes. Venus, Mars, the Moon—the only possible candidates for life —seem now to be but great soulless chunks of rock and lava, hurtling mindlessly around and around their orbits until the end of time. We are alone in a dead and pitiless solar system, and all we have to console us are the wonderful, mysterious, furred and feathered creatures who share our destiny and our doom.

If man's numbers continue to proliferate, and the numbers of other creatures continue to shrink, the time will not be far off when human lives will become cheap, and animal lives precious as we fight to purchase them for museum specimens. The time-tested economic law that it is rarity that decides value has not been repealed for man any more than it has for the lemming. In all lands where too many people clutter the landscape and strain the economy, an individual life is treated as a burden of which society would well be rid.

An old Chinese proverb tells it all in three words more effectively than an encyclopedia of social customs. It is this: "Dead? Then, good!"

Part Three

Our Tarnished Standard
of Living

Chapter Ten

The City Syndrome

Seven-year-old Ann was making her first visit to her grandmother's in Los Angeles. One day the grandmother took her downtown and through the heart of the city. On her return a neighbor asked: "Well, how did you like downtown Los Angeles?" "I couldn't see much of it," answered Ann, "it was all covered with people."

In *The Web of Life,* an ecology classic, John Storer tells the story of uncontrolled growth using the example of the simplest form of life, the soil bacteria, which are vital to all other life on earth. Soil bacteria multiply by a process of fission, each individual under favorable conditions becoming two complete new ones about twice each hour. "Even if it happened but once each hour, and if each one lives, the offspring from a single individual would number 17,000,000 in 24 hours." By the end of six days the bacteria would form a bulk larger than the earth, and "every living thing on earth would have become engaged in a suffocating struggle for food and air and life." This is, of course, a statistical gimmick, a theoretical possibility of growth.

J. H. Rush, in his stimulating volume *The Dawn of Life,* offers another picture of growth, which is even more easily grasped. Again, we have the bacteria that divide to double themselves, but these do it every minute. He proposes to place one such cell in a test tube of nutrients at two o'clock. By 2:30 the tube is half full of bacteria. The question: At what time will it be full? You can hear the professor chuckle as he responds: "The answer is 2:31!" He adds: "The larger the population, the more serious the consequence of its doubling."

We have in each of these instances a glimpse of geometric multiplication; they illustrate with what unexpected swiftness, under the most favorable conditions, the engulfing end can come. The horrendous consequence of overproduction of the bacteria in the soil is, of course, only "on paper" a possibility. It is forestalled by the development of less than ideal conditions plus a great and insatiable host of predators.

In nature's original plan there were definite controls for all living organisms, an elaborate and intricate system that tended toward equilibrium. Insects (to use the most obvious example), which multiply prodigiously, are controlled, in Storer's words, by a "highly organized police force of flesheaters—bacteria, insects, mammals, and birds. . . ." That is, all reproduction is "figured." The survival of the species is insured by high multiplication rates; the danger of overpopulation is regulated by controls.

Of the 5,000 eggs which a chinook salmon lays after so much travail it is fortunate if even four make it to maturity and a return up the river to spawning beds again. The odds imposed by man's dams and silt and decaying vegetation have only added new obstacles to what was already a harrowing long shot.

People, however, although they are exploding geometrically, are doing so in an environment like a test tube, free of predators. One moment the world is half as full of people as is endurable; in a single doubling time the bounds of endurance have been burst.

Ecologist Paul B. Sears in *Bioscience* asks a very disturbing question indeed. "What conclusion would you draw if you observed a population curve, similar to that of man, in any other organism?" We would be terrified. In fact, there is no doubt that we would instantly summon every control measure from 1080 to the Bomb to save the globe from being eaten alive.

Loren C. Eisely speaks of man as a flame sweeping through the world and consuming it utterly. Says author Rush again:

> An advanced culture has been let loose in a primitive land, and for a moment, before our chance is lost forever, we have a glimpse of what life may one day be if man is willing to be man. Next to the insistent but transient threat of atomic catastrophe, the control of his numbers is man's most urgent problem; and it will be with him always.

Over the brief but tempestuous centuries of man's sojourn here, he, like all other species, has been subject to nature's controls of pestilence when overcrowded and of famine when natural catastrophe destroyed crops or game. But he also, as "a primitive in a highly technological and artificial land," learned to counter the effect of forces that would have controlled his numbers. Man has had a partial though perhaps only temporary success in the conquest of at least two of the three horsemen—war, pestilence, and famine. His victories over plagues have for the moment prolonged millions of lives in all their squalor. His phenomenal production of food paralleled the opening of the final stretches of new land as well as the initial and disproportionately productive introduction of scientific techniques. It has provided just enough nutriment to keep the vast masses lively enough to breed and yet not energetic enough to keep abreast of the countdown.

As for the controlling effects of war, we have computerized the effectiveness of hostilities and now estimate the death toll of the big ones in terms of "megadeaths," a fact that makes the ever recurring little ones seem cheap. Unless, of course, the big button is pushed, wars—limited wars—do not serve as the effective control on population that they once did.

The people of the world are not only multiplying

geometrically, they are at the same time packing their excessive numbers into urban areas. Cities and their environs are taking the brunt of growth. Within a decade or two, we are told, we shall be a nation of belt cities. There is a monotonous new megalopolis forming to extend solidly from Boston to Miami without a break. Think of a forest of billboards and commercialization, an artificial environment extending fifteen hundred miles. Think of it matched by another belt along the California coast all the way to Oregon, and still another from Detroit through the Midwest to Chicago and Milwaukee.

According to Sergius Chermayeff and Christopher Alexander, whose specialty is design, we are faced by this development with an elaborately complex challenge. "Either," they say, "he [man] must learn to preserve the existing equilibrium of life or he must introduce a new equilibrium of his own making. . . ." [1]

They said:

> Man was responsible in the past for the development of whole cities as coherent environments, but was only dimly aware of this fact through a preoccupation with buildings, streets, squares, statuary—the concrete aspects of the city. A balanced environment was provided by immediate contact with surrounding, untouched nature. Today it is becoming clear that the whole environment, as form, poses problems of quite a new order of complexity. . . . [2]

Ludwig von Beethoven, who came to the fashionable, music-loving, extremely cultured Vienna to further his musical career, could still within a few minutes' walk immerse himself in the natural beauty all about, from which he drew inspiration for his greatest symphonies. "Nature is my teacher," said this city man, who lived in a fourth-story garret in the heart of Vienna. [3]

In a world of the future we are committed to an artificial, to a man-made, environment. What this will do to man, what syndrome this will set up, we are not sure, but we have some clues. It has been discovered, for instance, that the designers of space capsules are challenged not so much by the problems of providing food and air and other physical necessities but by the need to keep the capsule's occupants human.[4] Somehow, because the capsule environment is completely man-made and envelops him without escape, it seems to create a high level of nervous stress. There would, in the professional belief of Chermayeff and Alexander, be some parallels with a crowded urban population. They say:

> At present humanity can still escape from man-made cities. But when man assumes responsibility for the whole earth, and the control of every part of it, a syndrome comparable to that found in the capsule may develop. An urban form that would probably reflect all the pressures of our time would be capable of sustaining balanced life within it, without need for escape. It would be a fully functioning framework for ecological equilibrium. Only thoughtful design can help deter further mayhem.[5]

The mayhem is with us, and whatever design can do for us is tardy. Crowded people take on a new and sinister complexion.[6] British biologist W. M. S. Russell has warned us that it will indeed be the crowded conditions that will make human aggression a desperate problem even before any serious food shortage develops. In his address before the 127th annual meeting of the British Association for the Advancement of Science, Dr. Russell stated that the most probable explanation for the rising postwar crime rates in countries abounding in food and employment is the natural reaction of any living creature toward overcrowding.

Although one must recognize the complexity of the phenomenon of crime, it seems pertinent to cite the observation of Inspector H. Lynn Edwards of the Federal Bureau of Investigation. On November 15, 1965, he said: "Since 1958 crime has increased *six times faster* than our exploding population." (Emphasis is ours.) This is not unrelated to the growing concentrations of people in small spaces. True enough, when Police Commissioner Howard Leary told New York policemen in March, 1966 to report crime more conscientiously, hiding nothing, the record on total felonies vaulted nearly 60 per cent in twenty days, demonstrating again that short-range local tabulations are notoriously unreliable. Nonetheless, the long-range FBI figures show the unmistakable trend toward increasing crime. And recently we seem to have become keenly aware of how easily the discomfort of a hot summer day in an unbearable slum—a capsule of confinement—engenders violence in the streets.

But more than mere elbow-shoving has created the most shameful crime rates in all our history. There is the loss of identity, of identification of the individual, which has helped boost serious crime at the rate of 5 per cent per year, says the Federal Bureau of Investigation. The biggest jump in the crime incidence has come in the fastest growing and in some senses most frustrating areas of the big cities—the suburbs, where it rises, if the statistical evidence is right, by 8 per cent a year.[7]

The President headlines our situation thus: "A forcible rape every 26 minutes, a robbery every 25 minutes, an aggravated assault every 3 minutes, a car theft every minute, a burglary every 28 seconds, all costing the nation 27 billion dollars a year." A fast-expanding city (Los Angeles) raised the murder tally from 177 in 1964 to 249 in 1965!

Says Dr. Russell again: "Crowded monkeys, muskrats, meadow mice and wild rats attack and even kill their young." By the same token, he adds that in the most congested section of British cities there has been a tremendous increase in the number of infants and children beaten by their parents.

Sally Carrighar documents the effect on animals—the "psychological discord—mental anguish, really—" of overcrowding. When snowhares over-produce, for example, they die by thousands "from a disease which seems to result from stress and . . . overcrowded living conditions."[8] In other animals enlarged adrenal glands, heart disease, extreme nervous conditions, even panic, result from too close contact with their kind. It is every third year that the prolific lemmings reach the breaking point, says Swedish zoologist, Professor Alf Johnels. They begin to quiver, then to run madly in every direction——anywhere where there are fewer lemmings——even into the sea.

Scientists find that in nature, birds' egg clutches decline in both size and fertility when environment becomes congested; that country mice, when moving to the city, experience a decline in fertility, too.

Man's cities, engulfed by more people than they can decently absorb, have in the process lost their own character, they have been effaced. Thus, there is now nothing left with which the city dweller can constructively identify. The city has become anonymous, the citizen faceless.[10] Little of the municipal heritage, either man made or natural, remains for him to admire, to cling to, to boast about, improve, or defend. The city itself has lost its cultural meaning. Much of it is a hostile jungle where Girl Scouts are banned in the name of safety from peddling cookies from door to door.

There is, indeed, a crisis in urban human activity, the dilemma of a mass society committed to consumption and denying to individuals the satisfactions of communal expression. "It may very well be," says the assistant director of the Chicago Archdiocesan Conservation Council, "that the preeminent task of the social actionist in the next generation will be to fight, not for collective bargaining and the minimum wage, but for beauty in its genuine sense." [11]

There is a withdrawal, a lack of involvement, in any pursuit except that of private gain. The urban society of which we are a part has deprived the mass of the opportunity for human confrontation except in commerce and denies them soul-satisfying outlets that informal neighborhoods once afforded. The crowds who surround us are rivals for space and become a nightmare of elbows. Because of the tangled multitude of problems involved in the caring for people, a city, to attain symmetry and health, must grow in measured, modulated steps with time for absorption. Today the city grows with a freakish speed, and the result, unplanned, is a Frankenstein.

The impersonality of the city permeates even those institutions that should be given over to compassion. Public institutions such as hospitals are metamorphosing from an attitude of personal care to a routine of mass care. According to Martin L. Gross,[12] errors of medication, anesthesia, blood transfusion, diagnosis, and surgery abound; incompetence, hospital-bred infections, indifference, and negligence kill patients without number, pointing up Kenneth E. Boulding's "Brontosaurus Principle: up to a point, the bigger the better; beyond that point, the bigger the worse." [13]

Much experimentation points to an artificial environment, unrelieved by natural sanctuaries, as the cause of emotional and mental stress. For whatever reason, we are now told that at least one out of ten babies born today is headed for a mental institution. Something is awry.

The renowned Professor René J. Dubos, in a plea for modernizing medicine, warns that adjustment to the "social pressures and regimentation of life caused by larger populations and crowding" may not take place. He points out that

> Life in the past was often dulled by solitude and lack of opportunity, but loneliness amidst metropolitan crowds is also cruel. Many of the weak or handicapped who used to lead sheltered though limited lives as accepted members of a stable home or in the role of village fools, now crowd our mental hospitals or commit suicide.[14]

Dr. Allen C. Barnes adds that of every 1,000 babies brought into this increasingly crowded world, approximately 35 die in eight weeks, 35 have brain and nervous systems badly damaged, and 35 bear hereditary defects—dead, damaged, or defective. Thus, we beamingly encourage prolific births (quantity) but we ignore the protection of the foetus (quality) in a manner that is iniquitous, even criminal.[15]

Dr. William Shockley, noted scientist, warns us that since our society nurses, fosters, and increases the deficients, defectives, and the unfit, we are disproportionately overbreeding these types to a shocking degree. He cites the instance of the sixteen-year-old girl, victim of urban disorganization, with three illegitimate children all being raised on public relief, which presumably frees her to start producing low-quality and perhaps defective fourth, fifth, and sixth state-supported infants—perhaps another dozen.

Illness, according to Dr. Dubos, is a response to the *total* physical and social environment, not merely to some single breed of virulent little germ that happens along. All the elements of our artificial and layer-living civilization with its technological side effects of pollution, competition, and irritation, too many chemicals, nutritional deficiencies, and assorted additives are making us push-overs for even a weak bug. How, for example, asks Dr. Jack N. P. Davies in the British medical journal *Lancet* do we account for the fact that four out of every ten cancer-stricken children in America have leukemia, while in Uganda and Nigeria, for example, the proportion is only one out of every twenty-three? What is there in our artificial society that invites leukemia in the very young? Dr. Davies, when contacted on this, could as yet make no inferences. The continuation of his research may some day offer the correlation we need.

The healing of man depends on the healing of the environment. Perhaps the city designer can introduce some artificial equilibrium in our surroundings, but the Great Designer, Nature, could undoubtedly do better. The balm of open spaces, the benediction of small refuges in or near the city, the temporary relief from shoving and elbow jostling—these are now recognized as therapeutic. Nature sanctuaries with the interests of wild vegetation and wildlife are becoming a necessity of survival in a society increasingly strained, crowded, and uneasy.

When tuna fishermen, probing the depths for a school, come up with a single tuna, they carefully observe the tail. If the tail is in fine condition, they conclude that the catch was a loner, and they move on. If the tail is frayed and beat-up, they conclude the fellow was one of a crowd and settle down to serious fishing. Will the city dweller of the year 2000 be betrayed by his frayed brow and beat demeanor? Or will he then have breathing spaces and beauty spots that will transform cities into gardens of the Hesperides not dreamed of today? Parks and nature areas give a city a soul. They give calm and solace to the citizen. Of course, we may be able to attain the same end with a few gallons of tranquilizers injected into the water supply.

Chapter Eleven

The Ultimate Horror—
a Septic World

"Today we are certain pollution adversely affects the quality of our lives. In the future, it may affect their duration."

These were the words of the President of the United States. Pollution of our environment has indeed lowered the quality of our lives in a thousand ways,[1] and the tragedy of it is that many Americans today do not know how wonderful life can be in a land of crystal-clean waters, air, and soil.

But in older civilizations pollution has already fulfilled the President's forewarning: it is limiting, crippling, and destroying lives. As if in echo, a United Press release of March 17, 1966, from Geneva, Switzerland, told us that "The World Health Organization Wednesday reported a worrying spread of disease around the world. . . . Cholera, it said, spread to 23 countries in 1965 and took 13,900 lives."

Afghanistan is a fascinatingly mountainous country about twice the size of Sweden, bordered in part by Iraq and Pakistan; it harbors about fifty-five persons to the square mile plus legions of sheep whose grease-rich tails provide the natives' butter. In ancient times Afghanistan was called Aryana, in the Middle Ages, it became Khorasan. Compared to America it is an old, tamed land, its mountain paths beaten down by millions of feet, its scarred slopes nipped by 4,000,000 fat-tailed sheep plus many camels and goats. The United States is at present superintending the building of a major dam for irrigation and hydroelectricity in the Helman Valley in revenge for which Afghanistan sends us castor oil and asafetida.

But the element in Afghanistan that sets the teeth of visiting Americans on edge is not its great stores of castor oil but its irremediable pollution. Not only are the surface waters laden with diseases and plagues, but the lack of proper sewage disposal over the centuries has caused permeation by pollution of the sparse soils until the deep aquifer—that vast and mystical lake of fresh water underlying Earth's surface—has become universally contaminated. All the excitement and allure of the exotic, ancient lands of the globe are somehow negated by the constant care that must be exercised by the visitor to avoid death-dealing disease from the excessive contamination everywhere in the environment.

The resident American in Kabul, Afghanistan, who serves his visitor from home a salad, must by all odds deserve the encomium of the perfect host. He will, first of all, have grown the greens within his compound, where the contamination is limited to only the ground and ground water.

He will, when it has matured, pluck the leafy vegetable and scrub it with a brush in detergent and water. He will rinse the lettuce or other greens thoroughly in boiled drinking water. Next, he will wash the greens in a strong solution of potassium permanganate and boiled drinking water or perhaps a chlorine solution. Now, he drenches the makings of his salad in boiled drinking water and revives his greens from the ordeal by thrusting them in the refrigerator.[2] Even after all these precautions he will ask a special blessing with his grace and pray for a guest with courage and intestinal resistance against the contamination of the soil.

In America in rural villages where the recent influx

of families has crowded in many new septic tanks and wells, the coliform bacilli (organisms found in all human and animal colons) are showing up with ever greater frequency.[3] Harmless themselves, they are danger signs, for they keep bad company.

Soil and underground contamination is still very localized in America,[4] and illnesses such as the community plague that ran riot in Ravena, New York, several years ago are still infrequent. That the great rivers that flow past our cities are foully polluted, we know—and we mostly avoid them. But to live in a country where the very soil in our garden and the ground water under our feet, put there over millions of years, are writhing with cholera, hepatitis, tuberculosis, typhus, dysentery, typhoid, diphtheria, polio, viruses, and hundreds of other plagues—where to drill a well in one's backyard is to challenge early death—must indeed be the ultimate horror. Mother Earth herself is then spetic, sick unto death; decontamination is physically impossible. A corner in the nation's life has been turned forever.

"Man," says Dr. Carl D. Shoemaker, honorary president of the Audubon Society, "is the filthiest animal that has ever trod the earth." Stark substantiation of his statement appears in the *Report* of the Senate's Select Committee on National Water Resources,[5] which forecast (not without a shudder) that "over and above a comparatively high level of waste treatment . . . approximately 90 per cent of estimated flows for 1980 in the East will be needed for waste dilution. . . ." The Committee also projected in this same year that our expansion thirst would be diverting *more than half* of the total stream flow of all our rivers and creeks to our water intakes. Taken together, these are, to say the least, interesting statistics!

Afghanistan is far from alone in its miserable predicament; it has much company among the older civilizations. And the same inexorable procession of events is occurring over the entire globe in faster or slower tempo as nations feed more and more untreated pollution into Earth's waters and soil. All nations with spiraling populations are cheerfully journeying down the road to a permanently septic world. Medical scientists predict new plagues of unimagined violence as the world becomes sicker and sicker with its human wastes.[6]

Reports the Wisconsin Federation of Conservation Clubs:

> The major water courses of the State of Wisconsin are so badly polluted that their use for other than sewers is practically an impossibility. The Wisconsin, Chippewa, Flambeau, Fox, Rock, and other rivers are almost beyond repair. . . .[7] Even the lakes . . . are carrying tremendous loads of pollution, and the bays of the Great Lakes are beyond human use for anything but boating.

As in Wisconsin, so it is in every state of the Union. Statistics of pollution volume here, there, and everywhere, and of the kinds of pollution—all of which appear almost daily in the newspapers—are almost meaningless because they are beyond normal conception. While we still report that we are currently spewing the sewage equivalent of 150 million persons into the streams from which we take our drinking water, the truth is that the figure is already outmoded and may be closer to 160 million.

The blushing fact is that, as Representative Robert Jones, chairman of a subcommittee on Natural Resources Power, noted recently, "we are using the same method of treatment that the Egyptians used 2,000 years ago" to alleviate water pollution by municipalities.[8] Those municipalities that do remove the suspended solids often do not bother to remove the dissolved material, which is costly. Another enduring fact is that treated effluent—even with the best of treatment—is not an elixir one would relish; it is simply plain sewage effluent stepped down in potency and in lethal qualities. For instance, the sewage effluent from a city of 100,000, after reasonable treatment, is still equal to the raw sewage of 20,000 persons.

Because of the mercenary attitude of the past,

Americans have come to accept as right an ignominious premise: That waste disposal is an essential use of surface water—that a basic function of a crystal stream or wholesome lake is to accept as much sewage and industrial filth as it can possibly handle without losing so much oxygen it turns into a festering, foul-smelling cesspool. On this premise we have built our whole national economy, and it is not to be disputed that had we invested a decent share of our profits in waste disposal research we most probably would have long ago evolved a method of protecting our waters. The President does not believe it necessary to progress that we commit this crime:

> There is no excuse for a river flowing red with blood from slaughterhouses.
> There is no excuse for paper mills pouring tons of sulphuric acid into the lakes and streams.
> There is no excuse—and we should call a spade a spade —for chemical companies and refineries using our major rivers as pipelines for toxic wastes.
> There is no excuse for communities to use the people's rivers as a dump for raw sewage.

In addition to the old familiar headaches—sewage, discharges from mills, furnaces, dye works, slaughterhouses, acid seepages from mines, silt from our denuded watersheds—we have lately added a few more competent killers: insecticides, herbicides, and modern chemicals, which, according to the Water Resources Committee, "defy treatment under present technical knowledge," not to mention radioactive materials. Our open sewers euphemistically termed rivers are swarming not only in the infectious diseases but even, according to Dr. Hollis S. Ingraham, New York State Commissioner of Health, with cancer-causing agents.[9] "I believe," Dr. Ingraham told us recently, "that man's wastes are going to prove his limiting factor." In our rivers the anaerobic bacteria (the bacteria which, with oxygen, break down organic wastes into harmless gases) have long since given up the good fight.

Not content to destroy our own living waters, we

have set about destroying those of our neighbor to the south. In 1961 the Bureau of Reclamation began flushing out the Arizona desert land and dumping the saline wastes into a tributary of the Colorado River. The Colorado River is the main source of irrigation water for the Mexicali Valley. The farmers of this valley complain that there has been millions of dollars' worth of damage to their cotton crops, and the land has been in great part permanently ruined. Thus, between our canny plots to drain down water from Alaska and then flush out our wastes into Mexico, we exhibit a strong tendency toward subjecting the entire continent to our commercial god.

That this slightly tarnished deity is still overlord in spite of the new movement to unseat him is being demonstrated all over the nation as grumbling city fathers continue to begrudge the necessary money to care for their own wastes. A Troy, New York, councilman told the Governor's Hudson River Valley Commission that were Troy to take care of its own sewage instead of dumping it raw into the Hudson through fifty outfalls, it would cost a tax increase of $7.00 per thousand. This, he insisted, was "beyond Troy's means." (At least, in a less affluent society they could afford to build an outhouse.)

Rensselaer, New York, pours its raw sewage into the Hudson and then turns around and draws its drinking water out figuratively within a stone's throw of its outfalls. Ottumwa, Iowa, recently gained a kind of scientific fame when it mixed one part water with one part Des Moines raw sewage effluent, shook it well with chlorine, drank it—and lived! Chanute, Kansas, when the Neosho River dried up, improved on the process. Like many cities on the Great Lakes they used their *own* sewage effluent. This is the height of some kind of efficiency and surely has a distinct time advantage over the natural water cycle.

Here, then, is where New York municipalities might save more than $7.00 a thousand. It seems a lot of unnecessary effort and hanky-panky to pump all the sewage into the Hudson and then pump the mess out again. Wouldn't it be less costly simply to add a little dirty Hudson water to their waste before processing it for re-use? This is only a suggestion.

Many smaller municipalities on the Great Lakes (Chicago dumps its wastes into the overburdened Illinois River) also get rid of their untreated sewage by befouling the world's largest bodies of fresh water. The major difference between towns that dump into a river and then withdraw their drinking water from the river, and towns that dump into a lake and then extract water from it, is, as noted, that river dwellers most often drink the effluents from their neighbors upstream; while lake dwellers must drink their own. Strangely, this is a very fastidious point with Americans. We show a strong preference for our neighbor's effluents over our own. Psychologists (and water officials) have long mused over this quirk without effecting, as far as we know, an answer.

The pollution problem is so complex and varied and so serious that it has spurred thousands of investigations and is today at the forefront of our domestic crises. If Lake Erie is already "a dying lake," Lake Michigan is treading its heels, sick with what Senator Gaylord Nelson calls its "dull, gray tide of pollution [which] is moving through our Great Lakes, following the path of human progress." For fifty years fifteen major and thirty-five minor industries plus many cities and towns bordering Michigan have relentlessly poured their wastes into this great, very deep lake until now the pollution is, according to a federal study, "practically irreversible." Even after submitting their wastes to some treatment, three giant steel companies and three big oil refineries alone discharge 7.2 billion gallons of waste each day into the Calumet River (which empties into Lake Michigan)—oil, cyanide, phenol, and nitrogen.

"In November, 1963," writes Senator Nelson in the *Sierra Club Bulletin*,[10] "10,000 gulls and loons died along the south and west shores of Lake Michigan" from pollution. Two of Milwaukee's four beaches have had to be closed completely and the other two intermittently since 1959. Yet 4 million Americans—60 per cent of all those in this area—depend on the Great Lakes for drinking water. Often their water intakes are clogged with filth.[11]

Desperately, a current $100 million rehabilitation process, which will help greatly to reverse the trend, has been ordered for industry. "Murray Stein, chief enforcement officer for the Federal Water Pollution Control Administration, was overjoyed," writes journalist John Allan Long.[12] "After a year of meetings between industry and the agency . . . the world's largest cluster of steel, chemical, and petroleum plants had just agreed to stop polluting Lake Michigan . . . a deadline was set for December, 1968."

But industry, faced with a $100 million tab, is not rejoicing. "We had little choice. . . . We were clubbed," groused one top executive. Doubtless it will be more resigned when the scores of municipalities now unloading their raw sewage into the lake are cracked down on by WPCA—all of which takes time and dogged persistence.

If Lake Erie, because of its unique shallowness, may with much help hope for a flushing from the strong waters of Superior and Huron within, say, fifty years, one engineer for the Public Health Service declared recently that "it would take over 200 years for the pollution now in Lake Michigan to be removed." However, WPCA's Chicago agent, Grover Cook, explains that thirty to forty years of the industrial ban will show heartening improvement of surface waters. Also he adds: "The immediate results will be an end to bacteria contamination, oil film, and bad tastes and odors." Only those who have traveled extensively in this region will understand what this means. Although we have easily refrained from tasting these waters, we have never been able to refrain from breathing while passing through.

Now small-lake lovers in the states of Michigan.

Wisconsin, and Minnesota are fighting a form of pollution more subtle but perhaps eventually just as dangerous to ground waters as industrial and sewage wastes. There are many thousands of recreation lakes dotting the countryside here, and the new waste problem stems from the septic tanks of lake-fronting cottages and from the fertilizers with which man saturates his lawns and farms, and which drain, like everything else, into the lakes and rivers. This brand of "nutrient" pollution,[18] common in rivers with agricultural watersheds, feeds algae to form a thick, stinking growth, killing fish and turning clear lakes into putrid marshes. With tourism at last threatened, lake associations and state legislatures are suddenly alarmed and have instituted research toward action.

There are, according to one survey, over 2,000 principal sources of pollution that pour their contaminants into New York State's waterways. Included are 1,167 communities and 760 large industrial sources that dump raw or half-treated sewage and industrial wastes into its streams. Added to these are many institutions, homes, farms, and, of course, boats. Herbicides and pesticides complicate the problem.

When in the summer of 1964 a group of children contracted typhoid after eating a watermelon they fished out of the Hudson River, public attention was drawn to "the disease, stench, ugliness and degradation" of what was once the nation's most majestic river. In the fall of 1965 New York voters, setting a nationwide example, went to the polls to endorse overwhelmingly Governor Rockefeller's proposal to borrow $1 billion to begin the rehabilitation of the state's waterways. It was the largest single borrowing ever authorized in this, the richest state. Today polluters are being hauled into Albany for hearings at the rate of twenty a month.

Is the new Federal Water Pollution Act, supervised by the Department of Health, Education, and Welfare, shot so full of loopholes and opportunities for delay that it is, in the words of an NBC commentator, "a sell-out"? There can be delays of six months, then six months, then six months . . . for establishing standards, for persuasion of the state, for legal maneuvers. Court proceedings are provided for, at which it appears to be the standards, and not the violators, who are actually on trial.

Remarked one noted conservationist: "You have two more years of hanky-panky and then you will really be in the business"—of fouling things up, apparently. Congressmen who tried to protect the rights of the states weakened the Act. Some feel that the standards hassle and politics will really "lock in" pollution at its higher level and make a travesty of it all.

It is often said that people who can't remember ever swimming in a river can't imagine its delight and will lack concern. That people who have never walked along a river's banks and seen and smelled the outfalls from dozens of industries and city sewers can have but little conception of what a foul thing this civilization is doing to the country. Yet, strangely enough, it seems that it is the city-bound persons, limited in time, energy, and sometimes in strength, who most often exert themselves to insure the joys of parks, river sports, or mountain climbing to other Americans. Many a successful drive for a new park or a cleansed river is directed from a top story of a Los Angeles, Chicago, or New York office building.

Unless powerful citizens with an overall view of the nation monitor the new Act, pollution levels may well be raised instead of lowered year after year as local Chambers of Commerce clamor for more lenient rules for new industries in their localities. With ever bigger cities who but an alert citizenry will force better and better ways of sewage-waste control *before* the effluent stains the river? Here is an act well intended but shorn of teeth; its bite will be only from teeth installed by and at the people's demand.

There is considerably more to the waste problem than the water issue. On her November, 1965, television special in defense of beauty, the First Lady said:

"Four pounds of junk are discarded every day by each of us, and by the end of this century we shall all be standing on junk piles." Howard James elaborates on this picture: "It seems those who say we will be jammed shoulder to shoulder in a few years because of the population explosion may be in for a surprise. We may be standing on one another's shoulders soon just to see over the trash." [14]

Keep America Beautiful, Inc., tells us that "The average American annually disposes of eight times his own weight in trash . . . we dump up to 20 million cubic yards of trash a year along the nation's public highways." According to KAB's executive vice-president, Allen H. Seed, Jr., "That is $100,000,000 worth of litter, and it has to be paid for by the taxpayers."

Robert D. Bugher, Executive Director of the American Public Works Association in Chicago, states that Americans must lay on the counter nearly $3 billion a year to rid themselves of junk—stuff that the engineers call "solid waste." Chicago's three huge new incinerators handling 3,200 tons a day and costing $12,000 a day to operate are already outdistanced, as well as being attacked for the masses of black smoke and soot they add to an already overburdened atmosphere, says Mr. James.

What shall we do with all the discarded plastic, metal, glass, cardboard, waxed paper, aluminum foil, cartons, old shoes, clothing, furniture, gadgets, etc., that we daily discard? The Solid Wastes Act seeks a solution. [15] The wrapping of food products has become not only preposterous but a source of immense and shameful waste. Always, there is the question of where to find another dumping hole.

In Britain a big hole in the ground is worth a fortune. In an $18.2 million project Britain's central electricity generating board has rented twenty massive holes, which it took the brickmakers sixty years to dig out of the clay. The board wants the holes for fifty-three million tons of ash dust to be produced in the next twenty years by the power stations of the Midlands. "If you think this is costing us too much, we say to you, just go on out and try to find yourself a hole." Added a district council official: 'He's right. Holes are in desperately short supply."

We are removing the good raw materials from Mother Earth and converting them into junk at a rate never dreamed in all of history. Walter C. Loudermilk, speaking in Israel, wondered "if Moses, could he have foreseen this wastage and neglect, might not have been inspired to deliver an Eleventh Commandment."

When Peter Blake wrote his best-selling book *God's Own Junkyard* he said in his Preface that his book was not written in anger. Then he added: "It is written in fury—though not, I trust, in blind fury. It is a deliberate attack upon all those who have already befouled a large portion of this country for private gain, and are engaged in befouling the rest." We need more fury—of the cold, deliberate, hard-hitting type.

Good things are promised in the new conservation that is bringing belated awareness to the rank and file. The President promises that the Potomac, with its evil odors and fourteen feet of sewage sludge lining its bottom, shall be cleaned and beautified to become the nation's number one example of what all our rivers must some day become. All the nation waits for this miracle.[16]

The President's Science Advisory Committee strongly recommends adding anti-pollution rules in all federal contracts, grants-in-aid, and the Government's own extensive building and operating activities. This would seem to be the least we could do. The Advisory Committee also advises that means be devised for taxing industries and other polluters according to their pollution. This method, which has been adopted in the heavily industrialized Ruhr Valley in Germany, has rendered the once-burdened Ruhr a far cleaner stream than the Rhine or any other of its sister streams.

American business ingenuity is taking hold in many small ways. The Salvage and Conversion System of Shawnee, Oklahoma, has just enlisted Westinghouse

Electric Corporation's help in the operation of its "nuisance-free community refuse-disposal plants," which would avoid the griefs of incinerators and sanitary landfills. A conveyor hopper takes all the collected refuse to the salvage section, where all marketable materials, including tin cans, rags, paper, plastics, glass, and rubber, are removed and sorted. Remaining matter then enters a pulverator and grinder and is readied for organic decomposition. It is composted quickly with bacteria additives, then screened and sold as a soil conditioner by bulk and package.

On a cross-country trip to California a couple of years ago, we could joke that we "went out on the Schaefer route and came back on the Pabst." The desert glittered with cans, and at one random stop far from anywhere we alighted to count 120 cans among the cactus within forty feet in all directions of where we stood. The Adolph Coors Brewing Company of Golden, California, has launched a campaign to retrieve every container it can and to reduce littering, and it pays a small amount for bottles and one cent per can, though a can is worth less than half a cent in salvage. In 1964 the company rescued 12,409,176 cans from the nation's highways; since 1959 sixty million bottles and cans have come home.

A somewhat less appealing suggestion for the excessive wastes of too many people concerns the disposal of city sewage. *The United Nations Review* [17] suggests a discovery that "may turn out to be one of the most remarkable of our time." This is not to be doubted. It is a scheme to turn the thick green slime, or algae, that forms on exposed pools of human body wastes into human food. "Algae may provide one of the richest and cheapest sources of food available to man. They have a protein content of some 55 per cent and can be harvested every two days. . . . The greater the population, the greater the number of food-growing plants which can draw sustenance from its waste products."

After you have recovered from the shock and the first squeamishness, you will come, sensibly, to the realization that at last humanity has it made. The perfect ring! The endless chain! Why have we taken so long to think of this neat solution to our problem of how to feed the ever mounting millions? *Bon appétit!*

Chapter Twelve

"38 Cigarettes a Day"

A recent scientific analysis of New York City's atmosphere concluded that a New Yorker on the street took into his lungs the equivalent in toxic materials of 38 cigarettes a day. Suddenly all the scientific jargon, official warnings, reams of statistics—the overwhelming avalanche of damning facts concerning America's air pollution—took focus. Here was a reduction of the tons of soot, sulphides, monoxide, hydrocarbons, etc., into simple, understandable, personal terms.

These figures are of vital interest to two-thirds of the population, which is the percentage of Americans who already live in 212 standard metropolitan areas having only 9 per cent of the nation's land area but 99 per cent of its pollution. Some cities outdo Manhattan and on days of cloud and atmospheric inversion actually kill off small segments of their excess population (involuntarily, of course).

Smog production seems to be a cooperative effort among our great cities. "A great deal of the smoke and dirty air in New York City comes each morning from the industrial areas of New Jersey," accused former Mayor Wagner as, smiling apologetically, he testified at an October, 1964, hearing on air pollution. Then his innate fairness forced him to add: "We return the compliment each afternoon, depending on the prevailing winds, or we pass some of our smoke and gases on to our Long Island or Connecticut neighbors."

But, definitely, New York was getting the worst of everything. It is "the terminus of a 3,000-mile-long sewer of atmospheric filth starting as far away as California and growing like a dirty snowball all the way." New Jersey's champion, Chairman William Bradley of the state's pollution control commission, felt that it was New Jersey who was really behind the eight ball or, rather, dirty snowball. "We feel incapable of coping," he sighed dramatically.

What, actually, is it we are talking about when we rant about air pollution? What it is varies from city to city and from industrial complex to industrial complex. There is a conglomeration of particles—bits of metal, the metallic oxides, tar, stone, carbon, and ash, the aerosols, mists of oils, and all manner of soot.[1]

Strangely enough, Anchorage, Alaska, in the clear and pristine North, excels in this air filth, with Charleston, West Virginia, East Chicago, Phoenix, and Los Angeles treading eagerly on its heels. The electrostatic precipitator in a factory chimney or the use of a whirling water bath for smoke emissions can remove many of these solids, but such devices cost money, and money (and the treasuring thereof) is still our number one consideration.

Much more serious than filthy particles is the sulphur dioxide that comes from the combustion of all heavy fuel oils, coal, and coke. We have visual evidence that this substance eats away brick, stone, and metal bridges, but we have not taken time off to discover what it does to the human lung.[2] A derivative, sulphur trioxide, is the common sulphuric acid, which we know eats into the lungs, eyes, and skin, but again research as to how to extirpate it from the air we breathe does not add appreciably to the GNP.

Technology's contribution to the air we breathe includes—in addition to the particulates, aerosols, and sulphur oxides—a whole legion of grisly gases, among them, carbon dioxide, carbon monoxide, hydrofluoric acid, hydrochloric acid, ammonia, organic solvents, aromatic benzypyrene, deadly ozone, and perhaps another 500 or more lethal emissions (some day we shall have discovered thousands). A few years ago the oil refineries and factories were assigned most of the blame for city smog; later, incinerators took the abuse; at length it was demonstrated beyond a doubt that from 60 to 85 per cent of most city smog is caused by man's best friend, the effusive automobile.[3]

Such smog, strangely enough, has lately been discovered to be the result of the action of sunlight on the incompletely combusted automobile exhaust gases, mainly carbon monoxide, the hydrocarbons, and nitrogen oxides. An unbelievably complex and varied "mishmash" of photochemical reactions takes place all day long from dawn to dark. Out of this witches' cauldron, whose catalyst is the sunshine, emerges a whole army of killing compounds: olefins (synergetic hydrocarbons "hungry to react to something"), ketene, peroxyacetylnitrate, sulphuric acid, aldehydes, and, probably most vicious of all, ozone.[4] The automobile is a versatile chemical factory that can produce almost anything you might wish to dial. Of all these perverse and malicious agents, man knows as yet almost nothing about what they do to humans over a period of time.

Nor is there much evidence that he greatly cares.

Senator Edmund S. Muskie of Maine, who has interested himself deeply in the pure air campaign and the Clean Air Act of 1963, says that, regarding air pollution, we are as ignorant of the components and what to do about them as we were about water pollution fifty years ago. There are about eight of the possibly thousands of constituents of automobile exhaust whose presence and amounts we have documented. According to a competent study [5] the automobile emits into the atmosphere for each 1,000 gallons of gasoline consumed:

carbon monoxide	3,200 pounds
organic vapors	200–400 pounds
oxides of nitrogen	20–75 pounds
aldehydes	18 pounds

sulphur compounds	17 pounds
organic acids	2 pounds
ammonia	2 pounds
solids (zinc, metallic oxides, carbon)	.3 pounds

Now, much has been made of the sulphuric acid fumes that burn the eyes and make holes in ladies' nylons. Lately, pushed by such indomitable souls as Senator Muskie, the unburned cancer-causing hydrocarbons (organic vapors) have been getting their share of attention in the mandatory action taken in smog-bound California. Thus, it was California who led the way for the imposition, in March, 1966, of limitations on the amounts of carbon monoxide and hydrocarbons that may emerge from automobile exhaust pipes. The standards, to take effect on the 1968 models, both of domestic and imported large cars, were to raise the price tags on new models not more than $45.00.

Sighing, an industry executive admitted that the automobile manufacturers had not the ghost of a chance of evading the afterburner hassle any longer. "Politicians, it is quite clear, have come to regard this issue as they do home and mother," he said. All would seem to be set for a cleaner, more wholesome atmosphere in the cities where the automobile is king.

But now a sinister new note has been sounded that suddenly cloaks the whole campaign against the hydrocarbons and the affable acquiescence of the auto manufacturers with the faint smell of herring. Why are we so cavalierly overlooking the nitrogen oxides, perhaps the most dangerous family of all produced by internal combustion, which will not be affected by any afterburner or catalytic muffler ever made? In our first efforts to eliminate a portion of the smog problem have we actually done no more than introduce a placebo that will lull the public into a false and fatal reassurance?

Nitrogen oxides are formed in all combustion processes; the greater the pressure, the greater the amount of them. If we eliminate the hydrocarbons with which they react, what will happen? Will they then turn on us and cause even greater havoc than at present—perhaps greater havoc than the hydrocarbons and all their relatives together? We know that irritations of the mucous membranes would greatly increase. And while hydrocarbons build up in the body for the kill, nitrogen oxides like to do a faster, neater job.

Yet we are ignoring them. The truth is, the complicated and expensive accessory needed to deal with the nitrogen oxides would be almost exactly opposite to that necessary for dealing with the hydrocarbons. An automobile properly equipped to get rid of smog effectively would probably be an elaborate mess—costly, slow, and demanding of much maintenance. Coming into this new knowledge which proves so distressing— that our dearest companion, the automobile, is completely incompatible with our health and well-being— how long will we cling to it in this embrace of death?

We have noted that long after the exhaust smells have wafted away the hydrocarbons, in the presence of nitrogen oxides and that much publicized California sunlight (or anybody's less glorious, less publicized sunlight), keep on producing a veritable legion of lethal agents to inhabit the smog.

No American city is spared.[6] Two years ago in San Francisco we were driven by burning eyes to flee the city to the skyline drive high above.[7] From that height we looked down on a city swathed in a thick mustard-colored robe. This was a blanket manufactured by man himself, which he had drawn down over the once sparkling countryside and golden bay, and it was slowly smothering him to death. How long, we wondered, will man continue to sacrifice his cities, his enjoyment, his life, because of the fetid breath of a monster never built for meandering in city streets with their stops and goes and halting, jammed traffic? An ungainly, unadaptable monster whose 80 mile an hour cruising speed was geared to the long sweep of thruways and not to the bumper-bumper creep among the city's canyons?

If we would still cling to our 300-horsepower monsters in city lanes built to accommodate at most a 4-horsepower carriage, we have but two choices. Shall we choose mass poisoning in a slow fashion by the vast armies of hydrocarbon derivatives or a faster (perhaps more dashing) suicide from the nitrogen oxides? Apparently, technological difficulties so far obviate relief from both.

This small book, intent on presenting an overall view of our most pressing modern problems, does not pretend to medical authority regarding the effects of air pollution on the living community; many health authorities, specialists in the field, have performed this work with shocking competence. But one piece of medical research will be noted. As early as 1957 Dr. Paul Kotin, pathology professor of the University of Southern California, reported at Yale Medical School his findings of five years of study on laboratory animals. A group of mice exposed to the day-by-day Los Angeles air developed one and one-half times as many lung cancers as those who breathed clean air. Abnormal changes were found in the lungs of experimental animals after only a few months of this Los Angeles brew. Concluded the scientist: "Similar rapid changes can be expected in human beings, with many air pollutants combining to make the lungs more susceptible to cancer in a shorter time than previously believed." [8]

Dr. Thomas P. Manusco, industrial hygiene chief for the Ohio Health Department, told the 1958 National Conference on Air Pollution that the urban lung cancer rate "increases by the size of the city." Since these reports, studies have confirmed the findings.[9]

A man is not a mouse—usually. He has a bigger body; he may have more resistance, slower reaction. But every day the air a human breathes comes in direct contact with an area twenty-five times as great as his exposed skin area. This is the exposure surface of the tender membranes that line his lungs. Dr. Morris Cohn impressed on a New York Joint Legislative Committee on Air Pollution that while "man consumes less than ten pounds of water, fluids, and food daily, yet he requires over thirty pounds of air in the same period—and thirty pounds of air is a lot of air, 3,500 gallons of it!" It is not necessary to be an alarmist to conclude that man is not immune to what affects the mouse. Indeed, physiologically, he is more like the mouse than he wants to believe.

A cartoon of a few years ago presenting the inside of a U.S. weather station of the future depicted the weatherman making the following report: "Our latest analysis of the stratosphere, Dr. Figby! . . . 21 per cent hydrogen, 7 per cent oxygen . . . and 72 per cent automobile exhaust fumes!" [10] By 1985 this cartoon will no longer amuse. Predicts sanitation expert A. C. Stern of the Taft Sanitary Engineering Center, Cincinnati: By 1985 the U.S. Weather Bureau will be issuing daily air pollution reports as well as weather forecasts. People will be "more interested in whether it will be safe to breathe than whether it will be rainy or sunny." Our only comment here is that his prediction is for ten —probably fifteen—years too late.

One more word about our shiny master, the motorcar: As motors are stepped up for higher compression, year by year, nitrogen oxides are stepped up also. And as gasoline manufacturers vie for more "pick-up" by adding new substances like tetraethyl lead and nickel to the gasoline, these extremely toxic substances are also added to our atmosphere. The insane competition for speed and power bows neither to safety nor to health.

It is unreasonable to blame the manufacturers. In the end they put out what the public demands. Indeed, some of them are ahead of public demands as a matter of company pride. Some persons claim that the industry has the know-how to combust completely the fuel within the cylinder and does not do it. But how many American buyers, when dickering for a new car, ask anything more about an engine's performance than horsepower and the fast getaway—and perhaps mileage per gallon?

True, there is the gas-turbine engine that would get rid of all the nitrogen oxides and most of the smog. It will also burn practically anything. But will Americans accept (as the Russians are now doing) conversion to an engine that gives slow starts, noisier action, a trifle less "guts"? Detroit is convinced the customer prefers the fast jump to a long and happy life.

But the Man from Mars, standing beside a super-highway as the shiny monsters hurtle by at 75 or 85 miles an hour, the drivers bent tensely over their steering wheels with riveted, lusterless eyes that see nothing but the pavement ahead, wonders what it is all about. What is this strange, strained Earth creature getting out of life? It is evident that he is not enjoying himself. And the price is high.

Air pollution in America is so varied, so complex, so changing a problem that scientists have so far only begun to scratch the surface.[11] It differs from city to city; turbulence, topography, sunlight, whether the majority of city dwellers burn coal or oil, the industries nearby, the number of automobiles and trucks—all these determine the quotient.

Typical of the great cities is the plight of Boston, described by Commissioner of Public Health Alfred L. Frechette.[12] He estimates that 2,600 tons of solid contaminants are dumped daily over the central 100 square miles of the city. A basic problem is the open burning of automobile bodies. Yet an effective city incinerator that would reduce by 85 per cent what goes into it costs about $5.00 a ton to operate, compared to the $1.50 a ton cost of open-air burning, or $3.00 a ton in a sanitary land fill operation. What shall the city fathers do?

There are two common denominators for air pollution from place to place: *first,* all air pollution is harmful, not only to people but to animals, plants, buildings, bridges, crops, and goods; and, *second,* all types are increasing everywhere at such a rate that researchers are left gasping. "Growing efforts to cope with this evil are having difficulty keeping pace with its fresh manifestations." [13]

What, ask the worried officials at the Boston Museum of Fine Arts, can they do about the black spots which have appeared all over the 300 or 400 priceless and irreplaceable bronze artworks—some of them from the first century—spots on the green patina that come, presumably, from the sulphur oxides in the Boston air? The sulphur oxides evolve from the burning of coal and fuel oil, as well as from gasoline, and their effects cannot be reversed, say officials. Or maybe the blackening comes from ozone? Nobody is quite sure what pollutant causes it, but it is decimating the Museum's treasures.

And what about the worsening air pollution in the region of the booming steel mills? Advanced science now employs oxygen streams to hurry up metal "cooking," and these cause enormous clouds of reddish-brown, acrid smoke that shuts off sunlight and air, has an evil smell, and cloaks and stains homes nearby. An electrostatic precipitator to eliminate most of the smoke and smell costs $1,000,000 per furnace, and even with greatly stepped-up steel production (and, we would assume, greatly stepped-up profits) nobody wants to pay out a million dollars each for ten or twenty furnaces in a row.

Aerial spraying of crops not only poisons rivers but may drift on winds for many miles to lodge in people's lungs. Only recently DDT has been found as a pollutant in the air far from the agricultural lands where it was employed. Nuclear explosions added the pollutants of fallout to our atmosphere, radioactive isotopes that will still be descending on us in the rains for years to come.[14]

In this connection the authors wrote in 1959 a small volume called *Our New Life with the Atom,* which raised several questions that scientists, then in the first blush of dazzling atomic predictions, were determinedly ignoring. One of these questions was: What would fallout—including radioactive iodine-131 from the multitude of Nevada tests—do to the bones and thyroids of children living nearby? The Atomic Energy Commission had been smugly assuring Americans and the entire world that the fallout it was causing was completely harmless. For example, an AEC spokesman on May 13, 1957, stated that the bomb tests would not have "the slightest possible effect" on humans.

On December 3, 1965, eight years later, an Associated Press release, originating in Salt Lake City, Utah, read as follows:

> Atomic blasts in the 1950's are suspected of affecting thyroid glands in a group of Utah children soon to be given medical tests in Salt Lake City. There are nine children to be examined at the University of Utah Medical Center. Southwestern Utah, where the children live, is crossed by winds from southern Nevada. . . . The children are 10 to 18 years old. . . . All have nodules, or small lumps, on their thyroid glands.

There is an ominous resemblance between the protestations of the "harmless fallout" experts of a few years ago and the "harmless insecticides" experts of today.

And what are we planning to do, wonders Dr. Columbus Iselin, Director of the Woods Hole Oceanographic Institution, about the possibly catastrophic effects of carbon dioxide on our weather? Modern technology is releasing great new volumes of this gas into the Earth's envelope, even while understanding that this gas is, over a period of time, a drastic climate changer. Man today is altering his environment faster than ever before, and little of it, to date, has been to the good.

Air pollution, like water pollution and all the other examples of our deteriorating conditions of living, is a by-product of too many people with too much push in the direction of economic progress and not enough in the direction of social progress. In a technology of surpassing wonders, wonders of dizzying impact, we still bear the body, psychological reactions, and evolution-

ary status of Cro-Magnon. Physically, we are emi-
nently better adapted to cave living than to space living
and will probably continue, if spared, in this retarded
development for another million years.

Thus, in a civilization whose air may be composed
of 21 per cent natural gases and 79 per cent automobile and other combustion gases, we shall be burdened
with lungs that demand an outmoded mixture of some
79 per cent plain nitrogen and 21 per cent oxygen. We
are trying to adapt a prehistoric physiology to an ul-
tra-modern technology and losing on every front. Pa-
leontology tells us that unless we switch and learn to
adapt our technology to our prehistoric bodies, we
shall perchance pay the price of the dinosaur and the
other unadaptable life species which have preceded
us.[15]

The depth of our present ignorance concerning the
hundreds of killer gases that we are generously releasing into our air blanket (and which, contrary to most
belief, will not simply waft away out into space somewhere) remains the most incredible and awesome element of our entire way of life. Such poisons will linger
in and densify our troposphere forever or until transformed into other substances. Their effects are therefore both acute and chronic.[16]

Crash programs to learn more about air pollution
and how to ameliorate it are in progress at all governmental levels. And in this field, as in others, scientists
are beginning to desert the torn standard of combat
against nature, to rally around the more solid standard
of learning to work with her or at least to use her help.

For example, Dr. Chauncey D. Leake, Assistant
Dean of the College of Medicine at Ohio State University, has called for extensive planting of trees and other
green things ("Maybe 10 trees for every automobile
and 100 for every truck") to depollute the air. In this
proposal he is strongly supported by Dr. Philip L.
Rusden of the Bartlett Tree Research Laboratories.
While humans inhale oxygen and exhale carbon diox-

ide, trees take in carbon dioxide and discharge oxygen, greatly helping to purify the air.

The extensive sums of money put into research by industry (including the American Petroleum Institute) throughout the nation to end pollution both of the common waters and the air are not generally known or appreciated. Leonard A. Duval, President of Hess von Bulow, Incorporated, of Cleveland, is only one of the many industrial magnates with a firm dedication toward cleaning up pollution. "Whenever I see a cloud of ugly brownish smoke pouring from a steel-mill stack," says Mr. Duval, "or when I see a stream of discolored water pouring from a plant or factory into a creek or river, I squirm a little and say to myself, 'Look at all those dollars going to waste. I'm going to get some of them.' " [17]

Already industry has learned how to recover many millions of dollars' worth of light oils, ammonia, and materials from coking coal—materials that go into drugs, plastics, chemicals, and many more products. Now Mr. Duval has dredged nearly 35,000 tons of exceptionally rich iron—washed-away mill scale—out of the Mahoning River near Warren, Ohio, for which he obtained almost $400,000. He is erecting another dredge and four-story processing plant at the cost of about $300,000 at Niles, Ohio, to work another 4,000-foot stretch of the river for a possible additional $400,000. Says Mr. Duval: "There are millions lying on the bottoms of these mill-town rivers and creeks waiting for someone to pick it up."

In like manner the massive brownish clouds of smoke that belch from modern steelmaking furnaces contain iron and zinc sulphides that persistent research will teach how to reclaim. Even the "fly-ash" emitted by coal-burning electric plants might have a use. When air and water pollutants are made truly commercial—that is, when scientists establish a cash-redemption value for each—then the nation's waters and air will be cleaned up with alacrity.

But research, like art, is long, while time continues

to be fleeting. Properly, the attack on our ignorance must be spearheaded by the national government. Not only would it be sheer waste for each community or state to duplicate each other's efforts; the call now is for such highly specialized atmospheric scientists, medics, chemists, engineers, meteorologists, etc., that smaller agencies of government could not easily recruit the talent called for in our emergency.

Once the facts are known and the solutions made available, the problem of applying those understandings is primarily local. As noted, one community may contend with a copper smelter, another with a chemical plant. One may suffer from atmospheric inversion demanding inflexible traffic limitations; another may have a soft coal problem. No distant official would be likely to work out the ingenious economical and effective program for trash burning, for instance, that Miami, Florida, did. There the incinerator will pay for itself by providing steam for a hospital and custom disposal for nearby Miami Beach.

There is an important role for the states, however. Enabling laws must be passed, rigid standards laid down, specialists provided for the smaller communities, and both intercommunity and interstate or regional problems attacked. The chief complaint of municipalities is that they have no "yardstick" by which to measure violations. It was partly to this end that an Air Pollution Control Board was created in New York State. And unless extensive education is carried on by all levels of government, there will not be the necessary public support to impel the large but needed outlays of money by either government or industry.

It took the Triangle Shirtwaist fire in 1911 to jar New York and then other states into enacting a labor law. It took a circus fire in Hartford to rouse us to more action. It took the near calamity of drought in the East to start pulling in the pollution violators for court hearings. We have already had some wholesale executions by air pollution in London, Los Angeles, and New York City on occasions of atmospheric inversion that hugged the smog close to the earth for a few days at a time. How big must the slaughter be to get real action?

Certainly what we need most is deglomeration of people.[18] Excessive pollution of air as well as of water can deglomerate, even decimate, cities unhealthily crowded with men and cars. But there must be more pleasant ways.

One way less unpleasant than mass biocide by gas asphyxiation would be to lean a trifle harder on that phase of research seeking to produce a combustion engine that completely combusts its fuel and emits a minimum of poisons. Our present combustion engines wastes oceans of fuel every year. Can the gas turbine engine be perfected? Chrysler's directional turbine nozzle is a smart advance in fuel efficiency and is hopeful. But why, ask the automobile industry's Members of the Board behind closed doors, throw in a wrench when you've got such a good thing going? No reason at all.[19]

But the White House has given out a hint that a reason may be made. The President's Science Advisory Committee, newly alarmed about the leads and additives that have pushed air pollution to critically high levels, has been mumbling (not too indistinctly) about tighter federal controls under a sort of Food and Drug Administration type setup. They are going so far as to suggest that the time is coming "when it will be necessary to get rid of the present engine and fuels altogether." They have asked automakers seriously to "mull the idea of scrapping present engines and powering cars with non-toxic fuel cells instead."

This is no small request. Fuel cells, while they would completely do away with auto smog and all its train of miseries, are rather far from perfection; indeed, they are far from any practical application. The fact is, the condition of our cities' air is so bad we cannot afford to wait for them. What, then?

Since most families have two cars already it is suggested that one of them be a small electric cart for city driving and the other a high-powered machine for the road. No, the electric cart will not leap forward like a rocket at the green light, but consider this: No more poisonous vapors, odors, smoke clouds, corrosion, gluey oils. inflammatory gasoline; accidents cut to a tenth. less noise, easier parking, the innovation of a relaxed kind of driving (not to mention the cut in incidence of lung cancer, bronchitis, heart conditions, and smarting eyes).

There are, in all, from 8,000 to 10,000 tons of gases, vapors, and solids being thrown into a large city's air every day—a generous two-thirds of it from the automobile—to saturate the lungs of roughly two-thirds of the nation's population. Years ago former Surgeon General Leroy T. Burney declared categorically that there is a "definite association between community air pollution and high mortality rates," a fact that is today universally accepted.

While cars get faster and longer, lives get slower and shorter. While Chrysler competes with Buick for the getaway, cancer competes with emphysema for the layaway. This generation is indeed going to have to choose between humans and the automobile. Perhaps most families have too many of both.

Chapter Thirteen

Crisis in Beauty

Before our eyes have passed, as in a magic lantern, the transcendant wonders of a primeval America: the majesty of the redwoods, the deafening thunder of an untamed Niagara, the world's only Grand Canyon, the Everglades, and more. Today the redwoods are being slashed into defenseless patches, the mighty Niagara's roar is cut in half, the Grand Canyon has been measured for hydroelectric harness, the Everglades has been drained—then callously flooded—for commercial advantage and its wildlife rots in the receding slime.

The list of indictments could go on and on; but let these developments stand as symbols of an ignominious fact: in American society beauty has been, in the words of Lord Byron, truly "the fatal gift." Briefly, we might view a handful of situations that the spotlight picks up as it swings over the continent.

In the year 1804 Thomas Moore, poet laureate of Ireland, visited the present site of Cohoes, New York, writes Edgar S. Van Olinda, sage columnist for the Albany *Times-Union*. The poet was so inspired by what he saw that he penned this exquisite poem:

> From rise of morn to set of sun
> I have seen the mighty Mohawk run.
> And I have marked the woods of pine
> Along the mirror darkly shine
> Like tall and gloomy forms that pass
> Before the wizard's midnight glass.

This was the forested fairyland we found; this was our American heritage. Now, listen to a modern verse by Charles H. Palmer, the Governor's assistant secretary, describing the same river, in the same paper, quoted by columnist Victor Ostrowidszki:

> Up the dirty river where the sewage flows,
> Say, anytime you're near there, better hold your nose.
> Swimmin' in that stuff, you had best avoid;
> Get yourself a mouthful and you risk typhoid.
> Up the dirty Mohawk, that's where industry
> Pollutes the running water far as you can see,
> If you take a chance and you water ski,
> Wind up on your backside 'mong the old debris.

And the verse ends:

> You keep going your way,
> I'll keep going my way,
> River, stay 'way from my door!

What, indeed, have we done to our incomparable country? Lewis and Clark wrote of the great hinterland of the continent as "lush and beautiful beyond compare." Old shanty boys reminisce of the massive fir trees—some of them fifteen feet in diameter—that blanketed the nation from Maine to the Dakotas, of fragrant cedar swamps "black and tangled as jungles," of the endless oceans of white pine that cloaked Wisconsin, Minnesota, and Michigan and the red Norways that "rose like masts along the shores of thousands of crystalline lakes." Now we travel mile after mile across the entire expanse of the nation and (until we reach the feverish lumbering centers of the redwoods in California and the Douglas fir in Washington) almost nothing greets the eye but scrub brush and spindling fourth-growth that never seems to grow any higher.

The traveler seeking beauty might ask: "Why couldn't they have spared even one small 'museum piece' of what this country was once like, along these interminable, barren highways?" The fringe remnants of our primitive forests, wherever they may be, assume a new significance as we search the byways and the parks for the privilege of looking at them. These last stands are all that we have left to link us to our history, to the spectacular beauty of our wilderness past. In these small oases some future Americans may relive for a moment that first sweet shock, that soul-stirring moment of stepping into a virgin forest, an experience no words can describe.

It has not been enough to pollute the great rivers and scalp the landscape; we have used most of our small beauty spots, the creeks, ponds, and valleys, as dumping grounds for wastes. Driving through the attractive little town of Gowanda, New York, we came upon Cattaraugus Creek, which should have been the center of an idyllic public park. Instead, the offensive smell it exudes impels the tourist to move on quickly —the farther the better. A filling station attendant told us a glue and tannery factory has been polluting this beauty spot for fifty years, thus denying all citizens the enjoyment of it.

Nothing whatever has been sacred. Bulldozers even invaded the famous (and protected) Walden Pond in Massachusetts to create an extremely ugly, white-painted bathing beach complex—what the Thoreau Society of Concord terms a "desecration" [1]—and misguided persons have been seeking to break out facilities for another such beach. With thousands of such beaches throughout the nation there is only one Walden. Nor is natural beauty all we have effaced. Everywhere historic shrines of great beauty go down without more than a passing shrug. "One final glint of gold . . . now twinkles faintly in the light of day as Boston's beloved Opera House bows to the swinging ball of demolition," sighed the *Christian Science Monitor* a few years back. "A heartless rubble of torn ticket stubs, crushed marble, and trampled crimson carpet gives opera lovers a nostalgic twinge. . . . The Metropolitan Company will be housed in a movie theater this spring."

Architect Edward Durell Stone, of the keen and penetrating gaze, wonders just how Americans will measure up in their new-found concern for beauty—an element of living that has been a determinant in European culture for centuries. "Look around you," he advises.

> Neon jungles, catchpenny honkey-tonks. Noise. Clutter. Building without concern for the neighbors, for what is appropriate, for what is in good judgment or taste. All in all, I thought I made sense when I said that if you give a damn, you feel like committing suicide when you look around.

Of the smaller American towns he laments: "Architecture without beauty or distinction, streets snarled up in automobiles, no harmony, no beauty, few trees, limited park areas. Nothing but an asphalt jungle where the big idea is to sell merchandise, put gas in the automobile, and move on." [2]

Even the lakes and rivers in our deep wildernesses are being secretly ravished far from the public eye. "Sometime during September, 1964," commercial logging interests in the Winchell-Omega lakes section of the Boundary Waters Canoe Area of Minnesota destroyed the exquisitely lovely Finn Lake (state owned) by bulldozing a road and fill completely across it. "That this could occur is wholly incredible," marvels an eye-witness. [3] Who was to blame for this contemptible and sneaky—there is no other word for it—accomplishment that replaced a spot of quiet, primeval charm with the ugliest of mud roads and a canoe barrier? Where were the Forest Service men while it was happening? Why has the state done nothing to fix blame and to punish it?

Continues Joseph W. Penfold:

> The Finn Lake incident brings into sharpest focus the fact that the kind of failure it represents in inevitable. As long as attempts are made to combine commercial logging with protection of wilderness environment, just that long can Finn Lake incidents be expected. Commercial logging and wilderness are incompatible. Commercial logging should be eliminated from all the Boundary Waters Canoe Area.

Do the American people know that famed San Francisco Bay is slowly being bulldozed in with trash, garbage, and fill? That the same thing is happening on Long Island? That five thousand ridge-line miles of the lovely Kentucky hills have been leveled and gouged out by strip mining? Concerning this last activity, a TV narrator [4] said: "Night comes to the Cumberlands. . . . The mountains are being decapitated. . . . The land dies, the water turns acid; it's a process which murders the land."

While conservationists appeal vainly for the early establishment of a Northern Cascades Park in Washington, where there still exist some of the ancient enchantments of the American wilderness, bulldozers are already busy mutilating the lower Cascades beyond recognition. In the words of a Weyerhaeuser representative: "It [the virgin, *not* tree-farm timber] represents millions upon millions of dollars, and so I say to the preservationists, the trees *must be cut down.*"

Yet with a hundred million people rubbing shoulders in the parks we now have, it is evident that we need new parks considerably more than we need more profits.[5] Nonetheless, while the crush of people becomes progressively worse, the crash of falling trees becomes progressively louder on all sides. Only the American public, and then only with much clamor, can call a halt to such blasphemy.

"The technology which has given us everything from the computer to the teleprompter has created a hundred sources of blight," says the President. "And in every corner of the land the Nation builds, and builds, and builds—highways and restaurants, factories, and neon signs. And far too often we find the marvels of progress, only to find that we have diminished the life of man." [6]

So threats and problems loom on every side. "It is not going to be easy," adds President Johnson. But every day that we delay, the backlog of ugliness and misery grows higher, ever higher. We presumably have no choice but to strike out before we find ourselves buried to the neck in our own offal.

Yet in taking this rough new road we are led inexorably to the following considerations: (1) So great has economic pressure on our resources become that we must now make conscious choice between practical utility and the preservation of such beauty as remains to us. (2) The ethics and values we have always proclaimed as a nation contain no commitment whatever to beauty. Indeed, we have been committed to its undeviating destruction and to a scathing scorn for it.[7] (3) So much has already been destroyed and the hour is so late that a reversal of policy (including the rescue of any worthwhile portion of the ancient grandeur left us) must be quick and, from our standards, drastic![8] And measures of rehabilitation will require effort of such magnitude that they must enlist not only all layers of government but all citizens and groups of citizens as well.

Considering the foregoing, point by point, we come to a realization of the crisis we are in and the difficulties we must surmount. For all our history our gestures on behalf of natural beauty have been cheap. We could preserve the Grand Canyon until now because we were busy building other dams on the Colorado—"already more dams," says Dave Brower of the Sierra Club, "than there is water to fill them." We could save Boca Ciega Bay near St. Petersburg against the real estate developers because we hadn't built up the more available sites.

Our national parks and forests were largely excess beauty. Even so, the saved *2 per cent* of our original heritage that they represent had to be bought with the blood of a handful of men—men like John Muir, and Gifford Pinchot, Olaus Murie, and Howard Zahniser, who had to battle the American creed every inch of the way.

Today, under the twin pressures of increases in population and gross national product, we have come to a political crossroad. Today the timber glut, the mineral glut, the water glut, the space glut, are no more. We face the demands of unlimited population growth in a finite, limited nation and world. We can no longer toss a spare crumb (a small chunk of all but inaccessible wilderness or out-of-the-way seashore) to the conservationists—because there is no longer an excess.

We now face many choices and a test of our kind of civilization. For each beauty spot there is now a pressing alternative use.[9] Every such oasis that we thought we had protected is now being attacked in some manner. Even our national parks are under pressure of encroachment. (Our national "forests" have been industriously and indiscriminately lumbered down to lamppost size from the beginning.) The forcing of such choice and the need for quick action make the matter a political one. The battle is joined.

Having subjugated the continent from shore to shore and flayed it in the most brutal exhibition in all man's history, we the public never matured. We have never reassumed the reins of our destiny from the exploiters. That is why it will take some strong efforts to change to the driver's seat now.

How bitter the choice will be is forecast in the battle now raging over the previously mentioned Boundary Waters Canoe Area of Minnesota. Swarming into the pine forests of the North Star State early in the twentieth century the lumbermen clear-cut everything and then dropped matches in the slash to leave behind them great reaches of charred wastelands.

Duluth papers at the turn of the century are filled with braggadocio about the "inexhaustible forests." Yet in about thirty-five years Paul Bunyan's legions had scalped the 40,000 or more square miles of prime pine as cleanly as though the great Bunyan ax had been a razor. Then they were off to the lush timberlands of Oregon and Washington, leaving only a swathe of timber along the Canadian border. There, beyond the continental divide, the rivers flowed north, not conveniently south to civilization, and who wanted to float his log rafts up into Hudson Bay?

But with the discovery of rich hematite iron ore on the Mesaba, mining towns sprang up in the deep gray ashes—towns as uncompromisingly bleak as the sub-zero winter nights but soon rich as Croesus from the profits of World War I. Roads pushed northward, chain saws and logging trucks replaced Paul Bunyan's ax and oxen, and now lumbermen settled down to harvest methodically the Superior National Forest in the approved manner: one tree (preferably deformed and unmarketable) to be left every 50 or 100 feet and, benevolently, no more scorched earth.

For many years Minnesota conservationists have deplored the government-approved cutting in the canoe country, where trees grow so slowly. The cutting left so thin a shell along the rivers and shores of the many thousands of lakes that the pleasure of a canoe trip was marred by ugly slash and every high wind toppled swathes of the remaining trees.

On January 12, 1965, impelled by the new ethic in conservation and the growing pillage, U.S. Secretary of Agriculture, Orville Freeman (former Governor of Minnesota), braved the interests to remove 150,000 acres (60,000 virgin) of lake-border timber from the logger's market. So shrill was the cry of the exploiters that a special appeal for conservationist support had to be mounted. Uneasily, this tardy victory for the public interest in the Boundary Waters Canoe Area stands until a new offensive by the lumbermen challenges it.[10] It is not difficult to see why a former director of the National Park Service reiterated that were the parks to be turned over to the states, they would swiftly be gobbled up and disappear.[11]

So we have come at last to the split in the road where, because of our mushrooming needs, every beauty spot requires a flat choice between aesthetics and profit. It is our *second* point—that natural beauty has always been incompatible with the American creed, always cheerfully expendable—that renders our choice-making doubly painful.

Thoreau said that "the perception of beauty is a

moral test." But to this day commercial advantage in any deal has been the only understandable motive, the sole motivation immediately accepted and never laughed at. Forests, swamps, rivers, impeded our progress; quite humanly we went at their destruction without mercy. The past three generations have been bred in an ethic which places all values subordinate to economic demand, an ethic that forces every defense of beauty to justify itself *ad absurdum* against the dollar. More, it is an ethic which condones any subterfuge of exploitation in the philosophy that the advancement of business is sufficient to excuse any deceit.

Recently, a rather extensive movement to cut strips in the Adirondack Forest Preserve was launched "in order to increase the browse for deer so they would not starve over the winter." Actually, any private lumbering operation "will in its execution always have as its primary objective financial gain rather than range improvement," comments Dr. Fay Welch, special lecturer at the School of Forestry at Syracuse University.[12] In this instance as in many others it appears that lumbering interests were using the political force of the hunters for their own purposes.

But the mercenary philosophy that has developed our technological wonders has taken bitter toll of our resources—physical and aesthetic.[13] It has left us a polluted, bruised land, now far beyond the capacity of the few, self-appointed conservationists to salvage, despite their zeal. We have been a nation of leeches— leeching our enjoyment of outdoors and historic shrines from the sweaty efforts of the few who have labored to preserve them.

Too many gaping tourists consume beauty but never think to contribute to it. When Secretary Stewart Udall was visiting Robert Frost, he picked up a tourism brochure entitled "Come to Unspoiled Vermont for Your Vacation." Frost remarked, with his wry humor, that when he came upon one of these leaflets, he used to take a pencil and scribble on the bottom, "And help us spoil it." [14]

Far too many "bird watchers" are just that; they contribute little or nothing to the Audubon Society or to the Wilderness Society for wildlife sanctuaries but sponge upon the accomplishments of others as they roam about enjoying themselves with field glasses and picnic lunch. Every bird sanctuary, every untrammeled field of wild flowers, every inspiring forest, every waterfall, every historic shrine is there because somebody preserved it (or is now fending off the developers) and invariably at considerable sacrifice.[15]

Shockingly, we have been willing to barter on matters touching the very vitals of our civilization; we negotiate with the merchants of progress as though they had a claim to status. We are still coarse enough not to consider their propositions effrontery. We are even now willing to debate whether a few more kilowatts of electricity to prosper the night life of Las Vegas is not a fair price for the defacement of a natural wonder our children have not yet seen. (Strangely, this vastly overlighted city also boasts the highest crime rate in the nation.)

It seems a grievous waste of life—the only life, by the way, of which we are sure—to spend it with glazed eyes looking upon ugly things that oppress and irritate us. Yet how much will we pay to be "surrounded with beauty"? This is the testing time.

"There are higher values than private profit and bureaucratic convenience," writes the *New York Times*. "Are America's businessmen prepared to accept the social discipline needed to create a civilized environment for everyone?" Is Congress prepared to "discipline the relentless bureaucrats and their bulldozers?"

"Talk of heaven!" Thoreau cried out to his fellow Americans more than a hundred years ago. "Ye disgrace earth!"

Chapter Fourteen

The Redemption of Beauty

But recently a revolutionary development, as daring as unprecedented, has taken place in the nation. President Johnson, staunchly reinforced by a remarkable First Lady, launched a campaign for a "new conservation" ethic that would recognize natural and historic beauty as a valuable resource quite outside of its cash value.[1]

What is the "new conservation"? It is "not just the classic conservation of protection and development, but a creative conservation of restoration and innovation," said the President.[2] Not only must we protect the countryside from destruction, "we must restore what has been destroyed and salvage the beauty and charm of our cities."

With almost three-fourths of our people living in sprawling agglomerations of development called cities, we need not only the parks and forests to flee to on occasion, we need beauty right in close beside us and around us where we live, to keep us sane. Beauty does things to man, continued President Johnson; we can no longer deal with it as an element apart, something in a vacuum.[3]

Having to endure ugliness can tear us apart, degrade, and demean our lives, cause mental illness, crime, and misery. Beauty, on the other hand, has been shown to revive man's spirit, foster healing, bring satisfaction, and increase all the pleasures of the good life. *Beauty is therefore "one of the most important components of our true national income,* not to be left out simply because statisticians cannot calculate the worth." [4]

Strangely, this somnolent, passive public that had so long abjectly acquiesced in the priority of profit over all other values was overnight aroused to a kind of excitement not felt since the days of Theodore Roosevelt. A new and finer bugle had sounded. "The response has been overwhelming, and unprecedented," said the Secretary of the Interior. "In the vernacular, the President has struck a nerve. It was as if the entire Nation had been waiting for someone to point out that natural beauty and the good life go hand in hand." [5]

The way that the bugle leads will be over harsh and unaccustomed terrain. Because of long neglect the cost of following it to a more beautiful land will be high. It will be a wrench to learn to "crank beauty into the recreation plans of the states," but it will be even more difficult to maintain its priority on the drawing board and in the conference room. Yet the search for beauty is not a crusade in itself but a gathering-in of all the other reforming movements we must embrace if we would change our course and point it at last toward national greatness.

It is necessary to recognize this mercenary American philosophy in order to understand how difficult it will be to mount an effective support of the Administration's campaign to beautify the nation. Yet, to embellish our *third* point (and again in the President's words), "The same society which receives the rewards of technology must, as a cooperating whole, take responsibility for control." From the federal departments on down to the local Rotary and Kiwanis clubs, from Wall Street executives to Boy Scouts, there is work to be done.

Brought up in the piney woods of deep East Texas, "listening to the wind in the pine trees (there is no sound like it) and feeling the crush of pine needles underfoot, or paddling a bateau on a quiet lake that twisted between ancient moss-draped cypress trees,"

Lady Bird Johnson was permanently saturated with a deep love of the beauty of trees. Later, in Central Texas where she lived after marriage, she longed for trees in the endless pastures of bluebonnets behind her home, so "finding an old apple tree growing there, I planted a weeping cherry, a pink dogwood, and a crab apple, and laughingly told my husband my epitaph would be, 'She planted three trees!' " [6]

Almost anyone can cut down trees; it takes a little vision and faith to plant them. We still have too many cutters and too few planters. Yet, as Mrs. Johnson has pointed out, if each one of us should go and plant even *one* tree (she has planted so many she has lost count), we could transform the roadsides. "It may mean fighting municipal vandals, prodding neglectful leaders, exhorting the public. But it is worth doing," adds the First Lady. [7]

And, specifically, what do the people of America say about this "frivolous" new beauty crusade? Mr. Gallup found 97 per cent of them strongly behind it. "Clean up the highways, stop littering," came first with those interviewed. Then: "Clear up the slums and renovate valuable old buildings." The third highest priority was, "Beautify highways, plant trees and flowers."

Following these favorites were votes to "eliminate junkyards, eliminate billboards; improve and increase parks and campsites; encourage everyone to clean up his own property," and, of course, "eliminate water pollution and air pollution." Others wanted the shorelines parked, and one staunch old reactionary snapped: "Do away with the big cities!" "Clean up the people first," grumbled a sole responder.

Edward C. Crafts, Director of the Bureau of Outdoor Recreation, quotes a Western newspaper's poll which showed that, to 85 per cent of the people, conservation and natural beauty comprised "an urgent problem to which high priority should be assigned." Seventy-five per cent would gladly set a billion dollars on the counter for beauty, each and every year. (This is the cost of one year's foreign *military* aid.) Ninety-five per cent put the finger on the states and cities to spend more money on highway beauty, and almost the same number attacked the highway engineers for the unconscienced "felonies" that have so long heedlessly destroyed roadside beauty.[8]

Thus, the new voice of the people speaks. The federal departments of Agriculture, Interior, Commerce, Health, Education and Welfare, and Housing and Urban Development, as well as the Office of Economic Opportunity and the Bureau of Public Roads have all been directed to give help and advice to citizens' groups which approach them. The Cooperative Extension Service is stressing natural beauty in educational work with some 95,000 4-H Clubs, school groups, Boy Scouts, garden clubs, nursery associations, Chambers of Commerce, church groups, and county home demonstration councils. The integration of urban beauty into the curricula of the universities which train our manpower and provide technical aid, will soon be demanded if we are to bring beauty into our civic environment.[9]

"The Urban Renewal Administration's program of historic preservation is expanding, including the recent grant to aid reconstruction of the New Orleans French Quarter," comments a congressional report. "The Housing and Urban Development Act of 1965 makes it possible to relocate historic structures within renewal areas, and, for the first time, to sell them to non-profit organizations interested in maintaining and restoring historic buildings."

In this respect much could be learned in urban beautification by visiting, as we did, the old city of Savannah, Georgia, where every second or third square block throughout the city's heart has been converted into a small green heaven of trees, evergreen and flowering shrubs, fountains, sculpture, benches, and garden walks. Even on a raw January day we had never seen its equal in American cities.

The gearing of the great federal agencies' directives toward aiding citizen beautification is reflected in the district offices close to home. ("It seems to me that a man has a right to be able to open his eyes in the morning and see trees," says Secretary Udall.) For instance, a recent announcement in a small-town paper by the Schenectady, New York, County Soil and Water Conservation office states that its services are now available "to *land-owners* who wish to improve the beauty of their land." Not only will they help you to build ponds, check erosion, and screen eyesores; they will sell you any number of small trees wholesale, perhaps find help in planting. And you need no longer "take the oath," that you are *not* using the trees for landscaping! Soil Service has come of age.

As for open spaces and parks right within the limits of the city, such as Savannah enjoys, the going will be very hard. We have already crowded every urban foot with the demand that it annually yield the very utmost in cold cash. But the old chestnut that "a park is wasted space because it contributes nothing to the tax roll" has finally been smashed. Many an open field at the city's outskirts, which has been hastily bulldozed and converted to residences to forestall the "wastage" of such land on a park, is being rued by the city fathers today. (See Chapter VI.)

Hugo Fisher, Administrator of the Resources Agency of California, reminds us that cities, as fast as they can, are converting their car-choked streets into broad, beautifully landscaped pedestrian malls.

[Development practices] considered reasonable and economically sound just a few short years ago have now become esthetically unacceptable to the public and therefore economically intolerable for the business community . . . Quiet beauty and open space, and the pleasure and convenience of easy movement. This is the manner of things the human spirit wants, and this is what the public will pay for.[10]

Victor Gruen, Los Angeles architect and author of the Fort Worth Plan, bemoaning the fact that "highways, freeways, and expressways . . . cut cityscape and landscape further into shreds and pieces," says: "In the planning of our downtowns, let's not forget that quality has to do with cultural values as well as sufficient parking. . . . Let's not be satisfied with drab structures when we can create beautiful buildings and plazas that will be a heritage for the generations to come." And he continues, "Anything right and sound can be financed. And that's not just a platitude—*that's a fact.*" Adding to which, Professor Charles M. Haar, Harvard professor and adviser to President Johnson on beauty, warns that beauty is "a source of great value, indeed of far greater value than the mundane values and things which succeed it."

"Our present highway law permits the use of up to 3 per cent of all federal aid funds to be used *without matching* for the preservation of natural beauty," the President has reminded us. "This authority has *not* been used for the purpose intended by Congress!" In other less dignified terms our road builders and town and city councils have been cheating the public on beauty—a sordid trick that must now be exposed and remedied.

There are, then, two basic needs of immediate concern. Let Daniel M. Ogden, Jr., of the Bureau of Outdoor Recreation list them:

> Should we set aside great scenic and wilderness areas now, while we can, before they are destroyed forever—even those which are remote from the centers of population? To acquire a sizeable California Redwoods National Park could consume the bulk of the National Park Service's share of the Land and Water Fund for a decade.
> Or should we seek to protect and develop areas which can be acquired near the centers of population—in a direct effort to meet the needs of the greatest number as close to home as possible?

(He adds: "I find myself preferring to preserve the great scenic areas before it is too late, even though some may seem remote today." With the transportation of tomorrow, he concludes, nothing will be remote.)[11]

The *Washington Post* wonders whether the great chain saws, the giant cats, the technological expertise, will make a gutted wasteland of the redwoods while our heads are turned tallying profits and clipping coupons? [12] Will we dally watching television while every last patch of open land around our cities is covered with cement and more buildings, filling stations, and supermarkets? Because of climatic and other changes not even two thousand years will restore the redwoods; and land once frosted over with asphalt is never reclaimed to wildness and beauty. [13]

How much does "our wolf mother, the wilderness" mean to us? In *A Sharing of Joy* Martha Reben, a hopeless consumptive who fled to a shack in the Adirondacks and by so doing was given a new and thrilling lease on life for many years, wrote that to her wilderness meant

> a memory of something beautiful and ancient and now lost . . . a forgotten freedom we must all once have shared with other wild things which only they and the wilderness can still recall to us, so that life becomes again, for a time, the wonderful, sometimes frightening, but fiercely joyous adventure it was intended to be.

Do we want to retain this "fiercely joyous adventure" which is our heritage? The choice is here; in five years —perhaps in less time—there will be, as has been so often repeated, nothing left worth fighting over.

City planners remind us that "cities are for people" and point to the outdoor cafés, great boulevards, and lived-in parks of Paris, Madrid, and Rome. Why do we not have outdoor benches and cafés? We are reminded that even in New York City there are but a few scattered benches placed there by a philanthropist, when the city itself should have provided them on all the popular avenues.

"Why don't we aspire to a Champs Élysées?" one famous architect asks fretfully. "It seems Americans can afford everything but beauty."

In searching the Southland in January, 1966, for

first evidences of the beauty campaign in the cities we came upon a most inviting sight. One is accustomed—but never reconciled—to finding a gasoline station the worst eyesore on the landscape, littered with ugly signs, old and new tires, gadgetry, violent colors that shock the eye, carnival banners, and the like. Citgo's service station in Coral Gables, Florida, however, is a small oasis of flowers, bushes, and palms, artistically bathed in colored lights.

Thereafter, we sought out Citgo stations at every stop, hoping to find its equal. Though we did not, we noted some hopeful beginnings. A Sinclair ad uses its full page for an exciting color photo of an idyllic virgin forest trail with the warning: "Each newly born baby has one-quarter acre less of such land to enjoy than the baby born a moment ago." Recently, also, the Union Oil Company used its ad to feature two giant old oak trees which, in the cause of "being a good neighbor," it did not cut down but cleverly used to backdrop and shade the station at Thousand Oaks, California. There are evidences that the oil companies (and a few other industries, too) have begun to get the word. The American people can reward cooperative oil stations with patronage. It would be a pleasure.

Truly, in resolving the dilemma of which we should protect and save first—our famed national wonders or our city beauty spots—there should be no contest. The fact is, a nation as affluent and stuffed with expensive conveniences, food surpluses, and gadgetry as are we, should not have to make so bleak and heart-rending a choice. We are well able to afford both.

We can well afford to be lavish and openhanded in returning to Nature some of her violated resources which has made us billions and put us where we are today. What we cannot afford are any more giveaways to private development or destruction of the small fraction of these natural wonders still with us.

And because of the lateness of the hour, beauty must not be weighted equally with commerce; it must be more heavily weighted, because, suddenly, it has become infinitely more precious.

As the examples before our eyes of China, India, Egypt, and the other worn-out countries of the Middle East can be a warning to us in this supreme moment of our ascendancy, so the resuscitative efforts of a once worn-out but resurgent country may be an inspiration to our endeavors. In the February 26, 1966, *Saturday Review* there was an ad that caught the eye. It was headed: "When was the last time you saw a miracle?" It continued:

> Some pretty strange things are happening in the northern part of Israel. Birds are singing where they haven't sung since biblical days, and rain is falling and crickets are cricketing. It's all because of the trees that weren't there 18 years ago. The people of Israel planted these trees where nothing could grow, and today the only thing growing any faster is the nation around them.

It is definitely easier to resuscitate beauty and well-being in a land where shreds of it yet remain, where topsoil and water are still sufficient for effective husbandry, than to wait until these indispensable assets have slipped away and the dust clouds and sand have closed over the great inner sweeps of the countryside.[14]

But the word "beauty" has been an embarrassing word ever since the industrial era began. Perhaps, says Mrs. Johnson, our affluence "has given us the courage to use the word right out in public." The truth of all truths was stated in the very peak of the industrialization era when President Theodore Roosevelt dared to declare: "There is nothing more practical in the end than the preservation of beauty."

Yet it is also true that, eventually, if we do not recover our sense of balance and limit our fecundity before then, the millions and millions of feet will trample to death every park, forest, beach, wildlife refuge, and beauty spot we can possibly preserve. But we can hope it will not be so.

There must be trees in my Paradise,
There must be pines with spires to lift the eyes.

The golden stairs I fear will go untried
Unless the mountain yew springs lush beside.

And pearly gates—how garish, and how bare
If I shall find no redwoods towering there!

I need a lake where hoary spruces brood,
I need to lean my back on living wood . . .

For heaven's streets will leave me unconsoled
Unless the elm can sink a root in gold.

If there's no green the dazzling gold to leaven
Then I shall be a foreigner in heaven.

                                        —L.R.

Part Four

The Destruction
of Ourselves

Chapter Fifteen

Noise, Nerves, and Neurotics

There is a tiny, isolated speck of an island about halfway on the trackless ocean wastes between South America and South Africa called Tristan da Cunha. After a violent volcanic eruption its handful of dispossessed and frightened inhabitants migrated to Britain and civilization. They didn't stay long. Homesick and disillusioned, they returned in 1963 *en masse* to the quiet and peace of their remote little isle, crying at the world of progress they were quitting: "Money, money, money; noise, noise, noise; worry, worry, worry."

Speaking about findings that more than three out of five American men have lost some hearing which they will never retrieve and that deafness is mounting in our civilization, Dr. Aram Glorig, director of the hearing and speech center of the American Medical Association in Dallas, stated: "It's a noisy world, getting noisier. And somehow we've got to learn to control it, or live with it, or go deaf."

The expanding world is growing one decibel noisier every year.[1] What is a decibel? Only five years ago the word was almost unknown in the public lexicon; today it appears almost daily in the press. In layman's parlance the word "noisy" is applied to any sound that makes it difficult to speak or to be heard. By this standard 80 decibels is considered "loud," 100 decibels labeled "deafening," and anything over 120 decibels is "dangerously high." How do the everyday sounds of our civilization line up against this standard?

According to a special report by Jack Dillon [2] a big jetliner soaring over Boston at 1,200 feet registered 103 decibels on the street. The meter registered 2 degrees higher inside a high-speed Harvard–Allston subway car, and two motorcycles zooming down Beacon Street rang up 107 decibels on the gauge three stories up. Jackhammers in the street gave 98 decibels at ten feet, but the unfortunate human at the controls had his ears assailed by 123 decibels of bone-jarring thunder. One big cotton loom registered 103 decibels: the horror of a dozen or so such monsters in a factory room can never be imagined by those who have not experienced it. "It is not," said a manufacturer, "economic to convert to less noisy equipment." [3]

As the population growth in metropolitan areas and closer, tighter, living accelerate in all continents, under capitalism as well as under communism, the growth in noise also accelerates. The World Health Organization of the United Nations has sent out a warning [4] that noise, "another prominent evil of the modern metropolis," can be harmful even at low levels when it is continuous, as in the case of city traffic. "It can even be harmful when it is not consciously heard," the agency adds with sinister undertones. Most abused and complained about by people are the jets, which daily take a verbal trouncing in every city of the world—an attack which, if words were barbed, would puncture the holds of the most impregnable leviathan of the skies.

So great was the public clamor around the John F. Kennedy Airport that in November of 1963 the town council of Hempstead, Long Island, passed the first such enactment on record—an anti-noise ordinance with limits that promised to cost airlines an estimated $25,000 a day in fines. More than half of the 500 airplanes flying over the town each day to and from New York City's two big airports create such constant thunder that they make church services and classroom discussions all but impossible; they destroy relaxation in the home and render the citizens so nervous they cannot work, eat, or sleep.[5]

Retorted the Air Line Pilots Association: "What shall we do—endanger passengers' lives by cutting back power to make the engines run quieter?" An industry spokesman called the demand "technically and economically impossible at the present." A town father responded darkly that the town had on order mobile detecting equipment, including candid camera shots, which it was prepared to roll out to gain the damning evidence which it would take right to the Supreme Court if necessary.

Administrator N. E. Halaby of the Federal Aviation Agency said in a speech at the MacArthur Airport that the noise of jets will not only persist but most probably get worse, which aroused former Senator Kenneth Keating to castigate industry's push for greater technological advances without first solving pressing problems such as jet noise abatement.[6] "This is but another example of our society's failure to tie together the loose ends of one stage of our technical accomplishments before going on to the next," he said.

Although people scream at the jets, it is the multitude of other more intimate, folksy noises that city dwellers grumble about the most. It would be a difficult search to find even a single city dweller without a dozen pet complaints.[7]

"It's my neighbor's noisy air conditioner that keeps us awake at night," said one angry flat dweller. Women on a Chicago radio program complained particularly of the screeches of paper boys, the clatter of women's spikes on the cement, and the groan of accelerating buses through the streets. In Cleveland, in addition to the scores of suburban aggravations, night-barking dogs ("the neighbors'"), and "revving" motorcycles (also "the neighbors'") ranked high.

In Midwestern suburbs in general the unsubdued drone of the neighbor's lawn mower and the squeaks and bangings of his outmoded truck in the drive under one's window were sore subjects. Everywhere the pounding, thumping, and groaning of street-repair machinery caused headaches, as did the relentless, unceasing clatter of bulldozers and building machinery. In California, Florida, and Arizona, in particular, as thousands of "little cement nubs"—in the words of our professor friend who lives in one of them—follow thousands of other little cement nubs, there is no respite from the din of the mechanical monsters. Any diminution in this development orgy will, an industry spokesman warned, mean our progress is slipping.

On a recent military inspection of the Ford Motor Company plant in Green Island, New York, we learned that there was another side to the story. My officers started in that part of the plant where, by a cold process on a huge press, spring leaves for new cars were being fashioned. The noise was so deafening that the guide had to lean over and shout and then all five of us could not hear him. It rated around a hundred decibels, much more at intervals when a workman slung a spring leaf onto the table for the next operation.[8] Hanging on a post next to the machine was an elaborately constructed pair of yellow ear muffs that looked like the protective gear of a football player. In these surroundings they shone like new. "Why," I asked our guide, "doesn't this fellow wear these things? They look effective; wouldn't they help?" After repeating this query four times (with gestures) our guide understood my question. All he could do was to laugh and shake his head. Later we were told that the operators consistently scorned such sissy measures. They courted deafness rather than to appear "chicken" with a pair of muffs.[9]

People living near the freeways of the great West, or the turnpikes of the East are particularly vocal. The Westchester (New York) County Board of Supervisors wants legal limits on the noise emissions of motor vehicles: 85 decibels at 50 feet, 90 decibels at 25 feet, and 96 decibels at 12.5 feet. At the same time, Britain's Minister of Transport, Tom Fraser, proposes motorcycles be limited to 85 decibels and automobiles to 80 decibels, all at decent British distances. If "the exhaust silencer has just fallen off the car, Officer," the motor vehicle falls out of the traffic until the trouble is corrected.

A foreign visitor loved American cities except for one aspect: the powerful motorcar horns used "indiscriminately and endlessly for no apparent reason." He could not have been from Italy. A letter to a Boston newspaper held that illegal parking was the prime cause of so much daytime horn-exercising. In Italy it is said the horn cacophony is exuberance and sheer love of noise. But a visitor to any American city, lying awake in his twelfth-floor hotel room, wonders what on earth causes all that horn blowing at three o'clock in the morning. There can't be that many jaywalking pedestrians left to blare at. Maybe the late drivers and taxi men are leaning on their horns to stay awake. If so, they are successful—as far as you are concerned.

Even more aggravating to the small town dweller stranded in Philadelphia, Sacramento, New Orleans, or any other grand city [10] are the eternally shrieking sirens of fire engines (usually false alarms) and ambulances that seem to follow each other on a pre-arranged five-minute schedule straight through the city's heart from dusk to dawn. Brownstone-front dwellers in Eastern cities, in their "Letters to the Editor," complain about "the cacaphonous, metallic clatterings of the sanitation collectors. . . . Must they bounce the metal cans and covers with utter disregard to the high decibel count they create? Also, why must these men shriek to their buddies, adding to the clamor?"

Most drivers blow angry horns—"after-the-fact horns," not danger horns—say the letters. "Noise pollution sets our teeth on edge, causes dangling nerve ends, and in a few tortured cases, deafness." Acoustical expert Lewis S. Goodfriend, in a paper read to the Acoustical Society of America in 1963, disclosed that not only are 100 suburban communities on the Eastern Seaboard becoming noisier but that complaints and lawsuits are continually on the rise.[11] Some kind of a climax is preparing.

In California during a recent twelve-month period of investigation there were 332 cases of hearing damage attributed to high levels of noise in "metal working plants where riveting was the chief offender; wood working plants where saws made noise; in boiler plants (long the champions in decibel rating); and in digging for building construction." New regulations covering more than 400,000 industrial establishments in California have since been put into effect, regulations that will hold employers responsible for maintaining the noise level below 95 decibels "except for impacts or bursts of sound. This is the noise level of a heavy truck twenty feet away." [12]

The insensitivity of a business is revealed in a recent bank ad in a local paper: "Putt putt putt . . . ZOO-OO-OO-M-M-M-M . . . IF IT MAKES A noise, WE'LL FINANCE IT!" The ad continues: "Automobiles . . . motorboats . . . outboard motors . . . motorcycles . . . refrigerators . . . air conditioners . . . dishwashers . . . you name it, we'll finance it. . . ."

On the other hand, a perceptive ad man, Stephen O. Frankfurt, Vice-President of Young & Rubicam, Inc., told the American Association of Advertising Agencies assembled at White Sulphur Springs, West Virginia, some hard truths about what ads were doing to American ears.

> The sounds of selling are all around us—in the streets, on the road, at the movies, on land, on sea, and on the air. And, oh, that sound of the air. What many of us in advertising sometimes forget is that the individual has only so much capacity to absorb sound, and his desire to maintain his sanity forces him to block out much of what he hears.[13]

Then he concluded:

> Your message has had it when the sound becomes noise. Do you know what noise is? It's sound, but in the wrong place at the wrong time. You cannot make either a

friend or a sale by yelling at someone. Sometimes just the fact that you are quiet will cause attention to flow in your direction.

The soft sell recently adopted by many very effective ads (we are thinking in particular of some captivating ads for dog- and catfood) are some indication that parts of the advertising fraternity are catching on. Nobody wants an audience that has gone deaf.

A medical columnist speaks of the work of Dr. Zhivko Angleuscheff, who has been alerting physicians and acoustical engineers to the progressive damage to hearing by the mounting clamor of our daily life. He, too, cites the thousands upon thousands of new damage claims now besieging the courts due to deafness and ear damage from technology's excessive noise, adding: "Constant acoustical injury to the ears can produce a slow, gradual, but progressive loss until it finally affects serviceable hearing." [14]

Results of recent studies have shown that isolated tribes in Africa, where noise is minimal, have maximal hearing. In fact, the excellent hearing of the tribal elders for the highest sound was consistently superior to that of city dwellers of the same age group. Even machine noise so high in pitch we cannot hear it apparently affects not only our ears but our total health.

The raucous and uncouth noise of modern technology invades everywhere; motorboat owners fight to take over the last refuge of canoeists on Yellowstone Lake's quiet bays, which would, of course, scatter the wildlife and ruin the scene for all who prefer nature to be natural. President Harry S Truman issued an executive ban on airplane travel over and on the border lakes in Minnesota's unmatchable canoe country, for which nature lovers will be entirely in his debt. The combustion motor, a boor and bully, is incompatible with wilderness; like beets in a stew it takes over the entire mess.

We can never forget our one and only visit to Damascus. Taking guide and limousine at the dockside in

Beirut to be driven over the mountain for a brief visit into Syria, we were unfortunate to have in our company of six a domineering person who also happened to be an amateur philatelist. Upon entering Damascus he at once ordered the dragoman to drive us to the nearest post office, overriding the restrained objections of his five companions by sheer voice power. There we sat before that post office for forty-five minutes of the two hours allotted us in Damascus (the boat sailed that afternoon), while our self-centered companion purchased a variety of stamps and sent them, with appropriate jolly notes, to all the philatelic dabblers he knew back home in Ohio, most of whom probably couldn't have cared less. But he was asserting himself and monopolizing the stage. Later, when news came to us of the stubborn insistence of the motorboat enthusiasts to monopolize the entire expanse of Yellowstone Lake without regard for the feelings of canoeists and others, we could not help recalling this fellow.

Speaking of wilderness values, there is a verbal battle currently raging between hikers and motor-scooter owners over the wild backcountry of the public domain. Motorized scooters, it is accused, shatter the primeval solitude and destroy the serenity of nature for the hikers, horseback riders, naturalists, and nature lovers. A recent test case involving the Boise National Forest in Idaho[15] bolstered the right of the Secretary of Agriculture to ban motor scooters in primitive areas. The noisemakers have taken over 98 per cent of the continent, where they disport without limit (so far). In a society whose growing noise, crowded conditions, and tensions parallel its mounting curves of deafness, neuroticism, and mental illnesses, the destruction of those last quiet places to which the harassed cityite might flee for relief would seem to be unthinkable.

With more people come more building, more ear shattering, more pounding of demolition balls and whining of dump trucks, more road construction, more jackhammers, sirens, trucks, buses, electric drills, cement mixers, clanging of hammers, sizzling of riveters, planes, trains, scooters, garbage collectors, dogs, and ladies' spike heels on the pavement, more "revving" of unmuffled engines, more groaning and shrieking of brakes, more tooting of horns, blasting of police whistles, whirring of buzz saws, and chugging of machinery.

Julius Caesar banned night joy-riding in chariots because so many Romans complained of the rattling of the heavy wheels against the cobblestones. Londoners, in their turn, groused a great deal about the "hammering of the multitude of iron-shod hairy heels" that went on all night over the rough stone streets of the 1890's. None ever dreamed in all man's history of the rumbling, buzzing, siren-shrilling nights of the future. None ever conceived of the sinister thunder of the supersonic boom.

The latest phenomenon of progress is at this moment the center of the bitterest airplane noise controversy engendered so far. As explained by *Saturday Review's* science editor, John Lear, who has the rare knack of scientific definition in phrases understandable by the layman, ships that fly faster than sound compress the atmosphere around them "and literally drag a cone of noise for miles behind them." [16] The faster the speed of the plane, the more intense the compression, the more ear-shattering the thunderclap which breaks down upon us. A supersonic boom may shiver window glass, shake foundations of buildings, crack ceilings, terrify chickens out of laying, stop cows from letting down milk; it sends humans into mild shock and swamps police headquarters with frightened calls. Already the ancient homes of the cliff dwellers in the Southwest have been seriously damaged by sonic booms of military aircraft overhead.

But some military officials say that the new supersonic plane now on drafting boards, which will "do" more than 2,000 miles an hour, is a military necessity, so a few years ago the Federal Aviation Agency [17] arranged for a prolonged test reaction in Oklahoma City to discover whether the American people would tolerate it. Since one in every four jobs in Oklahoma City has to do with planes—either at an aircraft factory, at Tinker Field, or at the Federal Aviation Agency's headquarters there, and since, also, the city was to receive $877,000 to build the runway, it would seem that a favorable verdict was a fairly good bet. Jet pilots thereupon proceeded on February 3, 1964, to break the sound barrier across the city eight times a day for a proposed period of six months.

In the first week of "Operation Bongo" 655 complaints came in, to which FAA responded airily that "nervous people may have to rely on tranquilizers." When the powerful League of Women Voters added its voice to the rising wails, the city council suspended the experiment; upon more mature reflection as to "economic advantages of the future," the same prudent council rescinded its suspension. Representatives—actually, three engineers—of the National Academy of Sciences were called in to "review objectively" the whole project.

Three months after the booms started, a total of 5,655 damage claims had been filed with FAA. Most were not considered serious. How much does it mean to a blind vendor to lose the services of his terrified Seeing Eye dog? Is it important that some elderly people fell and broke bones and others had heart attacks; that a schoolroom ceiling lamp fell and knocked out a boy over his books? Plate glass windows can be repaired as can the brick facings of houses that were shaken loose. Are three engineers competent to assess the damage done to the human bodies?

At the end of the six-month test period, the Oklahomans in general said they could learn to live with the boom, but the number who said they could not stand the boom increased by 27 per cent during the period. Of the sample 2,033 persons interviewed three times during the testing, says the final report, "about one-fourth of all the people felt they could not learn to accept the booms." Of the 4,629 formal damage claims filed, 3,869 were disallowed, 229 were approved for payments that totaled $12,845.32, and the remainder linger hopefully in the courts. The more than 15,000 complaints that rained upon headquarters must have entailed an emergency set of telephone operators, but the FAA is confident that "once the public understands the phenomenon" the operation of civilian supersonic craft will be "feasible," which means "profitable." [18]

The "military or economic necessity"—in fact, any necessity—of a plane which will fly 2,000 or more miles an hour, subjecting humans to unnatural stress that has not as yet been measured, is questioned by many in high places. William Littlewood, who but recently retired from the vice-presidency in charge of aircraft procurement for American Airlines, has stated there is no economic need for the supersonic transport; another airline president has stated that he would be "happy if we did not have a supersonic transport for fifty years." [19]

Why, then, are we insisting on this fabulous, expensive undertaking? Is it for international prestige, braggadocio, to beat our friends, the British and French? Surely a cultured society should boast of more mature motives than these?

The Twentieth Century Fund survey shows that in 1850, 15 out of 100 Americans lived in urban areas; 85 per cent lived on farms. Today 70 out of 100 Americans live in cities or suburbs, only 7 on farms, and 23 in rural non-farm areas. Today's population is about eight times that of 1850 but produces thirty-five times as much. In putting forth this great rise in material goods it also produces, as a by-product, thirty-five times as much noise. And whereas in 1850 only 15 per cent of the people were submitted to production's bang-and-clatter, today 70 per cent of the people are so afflicted. Nor is this development peculiar in the United States; it is an international problem of the whole capitalistic and communistic world. [20]

Something is going to have to give. In the category of aspirin we have the ear plugs and ear mufflers advised by an airfield official, the thick acoustical ceilings and sound-proof-vault houses advised by a building contractor, the double-paned windows advised by a glass manufacturer, the heavy insulated draperies and heavier carpets, the sheets of gypsum and acoustical tiles advised by the appropriate commercial proponents.[21]

But Nature, it now has been discovered, is building up a permanent defense against the nerve-dissolving, killing hubbub by gradually causing the ears of the citydweller to go deaf. It appears that the only adaptation the human ear knows to the constant pounding and thrumming it receives is by eliminating *all* sound stimuli. It is, without doubt, better to be stone-deaf than raving mad.

There is no hope that jets can be tamed to any degree; their noise is their power. But in the category of more practical medicine are the attempts being initiated to standardize noise limits in terms of decibels for all surface vehicles and machines and to fine violators with unbending diligence. In Pittsburgh, Pennsylvania, a home owner was actually awarded a judgment of $12,690 because he and his family contracted nervous conditions from not being able to sleep nights.[22]

Better yet, these captains of industry who callously proclaim that we shall "have to live with it" should perhaps be sentenced to confinement and submitted to a continuous charivari of 120 decibels for thirty days. Again, this is only a suggestion.

It cannot be honestly charged that the authorities are not, in a restrained way, trying. Paul Zimmerman, executive secretary of the industry-financed National Aircraft Noise Abatement Council, told Washington correspondents that besides working on reducing noise at the source, they actually are redrawing flight patterns to avoid the larger residential areas and working to establish parks and green spaces around airports. The Federal Aviation Agency and the National Aeronautics and Space Administration are pouring a few million dollars into noise abatement each year. One official couched the idea of building a six-mile runway out into the ocean, possibly on the theory that fish do not have ears. The sign that noise is indeed gaining stature as a problem is the recent involvement of the insurance companies, who have leaped into the anti-noise campaign as claims for ear damages mount and mount.

Noise has been defined as the greatest level of hub-bub *consistent with economic and operational consid-erations* that is acceptable to the worker, or victim. Only when the economic and operational considera-tions take second place in the definition will noticeable improvements in the decibel ratings be achieved.

But perhaps we are all off on the wrong tack in our research. After all, we know little more about what noise is doing to us than that it is causing us to go slowly deaf. Perhaps it is not the decibels that are causing the deafness, or that appear to make some people ill or mental cases. Perhaps it is the fact that the unremitting clangor, this uncoordinated racket of our technological age, is so discordant and grating. Perhaps it is the discordancies and not really the deci-bels that count?

Recently, thirty-seven nations gathered at Stockholm at a meeting of the International Standards Organiza-tion. They unanimously agreed that the basic tuning fork note "A" should be raised from 435 to 440 oscil-lations a second. They standardized the pitch of all the instruments of the world; humanity is now operating on one key.

Of course, bugles are included; it is reassuring to know that the future call to battle will not be marred by any musical discordancies. Undoubtedly the song of a missile in flight will now be pitched in harmonious range to reflect man's new concern for understanding. As for the thirty-five-mile swathe of the sonic boom of the international jet plane of tomorrow, we can relax in the knowledge that the pitch of "A" will now be true; harmony will reign in the heavens.

We haven't been able to hear an uninterrupted symphony in any pitch since World War II. One of the noteworthy savings engineered by our efficiency-expert-ridden economy has been the elimination of mufflers on trucks. It was a great day for the home office when they discovered they could track their trucks by seismograph. Even the school buses, without benefit of experts, roar through the countryside like snorting monsters, driving the taxpayers into ever more acute neuroticism. Perhaps all this will be changed. Perhaps now the mellifluous rumblings and resonant roarings of these vehicles will blend with the symphony rather than smother it, adding a new depth of dimension even to Wagner.

But what can they do with jackhammers? Somehow the construction industry equates progress with din. So long as the bulldozer operator is on the loose making so much noise he can't hear the public cries of distress, we are obviously getting somewhere. The main thing when in doubt is to "rev" the motor.

We are in favor of 440 oscillations. Any advance in international understanding is to be hailed. But maybe now that the tubas are in order, the international negotiators can get to the problem of sirens. How comforting it would be if, when the moment of truth for mankind arrives, when the holocaust is on, the sirens all over the world were to sound in perfect key!

For we are not alone in our noise distresses. In the tumultuous rebirth of Tokyo for the Olympics there was added to its interminable roar of traffic "the moaning of donkey-engine winches, the rattle of hammers and rivets, and the rumble of construction machinery in a maddening and unending racket." One university student, finding study impossible and driven beyond endurance, committed suicide in an appropriate gesture of protest: he lay his head under a pile driver.[28]

As we go about our business of Chinafying America, it is pertinent to reflect often and again on what it is really like to live in such a country. In the maelstrom of Canton the problem of noise goes far beyond the pitch of "A" in the "peculiar and high tones of its horns," as one complainant put it. Another would-be sleeper doesn't enjoy the factory break at 4 a.m. when workers "talk, laugh loudly, play the Chinese fiddle and sing Cantonese opera."

Factories carry on all night with bells and hooters; one cannot support so many people on a half-day shift. The Kwangtung Torchlight factory tops it all with its battery of gongs and drums, loud-speakers, the "heave-ho" of workers, the "bang-bang" of dropping metalware, the "dong-dong" and shouts of "bravo! bravo!" Smothering the head in pillows and moving beds into the kitchen are of no avail. So neurotic have the Cantonese become that one objector could no longer stand the "loud explosions of parching popcorn." This "blasting operation" should be prohibited after 8 p.m.! [24]

In a telling *Saturday Review* editorial [25] editor Norman Cousins was moved to describe a full day in the great city in terms of the decibels that tortured the human ear. His conclusion:

Whether or not they realize it, the American people are waging unremitting war against themselves. The weapons are tranquility-smashers, and are fitted out with decibel warheads. They penetrate all known cranial barriers and the innermost core of an individual's privacy, impeding the processes of sequential thought, breaking down the sensibilities, and unhinging the capacity for serenity. The noise level is rising and the level of common sanity is falling.

Since this editorial was written in 1962 the decibel rating in our cities has risen (it is estimated) some five points!

And the *Times* of London berates the defense of the rising noise level which asserts it to be something that we must nobly bear.

The inevitability of every technological stride that is taken is paraded nowadays quite as much as its supposed benefits. It is a dangerous doctrine, causing men to lose control over the conditions of their own lives; for it disinclines them to reject or modify those possible changes which do more to damage than to enhance the environment. High on the list of the deleterious factors is noise.

As with our average junk production of four pounds per person a day, we also have a certain "average noise production" per person. So far as we know, no research has yet been launched to discover what this per capita noise production is, outside of the vague estimate that the present annual growth rate of our cities is raising the noise level by one decibel a year. If the one decibel per year "intelligent guess" is valid, we supposedly have some twenty years before we take mass leave of our senses. Happily, deafness will no doubt come first and rescue us. Deafness in such a world will not be too much of a burden.

And even though we could not afford the necessary curbs on economic progress that would have saved our hearing, we shall still be able to watch television to witness the landing of our astronauts on Mars, a venture for which we could afford a hundred billion dollars. In the meantime there is a new lip-reading-school stock on the curb market. It might prove a really hot tip.

Chapter Sixteen

Our Rising Standard
of Poisons

Biologist Rachel Carson has been accused, because of her *Silent Spring,* of "pushing the panic button" in regard to the progressive poisoning of our total environment by man-made toxicants. It was not Rachel Carson who pushed the panic button. It was the production experts who have been leaning on this button ever since the baby boom with the cry, "We cannot possibly feed the growing nation or produce the raw materials for their needs without a mammoth program of chemical control." Miss Carson merely exposed our predicament.[1]

We are told that our varied diet—indeed, the ability of our producers to feed our growing multitudes at all —depends upon our willingness to accept an ever-increasing dose of poison not only in all that we eat, drink, touch, or wear, but in our muscles, tissues, and even in our brains.[2] If this is so, it would seem that our standard of living has slipped a big notch somewhere.

When we discover (July, 1966) that since the commercial introduction of DDT in 1946, the use of synthetic pesticides has increased from a million pounds annually to the "massive dispersal" in 1965 of nearly *one billion* pounds, we can be confident that we are "living dangerously" at last. When we learn that we are at present ingesting eight times as much poison as we did in 1940 and that by 1975 we will be absorbing four times as much as we are absorbing today, it is evident that the notches are still slipping at an accelerated rate. Again, quantitatively, as in other things, we are at the apex of production; qualitatively, we are starting downhill at a trot.

It is with great emotion that the chemical buffs reiterate that the more than 900 million pounds of unselective pesticides which drench the earth and air each year are *indispensable* to outwit the swarming pest population. How could we conquer the twenty kinds of mites and insects and eight species of diseases of apples, for example, without fifteen or twenty sprays a year? And what foolishness to bend the back to hack out the crab grass around the patio, when 40 million pounds of herbicides soaked into the soil (and possibly thence into the water supply) will do it for all our lawns and patios so neatly?

When grandfather reminds them that fine apples were produced not too many years ago by relying on the "natural enemies" of the pests and then for decades thereafter by relying on only one or two sprays per season, the chemical buffs have an answer for that, too. They respond that the protective species of insects, nature's answer to the pests, have long ago been eliminated by the sprays. Birds, lizards, toads, wasps, and other helpful animals such as skunks have also been killed off around agricultural lands and there is no longer any recourse but to spray more energetically each year. Worse: we are told that as fast as they invent some virulent knockout drops for a species of insect pests, that species becomes immune to the poison, and the chemists must produce another poison with still more kill-potential. "We not only need [pesticides]," declares a Cornell College of Agriculture bulletin, "we are highly dependent on them."

Apparently the Department of Agriculture and the chemical buffs are right; we are caught in a relentless vise. We are pursuing a path from which there is no longer any retreat and that hourly grows more fraught with danger. If so, we have come to a rather dismal pass. The *Insecta,* some 1,000,000 species of them (possibly 600,000 classified), have endured and flourished on this planet since the Silurian age some 250 million years ago, and it is an excellent bet that they will outlive upstart (1 million-year-old) man.[3] They are "the most successful animal on earth." Unless man comes to terms with the creatures or can enlist some weighty help from nature herself, he is fighting a losing war.[4] Yet undoubtedly he will remain in there slugging it out alone until he is too weak to lift another test tube.

In the meantime, regardless of how "indispensable" the chemicals in our food are, the fantastic amounts of food additives, both "intentional" (661 million pounds in 1965, a 58 per cent rise in ten years) and "incidental" foster a serious and foolhardy situation. As Dr. David B. Hand of the Department of Food Science and Technology at Geneva, New York, and other specialists insist, a volume of incidental additives—pesticides, herbicides, fungicides—although "not intended," may well be "unavoidable," *given our present and especially our prospective population demands* and *our philosophy of expediency*.

However, the intentional additives—some 2,600 chemicals used in food production by 80,000 or more manufacturers, processors, and packers—which are used to preserve, embalm, flavor, color, emulsify, thicken, bleach, leaven, clarify, acidify, brighten, or change the consistency of foods may well be another story. Dr. Frank Bicknell notes:[5] "Food which cannot go bad is bad food;" i.e., if it won't support weevils or even bacteria, it won't healthfully support you (just another living creature) either.

Many of these strange, unpronounceable chemicals are found on labels; many more (as in the cases of bread and ice cream) are not listed at all.[6] How many housewives realize that we are buying and consuming 8 million pounds of coal tar products in food and cosmetics every year?

When you read a label listing chickle, butadiene-styrene, isopropene, saturated aliphatic hydrocarbons, polyvinyl acetate synthetic resins, butylated hydroxyanisole, butylated hydroxtoluene, propyl gallate, would you know you were reading a chewing gum label?

Who can keep up with 45,000 or more chemical formulations used in food processing? And when a cow is fed a formulation containing "prednisone acetate, procaine pencillin, dihydrostreptomycin sulfate, methylparaben and propylparaben in peanut oil-aluminum monostearate-polyoxyethylene sorbitan-tristearate vehicle," who among the chemical wizards who dreamed up this monstrosity of artificial nutrition is competent to swear that what comes out of the cow and goes into the baby is either wholesome or safe?

When Professor of Civil Engineering Daniel F. Jackson of the University of Syracuse breakfasted with delegates to New York State's annual health conference at the capital in June of 1965, he waited until the last gulp of coffee had been consumed before he analyzed what additives—both incidental and intentional—they had just eaten. In the fruit juice: benzoic acid, dimethyl polysiloxane (antifoaming agent), DDT, parathion (possibly), saccharin. In the bacon and ham: DDT, chlordane, toxaphene or other pesticides, especially in the fatty parts: also stilbestrol (artificial female sex hormone), aueromycin, mineral oil residue from the wax paper. In the eggs: decomposition products from fatty acids, mono- and diglycerides, isopropyl citrate, mono-isopropyl citrate, DDT, various antibiotics. In the rolls: ammonium chloride (conditioner), mono- and diglycerides and polyoxyethylene (softeners), ditertiary-butyl-para-cresol, coal tar dyes, vitamin fortifiers. In the butter: nordihydroguaiaretic acid, oxidation products from interaction with hydrogen peroxide (decomposition), magnesium oxide, AB and OB Yellows (coal tar), diacetyl, DDT or other insecticides. In the coffee, in addition to possible cereals, traces of insecticides.

"You can see," concluded the Professor, "you are

really getting more for the money than appeared on the menu."

The Interior Department reveals that one part of DDT in one *billion* parts of water kills blue crabs in eight days;[7] one part per *billion* in more understandable phraseology is the relationship one ounce of chocolate syrup would bear to 10 million gallons of milk! The chemical people make a great deal of the "safety" of the various death potions "when used as directed." Yet an analysis of dead wild pheasants in California on lands on which "accepted and normal" sprays had been used showed them to be so saturated that one biologist remarked, "These birds are sizzling hot."

Millions of fish have died in the Mississippi River, reportedly from endrin. While 95 per cent of the fish that die in Missouri streams die from toxaphene poisoning, the swarms and phalanxes of spraying planes dive, whirr, and perform aerial acrobatics, flying from dawn to dusk over the wheat fields in an orgy of soil and water poisoning, says Dr. James Whitley of the Missouri Conservation Commission. In New York State spraying is eliminating the trout in Lake George, Blue Mountain Lake, Paradox, and Schroon; the Finger Lakes are losing thousands of fish from the spraying done at campsites and parks.[8] Few realize that such spray often drifts for many miles. The effects of Sevin, a new organic carbamate substituted for the chlorinated hydrocarbons, are unknown; although its residual life is much shorter, one of its breakdown products is said to be 1-naphthol, listed as "very toxic."[9]

While fish slaughter presents the most dramatic and observable spectacle as the victims float glass-eyed and odorous on rivers and lakes, the bird and wildlife kill is even more serious: pheasants, quail, and mallards at Patuxent, Maryland; ducks, bald eagles, geese, pelicans on the Tule Lake Wildlife Refuge in California; mule deer in Montana and Colorado and New Mexico; shrimps, crabs, and mollusks along the coasts, especially in Louisiana; doves, pigeons, foxes, badgers in the prairie states; salmon, hawks, gulls, golden eagles in Washington and Oregon; the myrtle warblers and red-eyed vireos at Hawk Mountain, Pennsylvania; all the ospreys in the Connecticut River basin; the peregrine falcon utterly vanished from the entire Northeastern states as a breeding bird.

Pesticides are especially concentrated in game animals that roam and feed. "For instance, approximately 70 per cent of the woodcock examined recently contained heptachlor epoxide (average 1.6 ppm) for which there is a 'zero tolerance'" in domestic meats. Deer collected from an area sprayed with one pound per acre of DDT for spruce budworm control, contained DDT residues, some in excess of legal tolerance for domestic meats, says Dr. John L. Buckley, Director of Patuxent Wildlife Research Center of the Bureau of Sport Fisheries and Wildlife.[10]

The New York State Joint Legislative Committee report continues that in California game birds are so "hot" they have all but closed the hunting season. In Louisiana 186 woodcock contained heptachlor. Both DDT and heptachlor are now present in woodcock in the northern states. "Are we paying too high a price in biological damage for the unquestioned benefits of pest control? I think we are," says Dr. Buckley, "and sometimes, as in use of DDT for Dutch elm disease, we don't even get the benefits we pay for." He adds, "One may well question whether it is rational to eat game meats containing residues that would be unacceptable in domestic foods." Add this to the perils of hunting.

Said Mr. Udall, speaking before the Audubon Society's annual convention in 1963, "The unnerving fact is that pesticide residues have been found in virtually every type of warm-blooded animal across the land. . . . Man himself is slowly building up in his body small, but relentlessly cumulative traces of chemicals." And the chlorinated hydrocarbons possess such "movement" (carried by winds, birds, animals, waters) over the globe that they are now found not only in the flesh of isolated savage tribes (who did nothing to deserve them), but even in arctic penguins, seals, and in the flesh of fish that live 100 miles out in the sea!

A report of the Department of the Interior listed endrin as "about 50 times more toxic than DDT.[11] The other pesticides—dieldrin, aldrin, chlordane, and toxaphene—fell in between." In other words, although we have mountains of evidence of the killing properties of DDT because we have been using it the longest, it is nonetheless far less toxic than the newer poisons of which we as yet know almost nothing. Comments a British Ministry of Health pamphlet for medical practitioners: *"no* specific chemical tests for endrin poisoning exist."

But in addition to "movement" and toxicity the chlorinated hydrocarbons also possess great longevity. Dr. Robert L. Rudd, Associate Professor of Zoology at the University of California, Davis, tells of plots treated experimentally with 100 pounds of DDT in 1947, which still had a residue of 28.2 pounds per acre in 1951. Chlordane, dieldrin, heptachlor, and benzine hexachloride also last for a long time in the soil.

"Most concern," says Dr. Rudd, "has been directed toward the surviving toxic fraction of the parent chemical. A new phenomenon has shaken dependence on this simple measure. Breakdown or conversion products have been found to be more toxic than, or to complement the toxicity of, the parent residue." [12]

Thus, when heptachlor "breaks down" it converts into epoxide, which is even more lethal; aldrin, said to "disappear rapidly," merely converts into the more poisonous dieldrin. Is the folly of such prolonged poisoning of the earth from which we gain all our sustenance, comprehensible?

Then there are the systemic poisons. A thorough analysis of Cygon 267, a typical systemic, describes how this poison not only keeps killing for two weeks after spraying but also invades the stems and foliage and is circulated to other parts of the plant to kill insects through the plant's juices.[13] (What is the difference, a spokesman for the FDA asks, whether the agricultural poison is *on* the fruit, or *in* the fruit, so long as the "tolerance" rating is the same?) This would seem to knock the last props right out from under all the millions of Americans who have been sedulously scrubbing and peeling their fruits and vegetables in the hope of avoiding the pesticide. They can, however, now save themselves a lot of time and trouble.

Query: Why do Department of Agriculture authorities assure us that systemics are very "short-lived" in their effects, when the ads for farmers stress their "long-lasting" qualities? Doubtless there are comforting answers to all these bewildering questions somewhere.

Because, as mentioned, DDT has been in use far longer than most toxicants, we know much more about it, and none of what we have learned is good. We have long known that it builds up in the fatty tissues of warm-blooded animals (including man), seemingly harmless until the host suffers some illness or stress. It has been proved beyond a doubt by many experiments that when something occurs to use up the body fat of an animal or bird, the insecticide accumulation is suddenly released into the blood stream where it often ends the animal's career in a very unpleasant manner.

We are not going to be unscientific enough to extrapolate the results of animals' reactions over to humans.[14] The House Appropriations Committee's *Report on Pesticides,* which came out on April 19, 1965, castigates Rachel Carson for inferring that mammals who breathe, move, eat, drink, and have blood, nerves, cells, and organs alarmingly like man's, might also react like man to unselective poisons.

The Committee agrees with her that certain pesticides do cause cancer, sterility, and other distressing conditions in both man and beast. But it continues, "However, [the book] is unscientific in drawing incorrect conclusions from unrelated facts, and making implications that are based on possibilities as yet unproved to be actual facts." We do not here wish to be guilty of such irrational reasoning.

Nor are we taken in when Dr. Clarence Cottam suggests that "metabolic and physiological processes in man are not greatly different from those found in other vertebrate animals." We stand safely by the House Committee *Report.* Dr. Cottam is Director of the Welder Wildlife Foundation of Texas (and former member of the committe on pesticides of the Ecological Society of America), so he is probably not as unbiased in his observations as, say, some of the medical authorities interviewed by the House subcommittee and subsidized by the national chemical companies.

Yet when we amiably accept the report's repeated statement that it is unscientific to infer that animal bodies react similarly to man's when faced with concentrated poisons, stress, and the like, we find ourselves in the arms of a strange dilemma. What, then, are all the laboratories doing with their millions of experimental animals? What is the excuse, then, for these gigantic outlays of billions of dollars and millions of small (and unimportant, of course) lives? (However, all this is but an irrelevant digression.)

Let us return to the report of the House Committee and its indignation at Miss Carson's "unscientific superficiality." (Witnessing the prolonged death throes of a robin can sometimes move one to irrational deductions.) Certainly man is infinitely superior to all other creatures. Most probably we have some built-in immunity that no other living creature enjoys. Admittedly we have the supreme intelligence, and this should enable us to avoid the consequences of a poison build-up in our bodies by the injection of some powerful antidote or something, to which animals do not have access. And surely the experts in our government would not permit—yes, encourage—us to ingest poisons that build up ominously within us unless they had reliable proof that we could handle them, even under stress?

Moreover, it is not scientific, we are told, to worry about an eventuality until after it has occurred. And

the House Appropriations Committee underlines that
we have as yet documented no single human case of
such weird consequences as we have witnessed in thousands of animal tests.[15] Therefore, it is scientific to assume that they will never occur.

But let the biologists carry on their quarrel with the
poisoners of life and earth. They are beginning to
make an impression. We are concerned here more with
the implications of the poison policy to the American
way of life.

We have considered the increasing degradation of
our standards of wholesomeness in food and environment. But there is more. What is happening to the integrity and trust that should exist between a government and its people? What does it signify that we are
willing to accept every year greater compromise with a
known evil rather than expend the effort to combat it?
What of the bombardment of untruths to which we are
submitted by our officials to maintain public complacency? When it becomes more important to sustain the
serene upward progress of the economy than to safe-
guard public health, what happens to a nation's well-
being? When it becomes more important not to rock
the economic boat than to be honest, what happens to
a people's faith in its leaders?

First, there is the "tolerance" fallacy. Pesticides un-
dergo at least two years' testing by their manufacturers, whereupon the FDA usually takes 1/100 of the
amount that was found in the two years' tests to have
visibly harmed or killed animal subjects and establishes
a permissive dose which is then legally acceptable for
swallowing *in unlimited doses* by the citizenry over
seventy-five years.[16] This little stinger, we are reminded
with passionate earnestness, is an absolute essential to
"our standard of living."

Very well. But instead of the repeated and highly
unscientific avowals that the tolerances set are harmless, we should be frankly told: *This tolerance is a
wild guess based on insufficient research. We cannot
assure you that it is "harmless" over a period of time.*

But since our pesticides have far outrun our research and we are moreover under great pressure to approve tolerances for these new poisons, you will have to make the best of it—that is, if you wish to maintain your supermarkets in their present bursting splendor.

The finest of our scientists readily (but secretly) admits that the only effective tests for new pesticides is to release them to the public domain for a period of several years, where they will be used freely under natural conditions. This is logical. However, surely the guinea pigs deserve some warning of what is being done, if only the symbolic skull and crossbones that used to adorn the iodine and rubbing alcohol bottles of old. Instead, every agency and dealer assures us that the product is "harmless if used as directed."

We have been, in fact, almost bludgeoned by the Department of Agriculture into using spray after spray after spray, many of them unnecessarily, but as "preventives." We are told by Department of Agriculture and chemical company representatives that the ingestion of this insecticide or that herbicide is very "minimal." They may be right.

However, we have as yet seen no shiny brochures that attempt to estimate the total ingestion—that is, how many and what infinite variety of "minute tolerance doses" one person on an average diet actually consumes each day, week, and year.

What do all the thousands of "minute, insignificant" tolerance-doses of chlorinated hydrocarbons, the antibiotics, organic phosphates, herbicides, hormones, systemic insecticides, rodenticides, fungicides, preservatives, arsenic additives, the omnipresent sodium nitrates and sodium nitrites, tranquilizer residues, coal tar colors, the emulsifiers, propionates, and possible carcinogens add up to in an average American's six-month diet, for instance? What, exactly, are the biochemical properties of the fifteen additives in a cake mix? Perhaps it is scientific to declare that all these additives add up to nothing—because one small tolerance-dose of parathion, for instance, may add up to nothing?

Although the courage of the federal Food and Drug Administration's banning of certain dramatic killers is to be commended, it is disturbing that biocides are often permitted to enjoy extensive sales, Department of Agriculture backing, and the opportunity widely to poison soil and human bodies over a period of many years before they are banned. Especially irritating (and dangerous) are the pontifical, positive assurances of minor local officials, who couldn't be more ignorant on the subject, that the man-made guesses called "tolerances" are dependable and not to be questioned. In every crisis, on every challenge, the tolerance is cited as though its guarantee was inscribed on a tablet of God instead of being what it is—an expedient compromise of truth with economic interests. *No official is competent to assert honestly that the tolerances permitted by regulation are without harm now or in the future.* We are getting a double dose of poison: literal and verbal.

There is another serious misunderstanding suffered by many regarding the safety of the food they devour. Dr. Robert L. Rudd expresses it concisely when he says: "specialists and advisers maintain the curious illusion that current recommendations actually control residues" [17] and loudly proclaim this misconception to assuage the public.

In other words the FDA "makes rules" that a product shall *not* be marketed with more than so many parts per million of chlorinated hydrocarbon residue on it; that farmers observe strict spraying rules for organic phosphates; that additives shall be harmless.

Then, amazingly enough, salesmen, sprayers, and officials all cite these "rules" as the practice! In the case of milk the FDA long "ruled" that there should be no DDT whatever in the milk fed to babies. In practice, however, whenever a national sampling of milk was taken, DDT turned up in the analysis.[18] Expediency prevailed and the FDA was forced to retract.

On June 2, 1966, the Division of Industry Advice of the Bureau of Education and Voluntary Compliance of the FDA responded to our query as follows: "There are no legal pesticide tolerances for milk, cream, or butter at the present time. . . ." *But:* "We have published a proposal to establish tolerances for DDT, DDE, and DDD in milk and other dairy products . . . published in the *Federal Register* of November 16, 1965. . . ."

When a proscribed poison becomes too prevalent in a product, we simply legalize it. It is a convenient system for our purposes. Thus, the tendency when "safe" tolerances are exceeded is toward a "creep-up" of the permitted minimum to conform with reality. But not only are the limits on established poisons creeping up; each day finds new and more virulent ones glutting the markets—and each of these boasts its own tiny contribution of venom to the American smörgasbord, a contribution that may be added to all the others for a poison total that has never been computed and to which there is no limit.

Considering offhand the thirty-seven poisons permitted to be present in minute tolerances on cherries (not to mention a considerable number of other contaminants, such as the copper compounds, that are also permitted in the field and for which there are no tolerances), the great amount of press attention given to the minor fracas over the addition of more mineral oil and glycerine to the children's peanut butter appears grotesque. All our standards of reasonableness seem to have collapsed. It is not without significance that an FDA release stressing the need for pesticides mentions their importance to "the nation's economics, health and recreational activities," in that order.

Once in a while an unfortunate incident breaks out into print; an adult man spills a little of a 25 per cent solution of an insecticide on his skin and dies in forty minutes; a carload of carrots is seized containing large amounts of a lethal spray; a few shipments of milk are dumped into the river; a plane pilot spraying a small

Minnesota town for mosquitoes gets his cans mixed and accidentally uses parathion intended for crops, and the town has to be evacuated. (Parathion is described as so deadly that if a child rolled in sprayed grass it would probably die, yet there is a one part per million tolerance established for parathion in all our food.)

But in each such report, however, some impressive authority is quoted in the second to the last paragraph, assuring the people that all is well; everything is in hand; the threat of pesticides is "insignificant from a health standpoint." Although DDT has been found "in every complete meal analyzed in this country," testified Dr. Wayland J. Hayes, Jr., Public Health Service toxicologist, before the Committee [19] chaired by Senator Abraham Ribicoff, its concentration is "small and harmless."

We were told that heptachlor was harmless when used as directed and that none of it was appearing in our foods. Then, considerably later, it was revealed that "ten times improved analytical procedures" enabled discovery of minute amounts of this killer in cows' milk, and it was withdrawn from dairy production. Aldrin and dieldrin were registered by our government as safe for years; then on February 2, 1966, after a closed-door conference of U.S. Department of Agriculture officials and the manufacturers' representatives, the registration of these pesticides for use on vegetables, grain, and forage crops was suddenly canceled.

How many other tolerances have been established and the public assured they were "safe" before the scientists even possessed the analytical procedures to detect them on marketed foods? We have no quarrel with the valor that it takes to admit an error and to redress it; but we sometimes wonder wistfully if it is necessary to be deceived with such conviction when the authorities are fully conscious of their own ignorance and are aware that they are responding to organized pressures of interest groups?

In answer to our query a letter from Senator Everett

M. Dirksen, fervent defender of pesticides, assures us that "pesticides we have today have been in use for over twenty years and science has observed no manifestations in man." Let us examine this statement.

First, the avalanche of the most deadly poisons we now use has been conceived in recent years—many of them are but two to ten years out of the test tubes. Second, science has "observed no manifestations in man" probably because it hasn't been looking for them.

The Fish and Wildlife Service found that a number of dead eagles picked up had accumulations of DDT not only in the body fat but also *in the brain.* Zoologist Douglas James at the University of Arkansas found that the same insecticide apparently affected the central nervous system of quail and caused a decline in learning ability. *Query:* How many human brains have been opened after death to investigate whether or not they were so damaged?

Men die from such "natural causes" as liver, heart, or kidney trouble—or so read, in the medical phraseology, the death certificates. *Query:* How extensive has been the research in such unspectacular deaths to determine the victim's poison burden as a contributor to the disease?

We all know the answers. Time and the chemical tide wait for no man, nor for his autopsy either (unless his death presented acute or suspicious poisoning symptoms).

"There are many new chemicals with no analytical techniques set up at all," Dr. William A. Tompkins of the Massachusetts Division of Fish and Game tells us.[20] And, to repeat: decisions which may affect health and life are only too often made on the basis of economics, expediency, and politics, rather than on human welfare. C. P. Snow in his book *Science and Government* comments with some disgust: "Some of the most important choices about a nation's physical health are made, or not made, by a handful of men, in secret, and again, in legal form, by men who normally are not able to comprehend the arguments in depth."

Query: If hot dog colorings are as safe as the federal government presumably certifies, why have seven states (Illinois was the seventh in January, 1966) now banned the red dye used?

Query: If the organic phosphates with their wicked little tolerances are justified on the vast, commercial market, how is it that we just now discover that chick embryos injected with these substances suffer such birth defects as no right wing, skull malformation, and so on?

Senator Ribicoff was deeply shocked to learn that long after poisons in foods and clothing ("You can walk downtown right now and pick up a sweater with 400 ppm [parts per million] DDT in it")[21] have been in approved use, the Department of Agriculture tells us it cannot set up sound recommendations because it knows too little about them! "The nutritionists among you," he says, "would be interested to know that we are going to *start* finding out whether the over-all nutritional value of the food supply of the nation has been significantly altered through the use of pesticides."

The big argument between the chemical buffs and the protesters may best be illustrated in a comment in the *New Yorker* of May 2, 1964. Secretary Udall wishes to ban the most persistent poisons and those which carry over to effect large kills of wildlife in streams and woods. Secretary Freeman, defensively parroting the Department lines, retorts that it is unwarranted to ban poisons about which "too little is known."

"The Freeman doctrine appears to be that the less you know about a poison the freer you should feel to use it," remarks the *New Yorker*. Did this quaint idea come over from the ancient legal doctrine that the accused person is innocent until proven guilty? With poisons, such a theory is palpably out of place; it is like playing Russian roulette. When the proof comes it is too late to retract.

To which might be added as postscript the memorandum issued by the Rural District Councils Association of Great Britain to the Ministry of Agriculture concerning pesticides: "Long-term effects indirectly harmful to humans have not been assessed and may not be found until the damage is done. . . . There is *no* reliable data so far on how much of these substances the human body can tolerate."

The government is not leveling with the public. A health official high in national circles recently remarked (in private) that "there are times when it is wiser not to tell the truth." We can rail against this treatment, but let us be fair. We have no conception of the pressures put upon the FDA and the administration and especially on our congressmen by the commercial interests involved.

Moreover, all indications have been that we are getting just what we subconsciously want—to be tranquilized and shielded from facts that might disturb us. If the American people rose up and demanded honesty from its officials, not all the commercial interests, economic growth wizards, and moneyed power in the nation could thwart their demands. Our bureaucracies encompass many men of rare vision and principle; they will give us just what we demand of them. We are afraid to face facts. It is easier and more pleasant to skid along without thinking.

We are a society of consumers who insist on a fabulous profusion of top grade produce (in appearance, not in cleanliness, purity, or essential nutriments). An apple or a peach may not entertain one blemish, but it may be filmed with a deadly spray that lodges in and builds up in our brains, heart, and muscles. We insist on cold cuts that will keep two weeks in the refrigerator, we pay for our convenience by ingesting a steady diet of sodium nitrite and sodium nitrate which, should an accidental "spillage" occur, might (as in New Jersey a few years ago with regard to fish) strike a few customers stone dead.

On top of all this we insist on straining the economy even more with our fecundity, constantly aggravating the problem of supplying great varieties of food to ever larger masses of people.

We are, as a society, entrapped in a pit of seething chemicals, and although the banks seem at present too slippery to climb out, plans abound to control the flood before we are submerged. Senator Ribicoff discovered the basic need for more rigidity and severity of control: organized, periodic pesticide plant inspection, policing of disposal of wastes, policing and stern control of pesticide labeling.

Secretary of the Interior Udall says that although his department is feverishly studying some 70 generally used pesticide compounds, there are more than 500 now on the market needing study, and his staff cannot begin to catch up. As for the popular belief that the vast quantities of food displayed in supermarkets and elsewhere are federally inspected, it is estimated that less than one-third of 1 per cent of all food products that reach the hands of the people suffer this indignity. Writes our FDA correspondent: "We are currently examining approximately 1 per cent of interstate shipments of raw agricultural commodities for pesticide residues. [About 25,000 per year.]"

Intrastate products are subject only to state regulations, whatever they may be or may not be. The Congress, while lavishing sums far beyond what the President asks on medical research, is niggardly indeed with food inspection: fifty inspection stations over the width and breadth of the land offer the spray-happy grower such astronomical odds against detection that even the most timid need lose no sleep.

Dr. Franklin Bicknell (an Englishman) makes a serious charge: "The United States leads the civilized world in chemicalized food and in degenerative diseases." The babies born today are born with "built-in" doses of DDT, heptachlor, and strontium 90; in fact, these virulent guests settle down in the foetus soon after conception.[22] Surely we should foster a better environment for the future Americans in whose hands lie the virility and hope of the nation?

A British committee on agricultural pesticides has recently given as its opinion that if all the organochlorines were withdrawn, the annual potential loss of crops would be no more than 250,000 acres out of a total of more than 7,600,000 acres now under cultivation in the British Isles and that the loss could be reduced to about 75,000 acres by the use of less harmful chemicals. With our great ingenuity and greater wealth we could undoubtedly accomplish comparative results if we willed it.

However, the effort would entail an agricultural revolution. It would encompass not only vastly more supervision but new legislation and appropriations for *independent* research, education of the public (and the crazy plane pilots), greater controls on poisons and their users, the outlawing of long-lasting pesticides, increased penalties for violators, new systems of licensing and distribution. Especially would it include research in biological (as opposed to chemical) controls of pests. There would be needed a small army of entomologists, pathologists, geneticists, biochemists, and ecologists to offset the present vast armies of commercial chemists.[23]

The situation, to say the least, is out of hand. As with our other mounting crises, it is the unprecedented population increase that has spurred on this poison carnival in order to meet the emergency of ever more customers with ever bigger appetites. And just so, it is by spiking the population rise that we can take off some of the heat, give society a chance to catch its breath, and perhaps evolve, after some fumblings, a less foolhardy and adventitious method of procedure in the production of its bread.

To the Editor of the [Albany, New York] *Times-Union:*
Give us this day our daily calcium propionate (spoilage

retarder); sodium diacetate (mold inhibitor), monoglyceride (emulsifier), potassium bromate (maturing agent), calcium phosphate monobasic (dough conditioner), chloramine T (flour bleach), aluminum potassium sulfate (acid baking powder ingredient), sodium benzoate (preservative), butylated hydroxyanisole (anti-oxidant), mono-isopropyl citrate (sequestrant); plus synthetic vitamins A and D.

Forgive us, O Lord, for calling this stuff BREAD.
Averill Park

J. H. Reed

Chapter Seventeen

The Death of Dignity

"It is a sobering thought," writes Hugo Fisher, Administrator of the Resources Agency of California,

> that in another twenty-five years, only the very rich can expect to live with the dignity of peace and privacy. . . . Far short of the population density that will tax our potential food supply there will be a limit to the tolerance of the human spirit, the advent of social and cultural stagnation, the disappearance of compassion and sensible morality and the dignity of man.

Speaking before the League of California Cities on May 10, 1965, this noted planner continued: "I suggest that as a prelude to each and every proposed council action you thoughtfully address yourselves to this question: 'What would be the ultimate effect of this on the soul and spirit of man?'" The crowding of too many people in non-expandable space is menacing to health, destructive to the mind, offensive to aesthetics and conducive to a thousand other miseries. But perhaps the most damning of all is what it does to the individual dignity of a human being, to his importance and self-respect as a person.[1]

Spread before our eyes, if we will see, are the graphic evidences of what overcrowding does to the importance of a man. In China with its 750,000,000 population, the individual is less than nothing; he is expendable without even a shrug if the ruler decides the group will be benefited thereby. In teeming Japan of the gracious airs and ancestral reverence it is a distinct shock to learn that the mores condone indifferently passing by a man who collapses in the street, with no thought of pausing to help him even in his death throes. In India the starving beggar with legs like pipe stems holds out his cup in vain and topples from starvation almost unnoticed before the passerby's eyes.

Also, from New Delhi in February, 1966, a news item reads as follows:

> The Assam government announced Sunday it will pay $210 compensation to each of the families of 12 persons killed in a stampede during a visit by Prime Minister Indira Gandhi on Saturday. Police reported a check of hospitals showed 23 persons injured in the mass rush by a throng to hear Mrs. Gandhi speak at Tinsukia in eastern Assam State.

Two hundred and ten dollars. And even this sum is more than an individual in that teeming, once fabulously rich nation is now worth.

On a lesser scale great cities all over the globe illustrate at times what happens to individual importance when a man becomes lost in the mass of humanity shoving into a subway, mobbing a bargain counter or a celebrity, or carrying on a protest demonstration. He is rudely jostled, pushed, bruised, sometimes knocked off his feet. No one pretends, even in America, to pick him up; unless he can escape on his own he may easily be trampled to death. For the moment he is not a man but chaff, a speck, a nihility, a straw, a squib, a naught, a nit, a fagot in the wind, a bubble on a stream, nobody under the sun. In an overpopulated country this is what he is *all of the time*.

The lost values of which we have been speaking in the previous chapters are all related, and not the slightest worthwhile element of living is surrendered to expediency or gain without some corroding of the human spirit. We do not forsake cleanliness without a loss of self-respect. We cannot turn our backs on beauty without losing cultural stature. We do not heed-

lessly either exterminate the passenger pigeon or decimate the Great Plains Indian without some stain on
the shield, without its effect on the national conscience
and character. We are what we have done. But what
we have created can destroy us.

The assault of mass living on the dignity and worth
of a human being may be considered from three angles
of his relationship: to people, to space, to society.

Increased numbers mean, without exception, a
deflated individual. To many, the computerization of
life, the turning of man into numbers, and the indifference of society to the individual present the most bleak
picture of all.

As Edgar Ansel Mowrer wrote in *Saturday
Review*,[2] it is

> obvious that the greater the crowding . . . the more the
> authorities will be obliged to curtail their liberties, not be-
> cause they are necessarily opposed to freedom but because
> they must do so if living is to be made endurable for
> many of them. . . Constraint and an overdose of popula-
> tion are inseparable.

The sorest point in a beehive world may be the loss
of human compassion, warmth, and personal attention.
We shall have to adopt wholesale, dispassionate ways
of getting things done. We shall have to be heartlessly
efficient as were certain shipbuilders of the olden days
who painted the decks of their battleships red so the
gore of battle would not show! A Chinese Christian
general of the old regime, faced with the problem of
the many time-consuming baptisms in the faith, used
to line his soldiers up *en masse* and squirt them with
the hose while reciting the baptism ceremony. Mass
weddings and mass funerals are the concomitants of a
crammed world.

Hideous and not at all humorous will be the hospital
of the future, when patients lose all personality other
than that of a name and number on a chart, when
nurses and doctors no longer look in with cheerful

greetings, when there are no flowers or visitors permitted, and meals are served on moving belts.

But even grimmer, more macabre, is the picture that a *Science Digest* news item foresees. In this nightmare the patient of the crowded future will be anesthetized at one of ten or twelve "pick-up stations," dispatched through a pneumatic tube to a soulless hospital where he will be shoved in a bare slot and kept in an unconscious state until his discharge, dead or alive.

There the body will be irradiated, dis-irradiated, chemicalized, drained, injected, probed, and subjected to mechanical and electronic scanners that will diagnose his (its?) case and then prescribe his (its?) treatment, after which an automatic therapy machine will take over and minister to him—unconscious, God help him—all without the benefaction of human hands. Feeding will be by vein or stomach tube, entirely automatic. "Attached to the patient will be electrical devices to measure pain, pulse, respiration, etc.," explains the piece. "No bother, no worry, no complaints, no noise, no glare, no odors, no incompatible roommates, no visitors, complete privacy and complete concentration on getting well. What could be more ideal?" [3] What could be more terrifying? Yet these are not idle speculations; they fall in the category of long-range planning!

The signs foretelling the denigration of human life become more clear every day. Not too many years ago a great national disaster—a fire or earthquake in an American city that took a few score lives, a flood disaster on the Mississippi or Missouri or Ohio, a death-dealing avalanche in the Rockies, a bomb explosion in a crowded theater—would excite the attention and compassion of the entire populace for weeks, even months, thereafter. Now a jet plane goes down with eighty or ninety people board, all lost, and if you are not alert or miss one newscast, you may never even hear of it. In another day it is quite forgotten except by the bereaved families. Lives are no longer precious because we are fast becoming too many. We are becoming expendable—and cheap.

We are still, as a people, a long way from Chinese attitudes, but the trend, especially in cities, is accelerating. Today two young women are hacked to death in two different cities, both within sight of dozens of their neighbors, who are so callous they do not even call the police, much less go to their aid. When a New York storekeeper braved a gang of hoodlums to help the police, it was so rare and unaccustomed an act that the police of Des Moines, Iowa, sent the brave fellow a check for over a thousand dollars.

Recent experiments have proved that rats actually go insane if too crowded in laboratory cages. But the draining of one's importance, the feeling of nothingness, is equally as vicious a threat. Very often it is the cause of suicide as well as derangement. It is well known that suicides among the oldsters over sixty-five is four to five times that of the entire population, and one of the reasons most often listed in the pitiful notes they leave behind is that "I am not wanted," or "I am of no use to the world or anyone." A person yearns for involvement, or as one old school teacher put it, "to be a part of the stream of life."

When the individual of whatever age comes to feel a sense of uselessness, frustration, of being nothing more than a number, his will to live dissipates. And why not? Of what infernal use would be a computerized, regimented, ant-hill life, devoid of creativity and the joy of challenge? Yet the loss of self-will and creativity are *infallible* earmarks of the crowded society, where man must conform just to exist.

But the increasing callousness of society, while it punishes the individual, soon arouses (if he continues to live) a corresponding callousness of mind and spirit in him. One of these authors appeared on a 1966 television program with the Fort Ann, New York, defector to the Chinese, who after twelve years returned home with wife and child and made his fortune through the sale of his "story." One of the lessons brought home during this panel discussion was the progressive, insidious brutalizing of the individual by protracted living in an uncompassionate society. He had told of the unutterable barbarities of his captors, of how prisoners were forced to stand in cages until they fainted dead away, then revived and forced to stand again until they blacked out, and of similar cruelties. At first these demonstrations bothered him, then it appears that they bothered less and less; at length he could become friendly with the perpetrators and at last become one of them. Is it possible that Americans, but now emerging from the crudities of pioneer living, aspire to such degeneration of spirit and decay of sensitivity?

Then there are the effects of too many people on the dignity and pride of the human spirit. Consider whether learning to drink our own sewage (call it by whatever euphemism you will) is not a certain kind of debasement, an erosion of self-respect? If such an unsavory prospect were unavoidable, the element of martyrdom might redeem its grossness; the fact that it will be the result of overgratification of self and the willful lack of self-restraint in breeding, robs it of any virtue it might have had.

But recently research has been instituted to determine whether ground waters of the drought-stricken Eastern Seaboard can be safely replenished by properly treated liquid wastes. What elements in sewage effluent must be removed or modified before waste can be "successfully" recharged into the now pure ground waters by injection wells? That this nauseating procedure (an irreversible contamination) is even being considered must speak for itself.

When during the summer of 1965 William C. Treon penned in the Cleveland *Plain Dealer* his graphic stories concerning Lake Erie, he raised not only some eyebrows but some retching, too. Speaking of this foul lake, strangling for lack of oxygen yet appearing so attractive from a distance, he challenged his readers: "Stand in it. Stick your nose close to it. Reach down and scoop it up and look closely at it. Scoop up some of the muck from the bottom. Spread it out and watch the thousands of needle-thin sludge-worms squirm." Then he adds: "And THINK. Think that tomorrow— or some day soon—your family will be drinking that water."

What will we *not* do to avoid facing responsibility?

Overlapping the topic "Man versus people" is the problem of man versus confinement, or lack of enough space. It has been discovered that in the classic case of the lemmings, which, when population explosions occur, go mad and rush to their deaths, abnormal functioning of liver, adrenals, and nerve ends take place; the sugar content of their blood changes and brain cells are damaged; in some cases neurodermatitis occurs and they become desperately sick. But men are not lemmings, and although we possess most lemming potentials, we can in most cases tranquilize them out before we reach the sea. But there are other facets of cramped space where science cannot avail.

Some great philosopher has said, "The man who is never alone is never with God." How important to one's spirit is meditation and solitude? How important is being alone for a small time each day, without the raucous clatter of human voices, the shoving and elbowing (yes, and sometimes the smell) of human bodies, the irritation of constant interruptions?

Perhaps a young student from Ghana who was lured to Red China to study medicine and who wrote up his experiences can tell us something of this. Emmanuel John Hevi wrote, in part:

Eight Chinese students occupy a room ten by twelve feet in size, sleeping in tiered bunks. Their personal belongings—boxes, bags, books, and clothing—are stacked higgledy-piggledy in any available corner. For lack of space, there are no tables, no chairs, no bookshelves. Students have to study in the lecture halls. The room has one door and one window. In winter, the window is sealed shut with wedges of newspaper, the room is always kept closed because of the cold. With eight people, those rooms get very stuffy!

Each accommodation block has three floors; each floor

containing nearly 150 students, has one washroom and a lavatory with five cubicles. In some of the cubicles the water system is permanently out of order. The result is rather hideous.[4]

Women and men use the same bathhouse in which bathing is regimented so that females must attend at a posted period of two hours, and men at another posted period—or go unbathed. "In China," writes Emmanuel John Hevi, "which for centuries has known huge mass populations, overcrowding has to be accepted as a norm of life." During bath hours, with 5,000 students attempting to occupy twenty-six shower stalls within two very limited periods, there must be a temptation to hark back to the glory that was Rome when people were few and baths were many.

As lots and land soar in value and are gobbled up for development, as automobiles rise from 75 million to 100 million by 1980, as more and more roads bisect and beribbon the countryside to invade every nook and cranny of the nation, privacy will be a forgotten luxury. Even in their homes "laid edge to edge and side to side," people will find no privacy.

Already today, flying over the United States (again to quote architect Edward Durell Stone because he is so quotable), you will see hundreds of acres "filled with these cheesy little boxes that line the streets, no privacy at all, and each having a picture window with a floor lamp in it." Nor are the multitudes of "large, ugly buildings, divided in myriads of barren cubicles" much better, and Mr. Stone adds: "We are starved for beauty." And the population boom has only begun to tell!

That we shall be forced to plant our dead in graves on top of each other offers no affront to human dignity. And while losing the long-accustomed luxury of one's own table when restaurant dining may do no more to one's dignity than ruin his evening or make him lose his temper, there are more unpleasant impingements on the ego.

Where, as space limitations close in upon us, will we put all our increasing mountains and landslides of waste? International agreement forbids launching them into space; we cannot therefore plan on orbiting our garbage lest China, India, and Russia orbit theirs and thus completely close off the sun (not to mention what they will do to the rain). If, by chance, one of those giant satellites of rubbish should lose momentum and crash, it would undoubtedly damage some more dignity.

And what does it do to our integrity and sense of moral responsibility when, pressed to kill off all other forms of life which attempt to hold their own or get in the way of our spreading, insatiable demand for *Lebensraum,* we resort to the hypocrisy of rabies scares and other fanciful plagues to calm our conscience in exterminating them?

Never to see anything except through somebody else's cigarette, never to get far enough away from human uproar and clatter to hear birds sing—these catastrophes may reduce us to pitiful chattering victims, but they do not necessarily demean us (very much). What does demean us is to watch what is happening to our own priceless environment—the raping of the last of our deep and silent forests, the shame of our great and silent rivers, the mutilation of our landscape—and to do nothing or perhaps engage in a few cheap, piddling efforts, contemptibly impotent, to save them.

The third assault on the dignity and integrity of man has to do with man and society. In the society in which man is submerged in the mob his political ends are defined for him and his approval manipulated. There is no opportunity for creative or individual solutions because the channels of communication are clogged.[5] They are clogged with the ravings of the demagogue appealing to the survival instincts of the mass. When all issues are biological, nobler conceptions are soon howled down.

This fear of losing identity is basic to the political philosophy of Kent, of Jefferson, of John Adams, of

Randolph, of great minds without number.[6] The pursuit of happiness in some creatively spiritual way is foreclosed by the impossibility of lifting oneself above the crowd.

But the situation has gone a long step farther. The greatest affront is not that, with growing numbers and pressing resource problems, we are likely to be ignored; but that we are compelled by the subtle processes of misrepresentation and engineering of consent to agree to proposals we do not understand.

One such worrisome example already at hand may be cited to give some insight into how this misrepresentation occurs. A few years ago U.S. Senator Thomas H. Kuchel, disturbed by the evidence of indiscriminate poisoning of 135 deer found dead near 1080-poison stations, wrote the Director of the Bureau of Sport Fisheries and Wildlife, U.S. Fish and Wildlife Service, to question this virulent poison's use. The Director informed Senator Kuchel that the matter had been greatly misinterpreted. He made this statement: "Furthermore, he [Senator Kuchel's informant] grossly over-rates the potential danger to humans. For example, *all the chemical used in the entire State of California would only be sufficient to pollute a small tank of water at a concentration sufficient to endanger humans.*" (Emphasis is ours.)

"Let us," challenges an investigating author, "take his 'small tank of water.' " This represents the amount of approved concentration 1080 solution used in one year by the U.S. Fish and Wildlife Service and the California Department of Agriculture alone. "If the 1080 manufacturer's estimate of toxicity of 2.0 mg/kg for 100 per cent human mortality be accepted, the Director's 'small tank' of deadly 1080-water solution would have killed, at a minimum, 1,378,022 Californians!" (Conveniently ignored by the Director were the "small tanks" of 1080-water solution used by military installations and commercial pest eradicators.)[7]

If we are being hoodwinked by some of our bureaucrats today, what can we expect tomorrow with individual concern denigrated and regimentation vastly increased?

But there are other affronts to human values today even greater than being made an ass of. There are the unspeakable plans of taking men and, through use of electrical and drug stimulation, transforming them into robots, mindless clumps of flesh and blood, to relieve them (in the words of Dr. Lorne D. Proctor of Detroit) of boredom on such long space voyages "as a 400-day round-trip to Mars," as well as to stimulate artificially these living corpses "to perform superhuman tasks of endurance and alertness." "Indeed," he said, "by the turn of the century—thanks to developments already achieved in the field of biochemistry and genetics—'the astronaut could begin to be a made-to-order human, both as to physical and psychological features.'" Of course it would take "several generations" to get this mindless robot down to perfection, thus coming one-up on God, who took a few million to make a man. We shall become hibernating beings by the year 2000, or men kept in a state of consciousness "at the desired level for the required performance" for as long as the human manipulators decide.[8] No comment.

The science of politics moves in behavioralistic directions, so that our response here also can be engineered by manipulating the stimuli. The greater the mass of people with instinctive responses, the more predictable the consequence of an appeal and the greater the frustration of the thoughtful, creative citizen.

The affront to dignity, which amounts to a corrosion of the soul, is that the citizen becomes smothered in the mediocrity, the conformism, of the mass whose role is decisive and determining. No longer is there the slightest hope of individual protest. If that mass has low horizons, its tremendous bulk is too heavy to elevate; if it is illiterate, the overwhelming darkness is too great to overcome. The trial of the age is that overpopulation with its staggering pressure on the political order coincides with a worship of mass rule and of mass appetite. In other words we have guaranteed a voice in public affairs to each man at the very moment in history when he is most pressed—yes, constrained —to exercise that privilege least responsibly.

In his Excise Bill speech William Pitt made a memorable peroration that has been quoted as the most famed defense of human dignity ever delivered. He said,

> The poorest man may in his cottage bid defiance to all the force of the Crown. It may be frail; its roof may shake; the wind may blow through it; the storms may enter, the rain may enter—but the *King of England cannot enter;* all his forces dare not cross the threshold of the ruined tenement!

In regimented China the Party, faced with an extremely acute shortage of protein foods, has ruled and transmitted to the populace the teaching that carbohydrates are interchangeable with proteins in the body and that, therefore, meat, milk, eggs, and fats are luxuries which the people can well do without. Indeed, says Mr. Hevi, this doctrine is actually taught in the Peking Union Medical College by an instructor who could not meet the inquiring eyes of her foreign pupils.

In an ant colony when one of the members gets out of line, he is tapped on the head with a crumb of a decayed tree to remind him that he had better get back in the swim. There is a plaque on the wall of the Hall of Free Enterprise beside a glass wall ant colony that reminds the admiring observer: "If ants are instinctively regimentized in order to survive, man is instinctively a creature of freedom." The trick, of course, is in remaining a creature of freedom after we voluntarily consent to become ants.

Regimentation of the populace marches ahead in equal step with marching numbers—otherwise the social processes would be lost in a tangle of frustration. Every new stoplight that appears, every new restriction levied—although necessary—decreases our individual liberty and either regiments or compartmentizes us that much more.

Dr. Paul Sears, the Yale ecologist, writes:

> The whole record of history down to the present moment, including that of our own society, shows the progressive loss of individual liberty as numbers increase and humanity becomes more crowded. The end is complete socialization in one form or another. It may be under an autocrat, or just as effectively, under an impersonal state. . . . If this is what we want, nothing more need be said. But let us not be deluded into thinking that when we arrive at the complete domestication of mankind we can escape the issues which, if dealt with now, can prevent that situation.
>
> These issues are the control of population and encouragement of a less consumptive economy. For assuredly, no sovereign force, personal or impersonal, will be able to dodge them. It will be obliged in the end to license, restrict, and ration everything from food and reproduction up or down. . . .
>
> To this end we can exhibit informed self-discipline in facing the question of resources and population, divesting ourselves of the fallacy that bigger means better. And as a simple, direct ethical principle on which to build I would suggest this:
>
> Every child that is born has a right not to be a mere biological accident. Each new human being deserves a welcome and the prospect of the good life after it gets here.[9]

"The chaos of a jam-packed world" will, in the year 2000, "propel people to a regimented society," says the *Wall Street Journal*. Every increasing regimentation will be the only recourse to insure order and obedience to law and to avoid anarchy. The Albany slum dweller who cried out to the city authorities to clamp down on his landlord because of unfunctioning plumbing, falling plaster, and stuck doors was adding to the clamor for more regimentation. (Like most people, when he grumbles, "A landlord shouldn't have any more buildings than he can properly take care of," he doesn't equate it with the fact that he himself has ten children who are hardly being properly taken care of.)

The death of the individual's dignity is his transformation from a spiritual, thinking being into a cog or "another mouth to feed," from a choice-maker into a computerized "case history." It is the destruction of his identity as a person. Thomas Mann in *The Coming Victory of Democracy* wrote: "We must define democracy as that form of government and of society which is inspired above every other with the feeling and consciousness of the dignity of man." If this is so (and who would refute it?), when dignity vanishes, democracy itself has been gutted.

Chief Justice Harlan Stone once remarked in disgust about some recreants: "If the damned fools want to go to hell it's not our duty to stop them, if that's what they want to do." Some myopic people today make much the same remark about overbreeding and the overbreeders in general. But when they take us and the nation to hell with them, we must be excused for showing a little more interest in the denouement.

Part Five

The Great Hoax

Chapter Eighteen

Growth, Greed, and Gung Ho

Every ninety seconds of a winter weekend a ski train pulls out of Shinyuku Station north of Tokyo. Altogether by bus and train some six million Japanese jam the skiing slopes on their one-day or day-and-a-half weekend. They pack themselves in the trains as tightly as fruit in a jar at the county fair; they sleep, when they stay overnight, ten to a room at the farmers' homes, or *minshuku;* they wait forty minutes between turns on the ski lift.

The Japanese have experienced a booming enterprise, a catapulting growth, and what any American would call miserable ski weekends. Yet the measure the Japanese use for economic success is the one we employ: constant growth.

Total up all the services Americans use and the goods we make and you come up with an unbelievable and astronomical figure—some one-third of all the world's production.[1] Surfeited with goods, we pay a bill of $500 a year *per family* just for the packages and containers to take home our loot.

By the mid-Sixties the gross national product (the total of goods and services produced) was jumping by 7 per cent in a single year. In current dollars the total had reached—and passed—$700 billion. Newspapers could not resist the alliterative headline "Soaring Sixties." The computers of the economists were a bank of green lights.

The American standard of living, said the President, hit an accelerated rise, going up as much in two years as in the previous eight. The increase for one single year was the equivalent of the total production of all of Italy. We were being blown up the highway of prosperity by the winds of growth.[2] Every workday morning 10,000 more people were going to work on a paying job than went home the night before.

Our growth was paced by a continued boom in the automobile industry, which was turning out over nine million cars and trucks a year. The whole of the population could sit in the front seats of its cars, for arithmetically there were but 2.8 people per automobile.

The McGraw-Hill economic projections bordered on the fantastic. They predicted an annual increase of 4.1 per cent, greater than we have enjoyed so far in this century. In constant dollars the GNP was slated, they said, to escalate to $827 billion in 1970, to $1,000 billion in 1975 and $1,200 billion in 1980.[3] If these economic soothsayers come close, we will have experienced an advance of almost 80 per cent in fifteen years.

"The biggest problem for the United States will be to make full use of its vast industrial capacity and to maintain an adequate rate of expansion," says the Twentieth Century Fund Survey.[4] Our biggest problem? There are those who disagree.[5]

And what does our commitment to growth mean to the individual American? It means more money for automobiles, but it also means more cars clogging the roads and parking spaces. It means more money for hairdos, and more people pushing for "prime time" appointments; more activity (and more waiting in line) at the bowling alley and golf course; more of everything everywhere he looks: more goods and services, and many more fellow Americans to share them with. So long as the cradles keep rocking, the individual allotment of goods may not actually go up much.

A major evil in this national worship of the GNP (an attitude shared by most of the developed countries of the world) is the lack of discrimination that marks its acceptance. The economist prodding a nation to growth is not disturbed by the beer-can-littered landscape or the unsightliness of a strip mining location. His concern is to stimulate the appetite, not to cultivate the taste. His is a kind of science of collective gluttony. It has been aptly remarked that "one of the weaknesses of our age is our apparent inability to distinguish between our needs and our greeds." [6]

So long as the production figures are refined the products can be crude. It matters not at all to the economist whether society chooses to build a race track or a hospital. Indeed, we tend to justify products not by what they contribute to the quality of living but by their impact on the economic curves.

Evaluations of resource use still are, to a major degree, bleakly indifferent to the intangibles—as if they never existed. An economic study by Resources for the Future sought to advise New Mexico as to how to use an allotment of San Juan River water. "Put it into agriculture," said the report, "and it will gross $50 an acre foot. Put it into fish and wildlife habitat and it will bring in between $200 amd $300. . . . Allot it to industry and you will reap $3,000 to $4,000." Perhaps the intangibles of a fish and wildlife habitat are too ethereal for an economic study to evaluate. But they are profound enough to deserve mention in all but the crassest appraisement.

We open national parks to the noisy impositions of motorboats in deference to an industry. We turn our Department of Defense into arms peddlers abroad to keep an armaments industry booming. The great worry now that the moon adventure is "in the pipes" is how to keep the mammoth space complex chugging along on all its twelve gold-plated cylinders. Plans are being rushed to start Mars and Venus projects—not primarily in the thirst for knowledge or because they will do the nation great good, but simply to keep a lot of people busy and the growth chart zooming.[7]

Even education, instead of pointing toward individual satisfactions, concentrates almost exclusively on productive skills and adopts an attitude of condescension when it considers other criteria. And as we automate, the individual is viewed and cherished not nearly so much for his creativity as for his consumptive abilities. It is not his soul but his appetites that society nurtures.

The creed of unlimited growth is the modern version of the primitive race worship of fructification—of Ceres, Frey, Isis, Baal, and Astarte. Conceived when man's numbers were small and the going precarious, it is outworn and anachronistic in the human glut which even now presses against the gates of the future. But it has at last begun to prompt the recurring question: "Growth—for what?" That is what James Reston asks in his *New York Times* service column:

"But growth for what? What are the ends to which this fantastic accumulation of wealth is to be directed? This is the question which officials are now debating in the privacy of their offices and to which so little public attention is paid at the time of decision." [8]

Less than prideful—indeed, rather nauseating—is the fact that, sated, we greedily press for more and more cramming, wasting, opulence. Mass production has reached such heights of efficiency that the main efforts of the government must be directed toward whetting appetites and propping up demand to eat up the products.

Under no conditions let us sigh nostalgically for olden times. Fifty or eighty years ago the growth philosophy was so vicious it martyred and even destroyed its critics. Such technological wonders as add so immensely to the convenience or pleasure of living are blessings not to be discounted. To the seekers after the past Alexander Dumas once sighed, "Oh, the good old times when we were so unhappy!" And it was Longfellow who first remarked that "there are no birds in last year's nest."

The only quarrel of the "new conservation" is with fanaticism, with an obsessed worship of the economy that blights lives and warps minds. Yet even as we nosed economic graphs upward, Gordon Ackley, chairman of the Council of Economic Advisers, shifted focus when he said:

> Economic growth is not the ultimate objective of our society or of any society. We want a strong and productive economy so that we can better achieve our objectives as individuals and as a nation. . . . We have undertaken a war on poverty. We have begun to face up to the ugliness and the social disorder of our cities, we have begun to deal with the blight on the national beauty of our landscapes. . . . In short, we have begun to build a society that will one day be called great.[9]

The growth doctrine has assured our nation of prosperity for a period, but not of greatness, and certainly not of longevity! We are reminded that the decline of nations is only *climaxed* by historical events. Underneath there has long been a moving current of erosion, to which the critical event is but the culmination. The ancient Sumerians (to use but one of hundreds of examples) were in the ascendant and prospered glowingly for two thousand or more years before Christ. Yet when the fresh inundations of vigorous barbarians poured in from East and West to overwhelm them, they had long been degenerating in environment, strength, and political fiber, although not in glamour. The growth doctrine, degrading the more noble purposes of our civilization, may or may not kill our society from sudden collapse, but it will surely damn it in civilized history for want of either purpose of meaning.

The *Wall Street Journal* once editorialized as follows:

> Growth in any organism is a result, not a cause of good health, and approaching the problem as if growth were all there is to talk about, and a thing to be bought at any

price, is to mistake the task. And to forget that happy stimulants to growth can also be deadly.

As we have noted, untrammeled growth in any species consumes its environment to its own death. To talk, therefore, about a forever-expanding economy is preposterous. There is an end. But first we invite a shambles of our surroundings.

The economist, confronted by the fact that capital goods expenditures, high employment, and accelerated economic activity characterize what we call prosperity, has concentrated on building up the productive plant to spur economic growth. We increase production with this year's savings and then save the same or a larger proportion of next year's production, which gives us even more productive facilities.

This inflexible pattern of development is fostered quite independently of all other considerations. Recklessly, it overrides any delicate limitations of the endowments of nature. A top executive has expressed it this way: "Perhaps the sum total of all the will of the officers and stockholders of a corporation is ridden with doubt and reservations, diluted with qualms, shot through with idealism and the finer motives. But the sum total of the corporation's will is 100 per cent financial." [10]

He continued: "This is as it has to be since the sole reason for the corporations' existence is to make profits. Undoubtedly, it does not represent its membership, but its will prevails." Yet to found an economic theory of growth in complete disregard of the best thinking in ecology is eventual suicide.

The dizzying spiral is hypnotic to the point that economic growth has become an index of international power. Competition of the nation-states stimulates rivalry. Great power leadership is assessed in large part by the buoyancy of a power's production system and the capacity to seed developing economies. [11]

There is a large kernel of validity and appropriateness in this evaluation of great powers by their economic virility. But, at the same time, the international preoccupation with growth-rates gruesomely distorts the goals of mankind. All competition tends to fall in the realm of the material, not the intangibles. It lies in paper production rather than book quality, in building construction rather than architectural beauty, in TV assembly lines rather than philosophical discourse. The drive for massive drug production overwhelms the need to establish the compassionate treatment of animals in laboratories; the productivity of the worker becomes a more important consideration than his dignity as a person.

De Gaff's law states that "the progress of a people is inversely proportional to the time and effort required to produce the necessities of life." [12] It might be said that the lasting greatness of a people is inversely proportional to the time and effort lavished on purely material considerations.

Nonetheless, the inexorable contest of growth-rates proceeds without let-up. What Eric Sevareid calls the "yammering commercialism" accompanies it. We are in the grip of a "tyranny of things." To keep our nation dominant we must patriotically consume our way to satiation and beyond. Of such tawdry components is public policy made. It is a shabby destiny indeed, this orgy of consumption, whose spokesman is the circus barker and whose sustenance is ballyhoo.

Truly, what has been called the "ugly underbelly of progress" offends not only our higher nature but beslimes the quality of our environment. But with our public policy firmly in the clutches of specialists whose yardsticks are not adequate to the measuring of vast endeavors, our national horizons must remain low and mean. Arthur Compton, the scientist, once illustrated this point by telling about his sister in India who hired a native carpenter to repair the window. The native boggled the job terribly, though trying to follow the sketch she had made. She cried out in exasperation: "But why didn't you use your common sense?" He drew himself up with dignity and replied: "But common sense, Madam, common sense is a gift of God. I have technical knowledge only."

Remarked Theodore Edison: "Perhaps more people could make direct use of the Taj Mahal if it were converted into a drive-in theatre, but what a loss that conversion would be to the world!" The economic expert's slide rule does not condone a Taj Mahal if it stands in the way of a profitable drive-in theater any more than it condones the retention of an historic old oak where a filling station might bring in more tangible revenue.

Theodore Sorenson, once adviser to President Kennedy, has pointed out that specialists are dangerous, for they use only one small spectrum. "We need men with bigger vision, not experts, to determine policy," he said. The direction, pace, and character of our "progress" are the consequence, the outcome, of our philosophy.

Unfortunately, this mass idolatry imprisons our political leadership as well. The President himself must bow too deeply to "butter and guns" accomplishment. Both for domestic and international reasons his administration must represent a milestone in "better and better living" and a record-maker in bigger and bigger consumption. His incumbency must prosper, glitter with mercantile trappings, no matter what the deluge to follow.

There is something frightening in the primitive lust of our economic drive. Against this harsh force the best-intentioned political leaders must struggle desperately to contend; it has become a heathen ritual demanding annual sacrifice of our finest both in ideals and vision.

Only rarely comes a whispered warning, as from the First National City Bank in its monthly economic letter, which said: "It is time to think less about emphasizing expansion and more about emphasizing stability." [13]

The natural scientists, however, are appalled. Dr. Alan Gregg, who devoted a long career to prolonging life by carrying modern hygiene and medicine to the far reaches of the planet, surveyed the resulting ecological imbalance with "grim dismay." He looked on the headlong and reckless increase in human numbers with its consequent disorder as comparable only to the spread of cancer cells within an organisim.

As Dr. Paul Sears reflects on this matter of growth —population growth and concomitant economic growth—he concludes as follows:

> To me, at least, it is disturbing to hear the current glib emphasis on economic "growth" as the solution of all ills. Growth, in all biological experience, is a determinate process. Out of control, say by pituitary imbalance, it becomes pathological gigantism and by no means the same thing as health. With the concept of a healthy economy there can be no quarrel, but to equate this with an ever-expanding, ever-rising spiral is to relapse into the folly of perpetual motion, long since discredited by a sane understanding of energetics.[14]

To talk about an "ever-expanding" economy is to try to conceive of infinity, a rather hopeless thrust by men who are something less, at this juncture, than gods. To continue to speak of resources as though they were infinite is scarcely intelligent. Yet the growth philosophy depends heavily on empasizing that many of our abused resources, such as lumber, soil, and water, are "renewable," which means "infinite." It would pay briefly to examine once more, and in this economic growth context, this euphemisim.

"Our timber is renewing itself" say the charts. It must be kept in mind that the time schedule of a climax forest or a fair replacement of what we are taking is much greater than the age of the oldest tree; it is, in northern latitudes, the outcome of a 700- to 1,000-year succession. On man's short calendar this kind of forest is *non-renewable*.

Moreover, as in the case of the redwoods, so in the overall picture of the nation's timber resource, "growing more timber than we are cutting" turns out, on close examination, to be a shoddy, even alarming deception, a kind of black magic. It matches the increased volume of the scraggly woodlots on the abandoned farms of the South and East against the massive mature giants falling before the chain saw in the West. Thus, we are sedated into exchanging (without realizing it) priceless virgin forests such as the Douglas fir and Sitka spruce for scrub. These scrub plots, then, are our "renewed forests" of the future.

Then, there is our "renewable" topsoil. Someone has said, "Civilized man has marched across the face of the earth and left a desert in his footprints." An Associated Press bulletin of February 16, 1965, tells us that some of the worst dust storms in ten years damaged 2.32 million acres of land in Texas, Kansas, New Mexico, Nebraska, Oklahoma, and Colorado, all in the preceding four months. Millions of tons of dry soils, shorn of their cover, were whirled away to the sea in winds up to seventy-five miles an hour. But topsoil is a "renewable resource."

Earth's soil mantle has been forming for 350,000,000 years, say Tom Dale and Vernon Gill Carter in their instructive book *Top Soil and Civilization.*[15] It kept building up until about 6000 B.C., when man first devised a cultivating implement and dropped a few seeds into holes, thus initiating the agricultural era. From that moment, the soil mantle has been (literally) "going downhill." In all parts of the globe not under the polar icecaps, many inches of topsoil have been lost to erosion; in richest sections the erosion is counted in feet, not inches. It is difficult to believe that the bared mountains of Italy, Syria, Lebannon, and even the Armenian hills were once thickly forested slopes.

But fresh regolith (the mantle of loose material overlying the solid rock of the earth) becomes topsoil much more quickly today than in the slow geological successions that preceded the last glacial age. According to the *Yearbook of Agriculture* of the U.S. Department of Agriculture, regolith deposited on a glacier was found, within 100 years of deposition, to show an

"A" horizon—that is, sufficient humus and nutrients in its first six inches to be likened to the fair-to-poor topsoil of the Eastern United States.[16]

But few stretches of agricultural land today may sit fallow for 100 years to renew six inches of tilth and nutrients through the natural processes of sun, rain, wind, vegetation enrichment, earthworms, bacteria, animal droppings, breakdown of the regolith, etc. Keeping the tilth in arable lands is a problem of worrisome and gigantic proportions, requiring not only long periods lost to food production by green manure crops, but outlays of labor, money, scientific know-how, and vigilant husbandry. The loss of an inch of good topsoil over an interstate valley is a matter for the consultation of kings.

Water, too, has been classified as a "renewable resource," but this is true only in a relative sense. Unless the environmental factors are held constant, unless the holding capacity of the soil is preserved, the odds on continuing to benefit from the water cycle are perilous.

Without control of the mountains that fathered its headwaters even the fabulously fertile valley of Mesopotamia was doomed; silt from lumbering tumbled down upon it in such masses in the rolling waters of the Tigris and Euphrates that digging to keep the hundreds of irrigation ditches free of the silt and full of water became the major concern and was for two thousand years the life-or-death struggle of the most glamorous capital of the world: fabled Babylon. With great legions of slaves the flagging fight against time could, nevertheless, be carried on until at last the Mongols and the Black Death rushed in to put the *coup de grâce* to a dying civilization panting for water and choking in dust. What good to man is the fact that water is "renewable" if conditions are such that it is not retainable for use?

In the name of growth and expansion we have, then, not only denigrated our values, but we have injected tensions and stresses into our problem of raw material supply. Because we insist on an economic orgy we introduce strain where there should be plenty, and corrode the goals of our civilization.

"Is civilization progress?" asks Charles A. Lindbergh, who, as much as any man, advanced aviation to its present status.

> The challenge, I think, is clear; and as clearly, the final answer will be given not by our amassment of knowledge, or by the discoveries of our science, or by the speed of our aircraft, but by the effect our civilized activities as a whole have upon the qualities of our planet's life—the life of plants and animals as well as that of man.

It is fair to ask whether our commitment to material standards is so complete that reappraisal is impossible. If not, we can profit by President Kennedy's oft-quoted admonition: "Our task is not to fix blame for the past, but to fix a course for the future. We must use time as a tool, not as a couch."

Chapter Nineteen

To the Rescue: The Seas!

There is a fairy-tale quality about the sea—mysterious, fathomless, eternal. Throughout the vast mid-continent of America millions of children who have never in their lives seen the oceans have memorized:

> magic casements, opening on the foam
> Of perilous seas, in faery lands forlorn,

and thrilled to the ancient fascination which the Earth's vast water kingdom has always held for man.

Again quoting immortal Keats:

> The ocean with its vastness,
>   its blue green,
> Its ships, its rocks, it caves,
>   its hopes, its fears—
> Its voice mysterious, which
>   whoso hears
> Must think on what will be,
>   and what has been.

"The sound of the sea," says E. B. White, "is the most time-effacing sound there is." We shall never be quite free of the sea's mystique.

But of late the eye that man has been casting with such fascination upon the sea has gained a covetous, even an avid glint. The sea with its uncharted depths fits the American credo, for it provides us with the frontier for exploration and exploitation that has sustained us historically. More, it now gives subconscious support and justification for our prodigality. "There is always the sea" to furnish food and space and water for the coming multitudes who will overtax the earth. "The sea will provide," we chant, paraphrasing the favorite maxim of the Puritans of old who cherished that same faith in the Lord.

The old fascination is still there but colored now with a new scientific curiosity that seeks to explain and tame all its mysteries. Charmed to the core, we scan the scientific report of Dr. E. G. Barham, who has discovered that the sound echoes from 600 or more feet beneath the ocean's surface are caused primarily by colonies of gas-filled jellyfish. We are comforted to know that the age-old sound of the sea is no longer the moaning of Proteus mixed with the voices of the millions who have died in its depths, but burping jellyfish and grunting turtles.

We are comforted because we are determined no longer to live in awe of so obviously rich and exploitative an element as the watery desert that envelops three-fourths of the world's surface. It has always been maddening to man to have this frontier that he has never been able absolutely to master, that has overcome him so many times, whose depths he has never been able either to plumb or to profit by. "Consider the subtleness of the sea; how its most dreaded creatures glide under water, unapparent for the most part, and treacherously hidden beneath the loveliest tints of azure," rhapsodized Herman Melville.

In the days of Melville we could shudder with delight at the terrors and presumptions of this great unknown. We had other frontiers not yet conquered, largesse not yet tapped. How profoundly has the tone changed today. Fantastically, the famed French undersea researcher, Captain Jacques-Yves Cousteau, discusses without a shred of Jules Verne tongue-in-the-cheek a new underwater species of man (*Homo aquaticus*) who will learn to inhale water, live under it, and carry on extensive research there. Scientific heads, otherwise sane, nod; research money of a serious sort pours into the watery pit. No one seems daunted by the problem of reversing 800 million years or more of painful evolution with a few drops of amino acid.

Yet once having gotten the small matter of growing back our gills out of the way, it now appears that we shall be more at home on the ocean floor than we would think. Ocean explorers report that empty cans, bottles, and waste of all kinds litter the floors of the Atlantic Ocean, the Red Sea, and the Indian Ocean. Captain Cousteau said recently that he would never forget his first deep dive in a bathyscaph: "I landed," said he, "in front of a spread-out newspaper!"

As we conclude despoliation of the land we regale ourselves with the promise and potential of the seas.[1] This is what the frontier has always meant to us—an escape from consequences. Because we know so little about the oceans there are no limits that reason can put on our expectations. Indeed, because we are ignorant we are so hopeful.

The Committee on Oceanography of the National Academy of Sciences reports that "we know less about many regions of the oceans today than we know about the lunar surface." We have almost no conception of the quantity of fish in the sea, how their numbers are determined, the supplies of plant and animal material to sustain them, or what steps to take to enhance their numbers. What situation would be riper for speculation? "We are most intrigued by the great potential that the ocean holds for the betterment of mankind," argues Dr. Harris B. Stewart, Jr., chief oceanographer of the U.S. Coast and Geodetic Survey.

The lure of diverting some of the funds that are being lavished on outer space—$24.6 billion in a ten-year period—must have some influence on the thinking and public statements of the oceanographers. How else can one account for the intriguing proposal that the excess population in the year 2000 can be accommodated in the sea! With between 6 and 7.4 billion people crowding the planet it is *scientifically advanced* that we can create living room by building cities on the ocean bottom. This makes about as much economic sense as the proposed migration to the moon, so it should share some of the moon's billions.

France's Conshelf operations team did work two to four hours a day at depths of 367 feet, an accomplishment of tremendous implications for industry, especially the oil industry.[2] Sealab 2 was set down in 205 feet of water off La Jolla, California, by the United States Navy and accommodated three teams for fifteen days each. M. Scott Carpenter, who sojourned some thirty days on the ocean floor, was quoted as saying: "It's in the state of the art now to build an underwater home for a family." The Urban Renewal Administration is not, so far as is known, accepting applications for relocating cities in the seas.

It is the productiveness of the sea that excites the most elaborate predictions. President Kennedy it was who emphasized that "to meet the vast needs of an expanded population, the bounty of the sea must be made more available. Within two decades, our own Nation will require over a million more tons of seafood than we now harvest."

That is a simple assignment compared with the task that Lord Boyd Orr lays down for the future. Within eighty years, he says, the world must produce *more than eight times* the present world food supply. And even Secretary of the Interior Stewart L. Udall is coming to the rescue of an overburdened earth via the seas. "Aided by men of science," he says, "we have set forth to plumb that 70 per cent of the earth that remains unexplored—the ocean depths. Thus, we may better discover and utilize the sea's bounties for the world's hungry."[3]

It is fish protein concentrate that is sought from the seas. "By utilizing the unharvested fish in United States waters alone, enough fish protein concentrate can be obtained to provide supplemental animal protein for one billion people for 300 days at a cost of less than half a cent a day per person." Few see anything askew about joylessly salvaging an excess population that there may be more breeding stock for a new burst of increase. We meet our social and political inadequacy as a species by casting an avaricious eye at the watery frontiers.[4]

The malnutrition of children is appallingly tragic; but the crime lies in society's unrestrained procreation, not in its negligence in producing fish powder. But wherever the population projections are contemplated, the answer to the problem is something like this: "There are few projects that could do more to raise the nutritional level of mankind than a full-scale scientific effort to develop the resources of the sea." [5]

Each year some thirty million tons of food products are taken from the sea, which account for 12 per cent of the world's animal proteins. Essentially what man does is prey on wild stocks. There are those who would practice a game-keeping technique to maximize the productivity of the seas. Others would "farm" the seas, feeding marine animals in enclosures or, for example, culling animals that compete with those bottom-living fish that we particularly desire. Since the whole matter of sea productivity is speculation, we need not limit our promises.

The cold war impinges on the problem, too.[6] Like the race to the moon there is the specter of defeat in a race to the exploitation of the seas. With the concern of a nation facing disaster we learn from a Senate Commerce Committee that the Soviet Union has more ocean research ships than the entire non-Communist world combined.

Thus, the frenzy of an outdistanced suitor combines with projected population needs to spur the pursuit of our share of the bounty of the seas. The National Academy of Sciences has shyly recommended a minimum expenditure of $165 million a year. The government of California has marshaled the state's oceanographers to set up a task force for marine resources development. The state with its swelling population must push westward into the sea frontiers for food, power, and water.[7] Private industry must now move into marine research and the federal government must make new attacks on the problem of marine resource development.[8] There is a tone of desperateness in all these designs on the seas.

But what is most startling is the assumption that the seas are a virgin resource unsullied and unmauled. The fact is that the seas have been, and are being, hurt, directly and indirectly, by the same forces that have abused the land. In the broad pattern of ecological relationships the seas are not separable from what happens on the land. The poisons that contaminate the soil and air wash in massive doses into the continental shelf waters. The salt marshes and estuaries that serve as breeding grounds for the sea are victims of the same development that pressure of population has brought to inland areas. The filth and pollution that spills from our urban sewers and industrial outfalls despoil our bays and coastal waters. All the border seas are already heavily contaminated by the same exploitation drives that have undermined the quality of life on land.

We shall not pause for statistics on what is happening to our harvests of seafood. Let the statement of Howard D. Zeller, Chief, Fisheries Division, Georgia Game and Fish Commission, serve as a fair example. He says,

> Harvest of oysters for human consumption has deteriorated from a high of 8,070,320 pounds during 1908 to 307,900 pounds in 1950 and to a low of 160,000 pounds in 1961. Vast areas on the Georgia coast have been condemned for oyster harvest due to pollution of coastal streams. The few existing areas are jeopardized by the continuing rate of pollution.[9]

For a thousand years man has relentlessly pursued the whale from one whaling ground to another. "As each area in turn became exhausted through overfishing," said Rachel Carson for the Fish and Wildlife Service, "the whalers moved on to new fields." With an almost insatiable demand for whale oil and the other products of the industry, and ruthlessly efficient whale fleets marauding throughout the Antarctic, last haven of the whales, the outlook is dismal. Nor is it easy to impose and enforce conservation regulations on the varied assortment of nations that have a stake in the annual hunt.

On many counts the sea is not nearly as big as it seems. So far as its usefulness to man is concerned, the coastal and surface waters are probably all that matter. There is where the food sources appear to concentrate and where man labors. In the light of the slow mixing of the lower and upper waters, the abuse of surface waters may not be quickly remedied by dilution. The great volume of the oceans is only partly meaningful. It was a grave matter, therefore, when Scripps Institute at La Jolla, California, announced that the oceans are becoming seriously polluted. It reported that the lead content of the surface waters is close to 10 milligrams a cubic yard, all of it stemming from the introduction of anti-knock gasoline in 1923.

Then, there are the pesticides that collect in the estuaries and coastal waters. Many of the insecticides in use in agriculture today were specially formulated to combat terrestrial arthropods—spiders, insects, etc., distinguished by their jointed feet and limbs, segmented bodies, and horny skeletons. In other words what selective toxicity is built into these pesticides is directed to the arthropods.

Unfortunately, it happens that a number of our most valuable marine food species, including lobsters, crabs, and shrimp are also hapless arthropods. Therefore, the millions of gallons of these poisons that wash off our farm lands and down our rivers pile up in the coastal homes of our most valuable and vulnerable seafoods.

Recently it has been discovered that exposure to lethal or near lethal concentrations of toxic materials may not kill shrimp and crabs outright; they remain in a moribund condition for a day or two.[10] The same research program that has us harvesting half-dead and poisoned shrimp indicates "that some species of plankton that are important as food for clams and oysters can be killed by very small concentrations of herbicides—much smaller concentrations than are used for weed control upstream."

No pollution of earth has been withheld from the seas. Traffic in oil has not only caused accidental discharges, but flushing operations commonly result in oil slicks that doom the waterfowl, blacken the beaches, and ruin spawning beds. A very loosely drawn international treaty seeks to impose some kind of restraint, but the sea is suffering. Only a few enlightened operators, such as Standard Oil of New Jersey, forbid dumping of oil on seas throughout the world. Meanwhile, the charm of places like Curaçao in the West Indies, where refineries abound, is darkened by a grimy line of black along the shores and a portentously quiet sky where only a few lonely gulls survive.

We are profligate with the sea, holding fast to the faith that in its size we can wash away our sins. Admittedly ignorant of the ultimate effect of our actions, we still run radioactive garbage ferries out to sea to dispose of thousands of tons of the wastes of nuclear reactors, hospitals, research laboratories, and industries. Britain pipes four separate lines of the wastes of its nuclear power establishment out to sea while protesting the innocence of the act.

Thus, the very ocean that seems to hold so much promise for so many has no protector against whatever nuclear contamination each of the separate states of the world might seek to impose upon it. There is little concern that what man harvests from the sea are those forms of life that climax the food chain and so concentrate many times whatever radioactive contamination we deposit there. We cut the throat of our dreams.

Not the least of the abuses of the sea are the mechanical developments for its more thorough exploitation.

Echo sound devices, radio telephones, radar, drift nets, balloon spotters, new and powerful gear of all types, factory ships—all put pressure on the "inexhaustible resources" of this water wonderland. One fishing country, Denmark, which markets the products of the sea in seventy countries, pushed with its new gear 136,000 metric tons of fish through its food processing industries in a single year, representing a triple increase in one decade.

But the fishing grounds are flagging. Salmon catches are critically lower. Sardines are becoming elusive. Halibut is under a hemispheric conservation plan. Fish wars are being fought between Korea and Japan, Iceland and Great Britain. The sea is, of course, boundless. There are relatively untapped grounds off the east coast of Africa and in the Indian Ocean. Nonetheless, most areas now show strain. If we approach them with the air of prodigality that has marked our treatment of the land and with the pressure of billions of hungry and clamoring people, the seas will not sustain us even in protein "retching-meal."

Today the fascination of the sea is something other than romantic. More's the pity. Experts are not sighing with D. H. Lawrence: "Ah, if one could sail forever on a small, quiet, lonely ship, from land to land and isle to isle, and saunter through the spaces of this lovely world!" Today they sail, but it is on a grimmer quest than that of seeking joy.

For the sea in all its awesomeness is scheduled for a $2.3 billion domestication. To be considered in the program are underwater experimental stations on the continental shelves, new devices for deep-sea mining, better forecasting systems to expand fishing catches and improve the speed of ocean liners, and the study of fish farming and "ranching." Altogether there will be mapping, exploring, and pioneering to find hiding places for atomic submarines in the ocean trenches, as well as to ferret out the last of the beasts of the deep.

Man, possibly because of his smallness and the sea's

unbearable bigness, has always harbored an underlying hostility toward the great waters. Just as we have fought the land we have fought the sea. "Between Earth and Man the contest never ends," began a recent television spectacular. "We found we could move the world around and do ingenious things with it. . . . More machines! More fuel! More pleasure! More ideas!" Gloatingly, the narrator shouted, "We took the world and shook it up!"

Picture after picture of us shaking up the Earth followed in dizzying kaleidoscopy, interspersed with shots of primitive tribes in darkest Africa to show the contrast between our happy, advantaged life and their miserable one. (Yet how many viewers noticed that all of the civilized faces we saw in laboratories, on city streets, absorbed in civilized planning, building, consuming, were drawn and perplexed? The only real joy we glimpsed was on the faces of the primitive peoples as they leaped and chanted in their tribal dances or strutted about, painted and bedizened, in their bootless ceremonies that accomplish nothing but time-killing.)

As we have "shaken up" the earth we shall now shake up the sea. We cannot conceive that this powerful force that slams our coasts and engulfs out shipping is at the same time a delicately balanced creation.

Said Byron: "Roll on, thou deep and dark blue ocean, roll! Ten thousand fleets sweep over thee in vain." But today the ten thousand fleets do not sweep over it in vain. They spew unmeasured volumes of oil flushings to slick the surface and destroy the waterfowl. They dump huge drums filled with deadly isotopes into its depths; they discharge nuclear depth bombs and rake the sea bottom with high-powered mechanical tools. And always, in a ceaseless stream from the land, man pours his wastes and poisons to transform this primeval cradle of abundant life into a salty graveyard. This is the "untrammeled ocean" in which mankind puts so much store.

In the sixteenth century when sailing vessels were

small and frail, George Herbert, the English divine and poet, said: "He that will learn to pray, let him go to sea." But today, perhaps, the prayers should be, not for ourselves, but for the sea.

Chapter Twenty

To the Rescue:
The Sciences!

The year was 1975. A splendid big super-supersonic air cruiser had just taken off from its New York airport with 3,000 happy souls bound for Europe. After the gangplank had automatically lifted, the doors had automatically shut and sealed themselves, the passengers been comfortably seated, and the take-off made, the automatic loudspeaker began its spiel.

"Ladies and gentlemen," it enunciated in the latest stereophonic super-hi-fidelity taped accents,

> You are now embarking on the first completely automatic flight in history. We call your attention to the noiselessly perfect operation of your automatic seat-confinement jackets, the automatic drink dispenser from which any beverage you may choose will be transported to your seat-table merely by pressing the proper button on the personal service panel before you. Everything on this plane—the pilot, copilot, the service, the starting, the entire flight, the landing—is completely automatic and completely safe. Relax and enjoy the flight! Nothing can go wrong, nothing can go wrong, nothing can go wrong, nothing can go wrong, go wrong, go wrong. . . .

Our society resembles these passengers, lulled into a baseless complacency over the environmental problems that face it by an exceedingly reckless confidence in the remedial potential of science. It is another of our substitutes for a dissipated frontier. There is in this smug dependence a surrender of our personal thinking and opinion making. Thus, apart from the question whether science can fulfill our expectations, there is a more fundamental issue. The myth of scientific infallibility is a convenient way of evading civic responsibility.[1] It has also a tragic consequence, for as an opiate it deprives us of initiative and response to what is a harsh challenge.

How do you measure the loss—the qualitative loss —to a society that has surrendered its critical sense, a society that maintains a wholly grim and self-deluding refusal to evaluate the problems of its environment on the grounds that Science has the answer in its magic test tubes? What serious public forum can you mount, what dialogue can you foster, what sense of reality can you expect, if from every complicated issue there is a craven, ostrich retreat—when every problem is met with a shrug and the idolatrous affirmation, "Oh, Science will fix that up for us; Science will find an answer"?

Commenting on a careful study of population pressures by the United States Department of Social Affairs, the *Wall Street Journal* typically dismisses what it considers the authors' undue concern for the future of the world's cupboard.[2] Haven't we always overcome anticipated shortages—of coal, of oil, of timber? Mustering its cheeriest vocabulary, the business editors aver their faith in science thus: "So when 1984 arrives we have little doubt that somebody's offspring who likes to eat will have come up with something for the empty plates. That's another habit [besides eating and having children] people seem to have."

The massive report of Resources for the Future buttresses the science idol by asserting that "the threat of scarcity has been held in check largely by technological progress," which, it adds, has become "the main escape hatch from scarcity." Thereupon, it concludes that our hope for adequate resources rests on maintaining the flow of new and improved resource technology.

But there is a rub. The deterioration of our resource position has proceeded hand in hand with our scientific advance. Science has provided some spectacular substitutes and stretch-outs, such as plastics and fiber board and artificial diamonds, but these efforts have not stayed the voraciousness of our technological system for raw resources.

Said Dr. Detlev W. Bronk when president of the National Academy of Sciences, "The thing that disturbs me is the idea that science can solve everything. For instance, when it is pointed out that we are using up a natural resource at a terrific rate, even relatively thoughtful people will say, 'Yes, but why worry—science will find an adequate substitute.'" [3]

A past president of the Association for the Advancement of Science, takes this analysis a step further. He pointed out (and some time before the 1965 "Great Eastern Blackout" that "could never happen") that "as dependence on ever more elaborate systems of technology increases, so does vulnerability to any slight breakdown at some point in the operation." The airplane pilot "who must depend on electronic signals to tell him whether his landing gear is down is less secure than one who can look below and see where it is in fact down." [4]

Another former president of the American Association for the Advancement of Science, Dr. Warren Weaver, in discussing our national commitment in science reminded his interviewer of its limitations. He said: "As dedicated as I am to science, I am definitely one of the individuals who do not feel that science is the answer to all of life's problems." [5]

The greater the scientist, the more humble. He admits that the scope of scientific ignorance in environmental science is, despite all the progress, almost boundless. In an official outline of research needs the gaps in knowledge are widely admitted. Even such a simple thing as "the role of various aquatic or terrestrial insects as food-chain organisms for other animals," says the document, "is not well known."

The New York State College of Agriculture in a fact sheet for agricultural specialists asks: "Are there satisfactory alternatives to chemicals for pest control? As of today, no." The sheet goes on to state that it is not intended to belittle non-chemical control principles but only to emphasize that our present state of pest control is quite inadequate. It brings home the immense field in pest control that so far has hardly been scratched: disease-resistant crop varieties, "the use of various microbial agents; use of insect and mite parasites and predators; manipulation of plant nutrition; and the use of various agronomic principles, such as crop rotation and time of planting." We are also woefully behind in research on the health hazards in existing control methods.[6]

And it is only recently, after twenty years of fervent chlorinated-hydrocarbon applications, wholesale and without legal limit over the face of the land, that government scientists have discovered they have poisoned our soil and wildlife irreversibly. (We are, by the way, still permitting these long-lived pesticides.)

The New York State College of Agriculture at Geneva makes much of its claim that "of the total land (and water) area of the U.S.A., more than 95 percent receives no pesticide in a typical year." This is misleading, even if true, which is doubtful. Do you, a gardener or a farmer or a road worker or a park official or an estate man or a range or a county agent, report to Geneva every time you take out the battered old spray can?

Moreover, one of the great and frightening mysteries of the chlorinated hydrocarbons is, as we have seen, what wildlife specialists term their "movement." When but a couple of years ago samples of young ducks and eggs collected more than 500 miles north of any known spray application were examined, the investigators were stunned to find that these eggs and immature ducks contained *more pesticide residues than any adult samples*. We have mentioned that fish hundreds of miles out from land are contaminated. Although it is well known that winds will carry airplane spray for hundreds of miles, these revelations rocked the scientific world. They opened up a whole new area of unanswered questions about our present pesticide programs.

In response to injunctive proceedings by citizens against further aerial spraying of their Long Island properties, Dr. Clarence E. Hoffman, one of the Department of Agriculture's leading entomologists, admitted to scientific groping. He said that up to that time there had never been a test to determine the overall effect of DDT on plant and animal life and their interrelationship!

Science is powerful, but the environmental challenges are almost overwhelming. Just as we think that we know how to purify water, even though we ruin its taste, Dr. Shih Lu Chang, a scientist from the Robert A. Taft Sanitary Engineering Center, finds quantities of microscopic worms—"under the microscope they look like a can of wriggling fish worms"—in purified water drawn from rivers in fourteen out of fifteen cities. The worms, called nematodes, by themselves aren't so bad; but having been raised in sewage they have fed on typhoid, paratyphoid, food poisoning, bacillery dysentery, etc., and now they encase the disease germs and completely protect them from treatment. (More, they smell bad.) [7]

Even industry finds itself slamming up against the frontiers of technology in such primary tasks as the treatment of its wastes. A. J. Von Frank, manager of the Industrial Waste Development Section of the Allied Chemical Corporation, traced the technical woes of a plant manager directed to find a wash liquid that didn't have significant water pollution problems, or treatment problems, that didn't boost his production costs or adversely affect the quality of his product.[8]

> He was told that a long list of things could be industrial waste problems and he should prepare to abate them *each to a different degree* if they were present. These were: oxygen demand of his wastes (three kinds), acidity or alkalinity, suspended solids, settleable solids, color, components that gave taste or odor to the water, separable oils, foamers such as the alkyl benzene sulfonates, temperature, turbidity, dissolved salts of heavy metals, nitrates, phosphates, chlorides, flourides, sulfides, cyanides, phenols, and coliform bacteria. . . . There were more but he chose not to go into it.

Although he was relieved when the engineers advised him that his manufacturing plant was responsible for only 40 per cent of these pollutants, he collapsed again at the mention of nearly a million dollars to install necessary tests, four acres of precious ground space, a huge slice out of his operating costs, his competitive position, the state of obsolescence of his plant, processes, etc. He called this hour of revelation "The Afternoon of the Trauma." It is the terrible morning-after headache of the progress orgy, and it must be met and grappled with not only for public welfare but for the very life of business itself.

Three years and several hundred thousands of dollars later, after many tests, surveys, consultants' advice, engineering reports, and intensive research, this manager was able to reduce his waste by 50 per cent and later by 75 per cent. But he had to evolve some ingenious approaches (such as the buying of higher class raw materials to eliminate waste). Pollution abatement can be effected, but we can in no wise belittle the problems that our decades of headstrong expansion without regard for consequences have loaded upon our generation and an overrated science.

There is great popular confidence in the capacity of science to extract the oil from our limitless deposits of shale. Colorado shale (which extends into neighboring states) has unfathomed quantities of oil. The Governor totals it up at *3 trillion tons.* "How much is that?" he laughingly asks, then offers us this homely little comparison: "Give your wife $3 million to spend at $1,000 a day and she'll be back in nine years asking for more. Give her $3 trillion to spend at $1,000 a day, and she won't return for nine million years."

Sadly, there is one catch to this dazzling miracle of abundance. In spite of a new Swedish cooking process, science has no idea of what to do with all this ocean of unrefined oil. No one can discover how to refine oil without water—great reservoirs of water—and Colorado is notoriously short of this dwindling commodity. Yet the comment of a journalist on the matter is interesting and typical. He dismissed the problem with this: "If the oil becomes necessary, some way to provide the water will be found."

Thus, we use science as the escape hatch from reality—as hashish. It deprives us of reason, undercuts the tone of the public forum, eliminates dialogue and the concern that might agonize through to an answer. We are like a group of shipwrecked persons set adrift on a life raft who continue to drift while they happily consume their two weeks' rations in two days in the confident expectation that thereafter gulls will alight on their shoulders. The least they could do, gulls or no gulls, would be to pull steadily and vigorously in the direction of the invisible, but charted, shore.

Since World War II the scientific control of mosquitoes through poison spraying has proliferated all through the country. Then it was found that generations of mosquitoes soon bred that were immune to the sprays. Stronger and stronger poisons were used. Now there are breeds of mosquitoes in the Midwest that are immune even to aldrin and dieldrin, two of the most powerful insecticides ever known. But the birds and wildlife did not become immune, and today many communities are bare of both. The mosquitoes will be back shortly but the birds will not.

On the other side of the spectrum from the heavy-poison advocates (and, amusingly, in the category of vinegar-and-honey medication) is the news from Griggsville, Illinois. There the Junior Chamber of Commerce stimulated the wholesale building of martin houses as a way of controlling mosquitoes without pesticides. Over an area of 125 miles in diameter the idea caught on. Not only is it a delight to travel through the region today, alive as it is with bird songs, but natives tell us that the project actually works.

Illogically, for all our great and abiding faith in scientific technology, it is this very scientific technology that is responsible for most of our problems in the first place. It created the admirable—but not-worth-returning—tin can; thus, every year we are buried in 48 billion of them. It invented the cheap, no-refund bottle, so 26 billion of them clutter our highways. Sixty-five billion metal and plastic caps and crowns are showered over the good earth as a by-product of our packaged economy. Let us wish all Godspeed to those scientists now engaged in creating a brown or green drinking cup that will deteriorate to humus quickly in the rain!

A few years ago scientists placed 2.2 pounds of deadly plutonium-238 in a small atomic battery that was supposed to power a transit navigational satellite. Because of a failure the deadly missile came down in the atmosphere off the west coast of Africa. With plutonium-238 described as a "fiendishly toxic" radioactive isotope (the maximum permissible tolerance for atomic workers is set at a microscopic two-billionths of a gram), this horrendous escape had the Atomic Energy Commission concealing the accident for three weeks. Then it dug deeply into its tote bag of pacifiers for one that would soothe the public.

Of course, whatever its effects have been on the life it has touched, no one will ever be the wiser. The point is that science, for all its wonders, has so many world-shaking and even world-shattering *side effects* that we cannot support it wholeheartedly, much less depend on it to rescue us from its own, and our, mistakes.

The contamination of our surroundings from radioactive fallout from the bomb tests of the 1950's falls in the same slot. Whether or not Dr. L. J. le Vann's correlation between high levels of fallout in Canada and the doubled rate of birth abnormalities in 1959 and 1961 was wholly justified, the alien element in our environment would not have been there had we not engaged in billions of dollars' worth of atom-exploding activity.[9] For that matter, it was the stupendous success of science that placed the hideous shadow of the mushroom cloud over our health and well-being, over our entire future and hope of survival.

Were it not for the success of science we wouldn't have had to spend weeks searching frantically for lost bombs in Spain's waters or scraping up 5,000 drums of their irradiated soil from the atomic accident there for burial in our own soil of North Carolina.

Were it not for the desolate and sterile countryside that the strip miners leave in the wake of their exhaust, great schemes for scientific restoration of the land's productivity would not now need to be troubled over and financed. When the World Health Organization discovers that the technical marvels of irrigation expansion in Egypt bring on a serious and advancing scourge, a parasitic disease known as bilharziasis, (a snail-borne affliction whose larvae flourish in the stagnant waters of new dams), we cannot honestly call it "an Act of God." [10]

Science, in short, is self-centered. It is cast awkwardly in the role of a social savior since it does not operate with ethical guidelines. If science can construct a theory that will result in the creation of a monster, the theory must be tested if for no other reason than to measure the horns of the monster. Further, much of the consequence of scientific activity is ignored or left to chance.

Thus, it is only lately that a panel of the National Research Council called the attention of the space scientists to the fact that alien organisms from other planets ought not to be introduced into the earth's living space. We have been carefully sterilizing our payloads to the moon and planets, but, say these questioners, maybe we ought not to risk the back contamination from the planets to us? It is well known by all scientists that one species of fungus, bacteria, or disease introduced into a new environment in which it has no predators could conquer the globe. Up to now the National Aeronautics and Space Administration has apparently not given thought to a quarantine.

Robert C. Cook, President of the Population Reference Bureau, points out that "we must get over our mystical belief that if a thing is technically possible, it is socially possible. Technology is not really magic. There is a price for progress. There are limits to science, there are limits to the earth's resources."

Clearly science is not our redeemer. An intern at a large medical institution told us recently: "There is no wonder-drug. Every one of these so-called wonder-drugs has side effects. The only question we bring up in their use is: which is worse—the condition or the effects of the 'cure'?"

There are so many sides to science and technology. They have freed mankind from many frightful plagues, reduced mother and child mortality, transformed our lives with conveniences and new pleasures, and poured a cornucopia of material marvels into our laps. Nonetheless, while providing us with the refinements and glamour of modern living, they have also caused foul pollution of our earth, water, and air; noise, strain, tension, mental aberrations, increased leukemia and thyroid growths, liver and degenerative diseases in the very young, the deposition of radioactive materials and pesticides in the bodies of unborn babies, the rocketing highway death toll, accidents and poisonings without number—not to mention TV "squint" and "stoop." Yet the excesses of science and their consequences are not so much the fault of science *per se* as of a public whose self-indulgence exceeded its wisdom. No public conscience has monitored the single-goal drive of a profession which admittedly places the acquisition of knowledge above race survival. As Madame Curie said: "In science we must be interested in things, not in persons."

Science is like electricity—a relentless blessing. But we know that electricity, our servant friend, and comfort, may turn, through the intermediary of a wet hand at an electric stove or the mere switching of an electric button while in the bathtub, into a monster of violent death. We therefore early establish our laws of dominance over the electricity we let into our homes. We have, on the other hand, given science, which is equally soulless and uncompassionate, a free hand, even a whip hand, to accomplish its end, regardless of the shower of dangerous side effects that pour over our heads and smother us in calamitous consequences.

The only possible answer is not "Let science work it out," but "We must direct science to help overcome our problems." The only accomplishments tolerable should be under social direction, on a collective, if not political, demand that the scientific enterprise be hitched to the social conscience, toward the remedying of the old science by-products as well as toward the proliferating of new products.[11]

On the credit side of the ledger, it is certainly heartening to observe the recent scientific efforts with new and less lethal (to other life) techniques. World-wide interest has grown out of the successful use of male screw-worm flies sterilized by exposure to cobalt-60 radiation to eliminate the pest from the Southeastern United States. It has started a whole new line of experimentation that may help salvage our poison-saturated environment. New chemicals have been found to confuse the sexual "orders" of insects so that they fail to rendezvous.[12] Such approaches are selective and point the way in this and other fields to improvement.

But the efforts in behalf of public health or ecology are so minuscule as compared to the efforts expended for the poisonous panaceas as to be discouraging. Indeed, the unexplored domains in insecticides are so extensive, the basic surveys so sketchy, the areas of ignorance so marked as to shake one's faith in human motivation, as well as in science itself.

For the major part we are still driving in the environmentally destructive direction. Of the $16 billion a year allocated to federal research and development, the vastly greater amount, some $14 billion, is tagged for defense, space, and atomic energy. Of the remaining $2 billion assigned to domestic civilian projects, such as housing, urban transportation, and pollution treatment, only the latter and some fringe experiments have to do with the preservation and enhancement of the environment.[13] Why should technology, for example, smash like a bulldozer through all aesthetic values? For instance, the citizens of mid-state New York, through private effort and contributions, sought to preserve Great Bear Swamp near Westerlo, one of the most splendid outcroppings of the giant pink rhododendron in the Northeast, as a scientific and educational sanctuary. When, however, the Air Force through the Corps of Engineers sent men trampling over the rhodendron bushes to survey for a 1,000-acre radar station, all but the defense goals got short shrift. A cut in the budget, however, slowed down the whirring of the defense machine, giving time for the citizen voices to be heard, and the swamp was saved.

The point is simply that we have not yet defined the national goals of our scientific activity with any consideration whatever for the national environment. Thus, in the face of the need for intense and immediate research in pest control, a federal report points out that "the number of insect taxonomists in this country today is no greater than thirty years ago."[14]

Only recently and on a very limited budget has a new watchdog agency called the National Environmental Health Center been set up. But again it represents but an isolated outpost on an otherwise undisciplined battlefront.

Science lassoed by the lariat of commerce can be and is likely to be a destructive force. Even unencumbered or unsubsidized, as in some of the research in universities, there is no guarantee that the contribution of science will be remedied. Yet Dr. Frank Stanton, the president of Columbia Broadcasting System, dedicating the Memorial Art Gallery at the University of Nebraska, showed that "federal commitments for basic research alone in American universities totaled, in 1963, $625 million, of which 98 per cent went to the physical, biological, and agricultural sciences, 2 per cent to the social sciences, and nothing to the humanities."

There is, indeed, great danger that, desperate and impatient to remedy environmental deficiencies, we shall without careful social considerations deface our surroundings even more. Faced with far-flung water shortages, the temptation of the engineers will be to launch immense public works—lower-stream big dams —rather than what science now knows to be the only permanent help—a program of control through upper-stream planting and many small impoundments. We have seen how all those "hydraulic empires" now long buried under Mediterranean sands went into a frenzy of dam and canal building only to find themselves every year buried deeper in upland silt from the stripped watersheds. Unlike the ancient civilizations we today cannot plead ignorance of ecological principles or that we do not have control of our own headwaters.[15]

The thrust of technology, unmitigated by the bird lovers, would push our television towers into the clouds. Unmoved by aesthetic considerations, it now strips our highways bare fifty feet or more back on both sides. With economic progress undisciplined, every point advance in the GNP gouges another point out of our environment. Science hitched to mercenary allies is a mindless killer; hitched to social and human ends, it is a preserver and enhancer of all life. If its wizardry is to pluck us out of the net it must be directed by our own radar. As Emerson said, "The best lightning rod for your protection is your own spine."

Part Six

Introspective

Chapter Twenty-One

Prolonging Our Moment in the Sun

Whatever pablum the seas and the test tubes produce to lessen the hunger pangs of the future, the insoluble fact remains that we cannot by the most superhuman efforts house any noticeable fraction of our unwanted human billions in the seas, nor can the test tubes produce some magic formula for stretching Earth's living space.[1] As for the planets, Joseph Wood Krutch suggests that our sudden interest in using space for people-disposal is because it is a technological answer, and we have become so technologically minded that it never occurs to us that there are other solutions.[2]

Even should there be some strange souls masochistic enough to be willing to inhabit under-glass colonies on the Moon or Mars, it is fairly certain there will be no exodus of the masses heavenward. Actually, though the skies were darkened without ceasing with the thousands of departing emigrant rocket ships, the drain would not be enough to put even a visible dent in our rampaging population curve!

All material solutions fail; the more we frantically turn here and there to avoid responsibility for our actions, the more we become enveloped in the shroud of futility. The more we shoo away the black raven, the more it returns to rest upon our shoulders. Technology can no more insure us survival than it can assure us of highway safety, freedom from insanity, or peace of mind. The solution must come from within.

For it is painfully, even disastrously, evident that as this nation streaks ahead at its breakneck pace, it cannot much longer cling to the same rough pioneer doctrines that carried it to its present material heights. The old frontier idea of producing armies of offspring to overcome infant mortality and push forward to conquer the continent is as discredited as bundling, witch-burning, and pond-dunking for shrews. Let all lovers of life plead for a new philosophy, a transformed social code, so that this nation and the world may survive.[3]

Dr. Will Durant noted that "a civilization is born stoic and dies epicurean." And Maeterlinck, in a rare moment of clairvoyance, set down the timing of that death when he suggested that "everything seems to foretell that Man, the last comer to this earth, will be the first to leave it." As a sort of addenda to these forebodings President Johnson recently declared: "So it remains for us, *who live in the summer of our greatness as a nation,* to preserve both the vision and the beauty which gave it rise." (Emphasis is ours.) This challenge indeed calls for a complete upheaval in our philosophy.

There are a number of great turrets studding the Gobi Desert—monuments once used as milestones—and they still stand sorrowfully pointing the way to the ancient city which has long since perished under Gobi's relentlessly shifting sands. To the pensive traveler who stands there alone, apart from the guide's bark and the milling of fellow tourists, there is transmitted a misted feeling of lonely terror. *Sic transit gloria mundi* was coined not for one city, or one people, or one time; it was designed for the profligate everywhere. As we have outsped any previous people in our wondrous advance to unrivaled opulence, so have we vastly compressed in time the signs of deterioration.

Perhaps the clearest and best expressed critique of Thomas Malthus' "dismal science," wherein he predicts that the population curve will eventually outrun the food curve and the world will starve, was written twenty-five years ago by William F. Ogburn and Meyer F. Nimkoff in their classic *Sociology.*[4] *First,* Malthus, they state, did not foresee agricultural and scientific advances which would forestall his predictions. *Second,* and more important by far, Malthus did not foresee that a rising cultural pattern, a changing and higher outlook, could and would in the years between 1860 and 1935 cut the Western World birth rate in half.

Considering the first contention, experts to date have concentrated their efforts on side-stepping Malthus' gloomy predictions by placing all their faith in scientific-technological advance. It has not been enough. It will never be enough. Even the most rabid anti-Malthusian cannot refute the simple truth that the geometric multiplication of people will sooner or later (and inexorably!) swallow up the arithmetic multiplication of food supplies. (Starting with 2, geometric progression brings us in 10 steps to 2,048; starting with 2, arithmetic progression brings us in 10 steps to only 22.) For that very obvious reason it is evident that all our thrusts toward the food solution have been (and can be no more than) feeble delaying actions to be swallowed up eventually as flood waters swallow up the carefully planted flood plains.

Now, to Malthus' *second "failure":* Here, and here only, rests the key to hope if we would thwart his augury of doom. Say Ogburn and Nimkoff:

> This falling birth rate [between 1860 and 1935] is a phenomenon of culture, and is not a function of biology. Malthus' doctrine was biological and quite inadequate as an account of cultural factors in this situation. *This one cultural trend of a falling birth rate has the potentiality of wiping away completely the doom to poverty* which followed from his analysis.[5] [Emphasis is ours.]

But once more history reversed itself. Even Ogburn and Nimkoff, keenly analytical as they were, did not dream that the birth rate would again soar and soar as fantastically as it has done since World War II.

How sophisticated, then, will we now show ourselves? Can we repeat the pattern that our ancestors voluntarily adopted after 1860? Can we again cut our birth rate in two and thwart the direful prognostications of Malthus for another century or so in the sun?

Tending to regard the population explosion as the exclusive offense of the benighted, undeveloped nation is fatal. "But they can afford seven children," we say smilingly of our own opulent overbreeders, even as we sorrowfully shake our heads at the seven children huddling about the mud shack in a Guatemalan jungle. It is no longer whether a family can afford seven children, but whether the finite, limited world (including a finite, limited United States) can any longer afford such excesses.

We are amused when we learn that some Asian and African tribes are so unenlightened that they make no connection between copulation and conception. We laugh aloud when returning American medics describe what happened to them in Guatemala. It seems that these medics were conducting a disease survey by sampling the blood of the nation's infants. They encountered stubborn, angry resistance and were at a loss to understand why. Finally, it came out that the Guatemalans thought the samples were being taken so that the Americans could find the healthiest babies to take home to the United States to eat! We shake our heads in patronizing disbelief when we cannot force the natives of the Middle East to give up their free-lancing propensities in favor of indoor plumbing. How can anyone ever teach birth control among people like that?

Yet it is beginning to become clear that in respect to ability to face this new challenge of too many people, the leaders of the underdeveloped nations are proving superior to those of the Western World. From India, for instance, comes a plea for help in sterilizing 2,500,000 men a year. And former Ambassador Chagla, observing the plight of his countrymen, cries out in wrath: "I am very impatient of the arguments which are advanced against birth control and family planning on the grounds of morality. What is this morality which condemns millions of children to poverty and destitution?" Viewing the problem on the "lighter" side is the Indian Minister of Agriculture, who insists that one of the most effective population controls we might proffer India is electricity. "In the state of Madras," he explains, "where 80 per cent of the villages possess electricity, the number of births is less than one half the national average. In dark villages they have no other amusement but procreation."

We need to remind ourselves that with births exceeding deaths in the world by more than thirty million a year, death control has indeed become a "bitter blessing." But it is the Western nations who delivered the unvaccinated world into this abnormal predicament; we with our little syringe have propelled them into this crisis. Despite our evident obligation to free them from the fateful consequences of our own interference, we are hindered not only by their sexual drive and primitive superstitions but by our own fumbling reluctance.

Actually, we are scarcely in a position to give the world lectures in population restraint. We have unflaggingly buttressed the sexual drive with billion-dollar commercial stimulation. Our ads belabor us day and night to keep ourselves bathed, pomaded, and perfumed for the sole purpose of alluring the other sex. We work, drive, eat, and play to the accompaniment of love ballads. Corn plasters, automobiles, and beer have been endowed with sexual appeal. We live in a fetid atmosphere of commercial eroticism. And we carry through. The intensity of our fertility worship (if not our birth rate) exceeds that of any of the "benighted" nations whose superstitions and cultural lag we so deplore. Our industrial complex still hails expansion in the diaper trade as the keynote of all good, and in the very same newspaper appear two items—one an article lamenting Brazil's 1966 baby bonus as "more bellies to fill" and the other the report of a board of directors of a large manufacturing concern rejoicing in the current United States birth statistics as "our wonderful crop of new customers."

While the Congress of the United States, in a mistaken effort not to tread in forbidden bedrooms, does the sword dance around the question of birth control, Japan solves its conundrum with energetic means, including abortions. Unenlightened Red China pushes a new drive for late marriages, contraceptives, and abortion to forestall a net increase of fifteen million annually. Twice the Chinese have called in Dr. Kan Majima, Director of the Tokyo Family Planning Association and inventor of a female contraceptive. Even China, avers the Tokyo dispatch, has come to appreciate that living standards can be lifted only if population can be kept at a level commensurate with national resources. Yet, adds Dr. Kan Majima, slyly, China actually has more undeveloped resources than the United States; if China judiciously balances its population against its production and waits, the tables will turn.[6]

We have considered the degeneration in our environment due to our heathen worship of quantity over quality. Now we learn that this same worship has begun to engender a decay in the quality of the citizenry as well. Proportionately we are reducing the intelligent element of our population and adding immeasurably to the "unplanners," the "frontal-lobe deficients," as Dr. William Shockley, Nobel Prize physicist, describes them.

These constitute the segment of our population incapable of rational planning, job-holding, or any constructive role. These are the public charges real or potential. Yet we keep on steeping these unfortunates in the fecundity myth and wantonly encourage their proliferation. Dr. Shockley, hypothesizing on the rot in the quality of our American population, indites the government as "scared . . . to pursue evidence that would permit establishing this as a fact or evaluating its significance."[7]

Meanwhile we are drifting: nearly one in four

American children—fifteen million—now lives in poverty. Almost half of all the children in families of five or more are listed among the poor—five times the rate for families with but one offspring.[8]

Families with four or more children have increased 60 per cent since 1951, and it is evident why John D. Rockefeller, III, philanthropist and chairman of the Rockefeller Foundation, has added his voice to the contention that population growth is second only to the control of atomic weapons as the major problem of our day. He told the United Nations Food and Agricultural Organization in Rome: "It is unfortunate that too few nations, including the United States, are fulfilling their responsibilities to their people by obtaining this knowledge. Each nation *has the duty* to summon competent, trained, responsible individuals to devote full time and energy to the study of population questions." [9]

The Lichty cartoon showing an American couple taking their bags out of a car with the caption: "That's no sound of a distant waterfall, dear! . . . just hundreds of dripping drip-dry shirts!" will no longer be so funny in 1975.

It is a cultivated unconcern for this future, and not ignorance, that forecloses birth restraint for the vast part of the American public. True, there is a slum, back-country, and mentally deficient minority which desperately needs and wants instruction in family control. But from the days when college girls used to soak their feet in scalding water for two hours to induce menstruation, to the modern pills, American women with an IQ equal to the total of their hip and bust measurement have known fairly well how to cope with the situation (and without abortions).

The point that overbreeding in America is largely the consequence of a state of mind, an attitude, has been proved innumerable times. Ogburn and Nimkoff demonstrated this phenomenon as it occurred in the nineteenth century. P. K. Whelpton, international population expert, Director of the Scripps Foundation for

Research in Population Problems, demonstrates it to us anew in the twentieth. Says Dr. Whelpton, in part: "depressions and prosperity have a big effect on the annual birth rate. . . . Now if you look at annual birth rates you will see that they were down during the depression; went back to the pre-depression figure in World War II, and then had a big upsurge after World War II." Since, then, married couples have, by voluntary action, lowered the birth rate by more than 50 per cent as it pleased them, we can assume that the majority of Americans are able to control the productivity of the bedroom. If minds were open to the subject and it were generally understood that we are breeding ourselves out of most of the good things of life, spontaneous controls would quickly appear.

Dr. Whelpton is only one of many scientists (whose numbers are increasing) of the opinion that this country's population has already passed its optimum for good living. In 1956 he voiced the opinion that perhaps the world can keep alive 4 or 5 billion by the year 2000 (the forecast now tops 6 billion) "on a level of living like that of India or China today." But if we would have the best of living for Americans, he suggested, we should enjoy a population not of more, but of from 25 to 75 million *less* persons than we *then* boasted.[10]

To reverse the trend, educational effort will have to be applied to the segment of the population who, because of low intelligence or emotional malfunctioning, have difficulty bearing in mind the connection between the sexual act and the crowded hovel. But even this depends for its success on the frame of mind that we develop in the population as a whole.

Says Robert C. Cook, President of the Population Reference Bureau in Washington, addressing the 15 million young women in the age group between twenty and twenty-nine: "If you choose the two-to-four-child family—the fashion set in the 1950's—then our nation is in for a baby boom of unprecedented magnitude

. . . [with] alarming implications." If, however, the young women of America choose the one-to-three-child family, then the nation may look forward to 300 million Americans, instead of 400 million in 2005, and "the shockwave hitting the schools and other vital areas will be less devastating."

Economist Sylvia Porter insists that whatever we do we are in for painful and costly overcrowding. But she, too, puts some confidence in the voluntary capacity to control as she cites the live births per 1,000 women of childbearing age, which have declined from 122.9 in 1957—the peak—to 99 in 1966.

On the narrower issue of access to family planning, the public viewpoint as usual streaks far ahead of congressional opinion. It indicates a readiness to reassess the big family syndrome. A 1965 Gallup Poll reports: "The proportion today in favor of the distribution of birth control information is the highest recorded in the twenty-nine years of the Gallup Poll's existence. The increase in favorable views over the last eighteen months is due largely to the opinions of Catholics." The question that was posed was this: "In some places in the United States it is not legal to supply birth control information. How do you feel about it—do you think birth control information should be available to anyone who wants it, or not?"

The results:

All the Population:

Should be	81%
Should not be	11%
No opinion	8%

Protestants:

Should be	82%
Should not be	10%
No opinion	8%

Catholics:

Should be	78%
Should not be	14%
No opinion	8%

As psychiatrst Dr. Marvin A. Block has noted with regard to alcoholism, it is social acceptance that is the primary factor in overbreeding. And conversely, social criticism is the most effective way to discourage it. Social criticism is growing fast, but the old myths persist in economic and petty official circles. Box 1776, Grand Central Station, continues to laud the 11,000 babies born every day in America as "more work, more jobs, more prosperity ahead, see free booklet." They do not mention "more schools, more buses, more institutions, more medical aid, more mental hospitals, more prisons, more accidents, more taxes, more crowding." We cannot seem, as yet, to cut ourselves free of the propagandists' tangle of umbilical cords.

Yet another Gallup Poll affirms that 64 per cent of the American public frankly favors the sterilization of women who have more children than they can provide for properly and who ask to be sterilized. The TV applause for "the wonderful mother of twelve" may change to hissing before too many years.

There are many proposals for shifting the thinking of the American public, for getting its mind off the subject of pullulation. Within the last few years American cities, spearheaded by Milwaukee, Wisconsin, have begun to seek federal funds to establish birth control clinics under the anti-poverty program. (It may be of more than passing significance that in Red China today couples who do not marry until over thirty are given an extra clothing ration, and those who have more than three children are refused cotton coupons for four, five, six, etc.) [11]

Professor Kenneth E. Boulding proposes in all seriousness "that a system of marketable licenses to have children is the only one which will combine the minimum of social control necessary to the solution of this problem with a maximum of individual liberty and ethical choice."

He goes on to explain:

Each girl on approaching maturity would be presented with a certificate which will entitle its owner to have, say, 2.2 children or whatever number would ensure a reproductive rate of one. The unit of these certificates might be the "deci-child," and accumulation of ten of these units by purchase, inheritance, or gift would permit a woman in maturity to have one legal child.

A respected scholar must be impressed by the desperateness of the situation to call for such measures as these. What disturbs us is that, added to the illegitimate, we shall have the poor "uncertified children" in our midst, to say nothing of the seven-tenths certified.[12]

Dr. Raymond B. Cowles of the Department of Zoology, University of California, favors a less complicated method and one with more political attractions. Dr. Cowles, as quoted in the *Sierra Club Bulletin,* suggests "an annual bonus administered on a monthly basis of an amount equal to or even more than present Federal tax exemption and that this bonus should go to each woman of reproductive age . . . who has had no children or was not pregnant during the bonus period." Because of the savings in education and general services required for each child such a reversal of tax policy would be economically feasible, says Dr. Cowles.

Nor does the Roman Catholic Church seek to take responsibility for the tragedy of overpopulation throughout the world. "The Church doesn't say breed, breed, breed. The Church endorses celibacy, continence, and the so-called rhythm method. . . . Actually, the Church is the greatest believer in birth control. . . . If everyone observed what the Church says on sex and control there would be a lot less population," declares Monsignor Luigi Ligutti, Vatican observer at the Vatican Council.

The Church is challenged as unrealistic in insisting that continence is the answer, but it is not unrealistic in its assumption that people are able to cut the birth rate if they are possessed of the determination to do so. Should the Church frankly denounce overbreeding,

the swarms of careless and indolent people hiding behind its frocks who have used it as an excuse for their
own lack of responsibility would be flushed out.
Whether the method of population control be the perfection of the rhythm practice or contraceptives, it
would seem at this crucial juncture in the progress of
humanity that it should be the results that condemn or
commend it. This may be the reason why, as
L'Osservatore della Domenica reports, growing Catholic opinion earnestly presses for the development of
those pills which regularize the fertility cycle and thus
make the rhythm method more reliable.[13]

The mumblings of new "reprisal" plans against
heavy breeders grow louder day by day. General William H. Draper, Jr., surveyor of the foreign aid program
for President Eisenhower—an experience that led him
into the vice-chairmanship of Planned Parenthood-
World Population—made this prediction in 1965. That
year, he said, "will be known in the future as the year
in which the American people reached a consensus
that the world population explosion represents a serious and imminent threat to the well-being of the
world, including the United States, and that something
has to be done to dispel the threat." [14] He is urging a
"new Manhattan Project—not to build another atomic
bomb which might destroy the world—but a grand and
noble project for knowledge and demographic understanding—a project to defuse the population bomb—
so that mankind does not multiply itself into oblivion."

We must concur with Professor Robert C. North,
political scientist of Stanford University, that "it is
not enough to have a pill. People must be willing to
take it—in many cases not merely to prevent the birth
of unwanted children, but also to prevent the birth of
deeply wanted, even longed-for children . . . an unhappy, even cruel, responsibility and sacrifice."

Much has been made of the very recent decline in
the national birth and fertility rates. In 1965 the baby
crop dropped below 4,000,000 for the first time since
1953. But even a 4 million baby crop is a terrific one,

with deaths totaling but 1.8 million a year. And as a trend of importance, the general figures are deceptive. They reflect an immense increase in the younger and older age groups, which have swollen the base figure on which birth rates are calculated. Warns Robert C. Cook, President of the Population Reference Bureau, "When this huge group of youngsters reaches child-bearing age, as it is now just beginning to do, this country [could] see a baby boom of unprecedented size." [15]

Everything depends, experts insist, on the "fertility pattern" chosen by "this upcoming surge of brides and mothers." Demographic experts wishfully believe that the young mothers, eye-witnessing the terrific strain now being put upon the high breeders of the 1950's as they struggle to put their brood through college,[16] are becoming more prudent. Experts do not denigrate "the pill" [17] but maintain that "human attitudes and decisions are the major factors."

It is already too late to dodge the dedication of great segments of our economy to food production, yet we can easily cease plugging "expansion," because the terrifying fact is that "expansion" will now—like it or not —jolly well take care of itself. Thus far in our history we have judged our success as a nation by our capacity to wring as much production as possible out of our environment without regard for what it can decently stand.[18] It is a harsh indictment to suggest that American passion for money has outrun love of country, but will someone come forth who can show "just cause" why this indictment should be withheld?

Today the land of our forefathers is an unhappy land—scalped, mauled, defiled, and poisoned. It has begun to turn on us in water shortages, in cancer, hepatitis, and virus plagues, in deafness, madness, personal degradation—and in a multitude of more subtle ways.

There is a fable about a dog that didn't catch the rabbit. He was asked why. "Well," explained the dog, "I was running for fun, the rabbit for his life." Where once we dawdled with nature preservation, with stream improvement, parks, recreational spaces, and the like with an eye toward communal "fun," we are now running for our lives. There is a difference. Our salvation lies in seeing it.

American fortunes today, large and small, are all built from the largesse of the land and its rich abundance, without which the most ingenious mind could not have created even a wheel spoke. How much, then, of our fortunes will we "plow back" to cleanse and redeem our benefactor the land?

The almost unearthly beauty of the primeval forests that once so charmed the eyes of Old World visitors is all but wiped out of existence, and forever. Those great oceans of trees in whose solitude "no one can stand unmoved," as the first Charles Darwin remarked of virgin forest, are no more. How much will we now expend to ransom their priceless remnants—the Olympic rain forests, the Northern Cascades, the Redwoods, the Minnesota border pines, and a few more—to pluck from the buzz saw and slash burner these last vestiges of our glorious wilderness past?

What pleasuresome vistas can man's hand create once the bulldozer has been corraled to its rightful place and beauty has been integrated into the contours of the land? How much joy of living can we add to our lives for fifty or sixty cents a head spent on roadside beautification? (It will astound you.) How much grief and pain can we avoid by replacing the distracting accident potentials of billboards for the shady solace of trees? What price shall we put on the shine in a child's eyes when first he glimpses the fragile beauty of a Florida Key deer? Or a wedge of greater snow geese piercing a Dakota sky? or a sparkling creek bearing the sign: "Swimming permitted on weekends"?

How much would we give for a rising water table in Texas and Colorado and Arizona, clean, rushing rivers in the great Northeast, a return of the bluebird to the Eastern Seaboard? How much to bring back to the Great Plains and mountains our vanishing national emblem, the bald eagle? to renew the exciting salmon runs and the shad and game fish of the Atlantic Coast, the deep-water trout and sturgeon in the Great Lakes? to bring back the joys of water sports and pleasure steamers to the Mississippi and the Hudson? to lift from shame, to regain national pride, in the storied Potomac? to save San Francisco Bay? to insure our national shrines?

Unless such matters as these become our passion and our priorities, we shall lose the very meaning of life even as we lose all honest pride as a people. And unless we find some way to control our pyramiding population, we shall have to cancel out our dreams forever as we bend to the grim and slavish task of grinding out new high protein formulas of rock, seaweed, sawdust, and, yes, *crude oil*.

Is this, then, to be the end of our worldly mission? Was it for this we vanquished our environment and came into our moment in the sun? Have we surrendered backbone even as we have surrendered beauty? Or can we still respond to Dr. Preston Bradley, famed Chicago pastor and unexcelled orator, who begs, "Let us, above all, and in all, and through all, let us upon the altar of our country place a sacrifice and stop treating that altar as a crib out of which to feed."

"We do not own the world," says Roy Phinney in *Vanishing Wildlife*. "Our place in it is merely leased to us by nature. If we persist in waging war against our natural landlord—if we continue in our efforts to reduce the world to a sterile desert—our lease will soon expire."

It is an illusion that our phenomenal plenty is a God-given birthright, a deserved recognition of our peculiar excellence as a people. This fantasy has blinded us to the reality that already we have passed our zenith. Only a powerful social effort involving the abandonment of aggrandizement as the national creed—in short, the acceptance of a totally new code of values —can bring us into equilibrium with our environment, and perhaps prolong our moment in the sun. The sacrifice must now be made, if not of much personal effort and much public money, then surely of more precious things even than these.

Sources and Additional Notes

Chapter One

Zenith

1. The potential (eventual) quantitative pinch on our economy is a reported lack of sufficient space on which to grow trees for the future, an unimagined contingency.

2. "One American may consume more paper in one trip to a supermarket than an inhabitant of East or South Asia may consume in several months. Gross annual consumption of paper and paper board has now reached about 40 million tons a year, about six times the paper consumption of any other industrial country, approaching one ton per family. In 1950 it had just reached 30 million tons, and in 1929 not even 15 million." *

3. Sylvia Porter, "Your Money's Worth," Albany (N.Y.) *Times-Union*, Oct. 13, 1965.

4. Alexander Campbell, "The Economics of Affluence," *The Nation*, June 2, 1962, p. 493.

5. In one of its continuing studies reported in the *Federal Reserve Bulletin* of March, 1964.

6. Chapter 3 of the *Annual Report of the Council of Economic Advisers,* transmitted to Congress in January, 1966, analyzes the problem of strengthening human resources from the point of view of productivity. Even here the ultimate focus is on making people more effective consumers.

---

* Hans H. Landsberg, Leonard L. Fischman, and Joseph L. Fisher, *Resources in America's Future: Patterns of Requirements and Availabilities 1960–2000* [Baltimore: Johns Hopkins Press, 1963], p. 170.

Chapter Two

Shadows at Noon

1. Arnold B. Barach, *U.S.A. and Its Economic Future,* a Twentieth Century Fund Survey (New York: Macmillan, 1964), p. 6.

2. "According to [the Social Security Administration's] projections, the continuation of the postwar birth rate to 2000 could produce a population up to 388 million persons [Table 5], the Social Security Administration's 'high' estimate." (Philip M. Hauser, *Population Perspectives,* Rutgers, 1960, p. 37, quoting *Illustrative Populations Projections,* Health, Education, and Welfare Dept. In this connection see *Population Growth and Development,* an International Conciliation periodical, by Jean Bourgeois-Pichat [New York: Carnegie, Jan., 1966]. See also the report of the National Academy of Sciences [May. 1965] in which eleven prominent scientists discuss high fertility as an American problem in comparison with the rest of the world.)

3. Copyrighted interview with *U.S. News & World Report,* November 28, 1958.

4. Hans H. Landsberg, Leonard L. Fischman, and Joseph L. Fisher, *Resources in America's Future: Patterns of Requirements and Availabilities 1960–2000* (Baltimore: Johns Hopkins Press, 1963).

5. Population problems of the Middle East are cogently discussed in *Land Reborn,* American Christian Palestine Committee, Apr.–May, 1960, pp. 4ff. An extremely interesting study on the effects of colonialism with regard to economic depression as it relates to population numbers is found in Folke Dovring's "The Opportunity to Multiply" in *The Journal of Economic History,* Dec., 1961, XXI, 4, pp. 599–612:

It is quite possible that economic conditions in North Africa are even more depressed than they would have been without the economic union with France—that is, in relation to popluation numbers; with an autonomous system, population growth might have been slower and more in balance with economic opportunities at large.

Increased security, health control, and opportunities for migration have often been countered in colonies by severe overpopulation along with a weakened spine.

6. Exclusive interview by Saville R. Davis, staff correspondent, *Christian Science Monitor,* October 4, 1965. Senator McGovern summarizes the inadequacy of our surpluses and also of our efforts to help feed the world's hungry and warns that our own security depends on equalizing food production and population—increasing the first and decreasing the second.

7. *Bioscience,* July, 1964, p. 5. Dr. Sears lucidly discusses the effectiveness of the ancient population controls in "The Rules Have Been Posted," Chapter 2, p. 20, of his small paperback *Where There Is Life* (New York: Dell, 1962).

8. *Population and Economic Planning, World Population and Resources: A Report,* London, 1955, offers the striking example of the almost total abolition of malaria in Ceylon by modern medicine. Ceylon's death rate slumped to the Western level; but its amazing birth rate remained high, with the result that the population is increasing at the rate of 2.7 per cent a year or thereabouts—twice as fast as India's. (p. 134.)

Chapter Three

The Hidden Price

1. The truism expressed by Philip M. Hauser (*Population Perspectives*, Rutgers, 1960, p. 66) that "greatly increased population means, all other things being equal, greatly reduced non-renewable natural resources per head, and operation of the law of diminishing returns as an offset to economics of scale," is perhaps one of the most disparaged great truths of all time.

2. Hans H. Landsberg, Leonard L. Fischman, and Joseph L. Fisher, *Resources in America's Future: Patterns of Requirements and Availabilities 1960–2000* (Baltimore: Johns Hopkins Press, 1963), p. 360.

3. Samuel H. Ordway, Jr., "Possible Limits of Raw-Material Consumption," an article in *Man's Role in Changing the Face of the Earth*, William L. Thomas, Jr., ed. (Chicago: University of Chicago Press, 1956), p. 989.

4. Arnold B. Barach, *U.S.A. and Its Economic Future*, a Twentieth Century Fund Survey (New York: Macmillan, 1964), p. 107.

5. *Ibid.*, p. 108.

6. "Esthetics and Economics," *Sierra Club Bulletin*, Sept., 1965, p. 5. A thought-provoking consideration of values other than commercial.

7. Barach, *op. cit.*, p. 112.

8. Landsberg *et al.*, *op. cit.* Landsberg incorporates charts of metal consumption for packaging—past, present, and projections for 1980 and 2000. For example, 1960 consumption of aluminum in foil and collapsible tubes per capita amounted to 1.41 pounds; the medium per capita projection of this metal for the year 2000 is 4.1 pounds. If dwindling tin supplies are replaced by steel (the first all-steel cans are on the market), the medium projection of

steel for "tin cans" will reach 6.08 million short tons by 2000. On the other hand, fiber consumption for the average American has remained on a plateau of 19 to 20 pounds per person per year since 1949. Nonetheless, the American consumes

> "twice as much as the Western European and four times as much as the resident of a country like India. Twenty pounds is enough for a man to outfit himself annually with something like a half dozen shirts, six sets of underwear, a suit, a pair of slacks, a dozen pairs of socks, and two sets of pajamas, and still have enough left over for ties and handkerchiefs. A woman could outfit herself with several skirts and blouses, several dresses, a half dozen pairs of hose, two nightgowns, a sweater, coat, bathing suit, and plenty of underwear." (p. 106.)

9. *Population and Economic Planning, World Population and Resources: A Report,* London, 1955, pp. 156, 322. In spite of the age of this report it reads, in urgency, much like many such reports today. Yet of the two rival "land-rich minorities" on either side of the Iron Curtain, the authors find the advantage in the race to rule the world with the U.S.S.R. because the Soviets "have a larger proportion of their non-renewable resources unexploited and have not yet begun to grow as dependent as the leading Western powers on remote sources of supply outside their full political control." (p. 318.)

10. U.S. Department of Agriculture, *Agricultural Situation* (Washington, D.C.: Government Printing Office), Jan, 1966, L, 1, p. 3.

11. Landsberg *et al., op. cit.,* p. 53. "But especially since the Second World War the United States has become a fairly large net importer of such basic items as crude oil and iron ore and has increased its imports of copper, lead, zinc, and certain other metals, which were already considerable." (p. 12) See trends of U.S. foreign trade in Figures 5, 6, and 7.

Chapter Four

Stoking Stomachs

1. On May 5, 1966, the President announced an increase in the allotted wheat acreage for 1967, an increase that would result in an additional supply of wheat equal to one year's total production.

2. "To provide a person with 3,200 calories a day for a year would at present take just a little over half an acre if the food were all in the form of bread, around two acres if it were milk, and more than ten acres if it were all beef." *

3. The detailed illustrated report compiled by W. H. Pawley of the Food and Agriculture Organization of the United Nations called *Possibilities of Increasing World Food Production,* Rome, 1963, despite a forced optimism, admits to disappointment at the current rate of progress and lack of hope that we can make the institutional advances necessary to meet the nutritional challenge. See pp. 5–8.

4. *Forbes Magazine,* Mar. 1, 1966, p. 20.

5. Joseph L. Fisher and Neal Potter diligently construct "escape hatches" from the pressure of supplying the world in a carefully constructed little volume entitled *World Prospects for Natural Resources* (Baltimore: Johns Hopkins Press, 1964).

6. After forecasting conditional continuation of raw material supply, Landsberg *et al.* remark: "Resource equality, however, is another question. Simply having enough oil, metals, land, and water would not spell a satisfactory life for most people." Of what use, they ask, is space when it

---

* Hans H. Landsberg, Leonard L. Fischman, and Joseph L. Fisher, *Resources in America's Future: Patterns of Requirements and Availabilities* 1960–2000 [Baltimore: Johns Hopkins Press, 1963], p. 89.

is comprised of burned-over forest land and "ugly and useless" abandoned strip mines? "The relationship of people to resources, which usually has been expressed in terms of quantity, needs to be restated for modern times to emphasize what is happening to the quality of resources." †

Says Philip M. Hauser (*Population Perspectives,* Rutgers, 1960):

"greatly increased population means . . . higher densities of population with accompanying gains in potential of interaction, range, and intensity of contacts, increased frictions, and greater tension and frustration in daily living. Growing population density, especially when accompanied by the increasing metropolitanization of population . . . has been accompanied irresistibly by greater governmental intervention into the economic and social spheres—expanded government functions on the national, state, and local levels." (pp. 66–67.)

The editors of *Population and Economic Planning* in their report *World Population and Resources* (London, 1955) comment:

"Intake of calories and fuel consumption a head can be measured, but the quality of human life is not measurable, and here, it seems, the harm done by unrestrained multiplication is at least equally great. A moderate number of human beings can be treated as individuals; an immense number can be treated only in crowds."

They add:

"The growing pressure of population on land and other resources is perhaps more closely reflected than is generally believed in the growing pressure of Governments of varying political complexions upon individual rights and liberties. Crowd psychology, uprootedness, the decay and destruction of ancient cultures and traditions, the growing encroachment on wild places important for amenity and for conservation of wildlife are only a few facets of the overriding need to feed, accomodate, and clothe more and more millions. Even the outlook and behaviour of people may be altered when they are increasingly herded together

---

† Landsberg *et al., op. cit.,* p. 18.

in congested urban or rural conditions. If human beings are to multiply, they must recognize that they are creating more regimentation and strain as well as children." (p. 304.)

7. *National Parks Magazine*, January, 1963, p. 10. This journal of the National Parks Association has in recent years published particularly thoughtful pieces on the space problem.

8. It is not uncommon for official pronouncements to underline the limitations of economic growth. "Economic policy," says the Council of Economic Advisers, "cannot make men wise, sympathetic, and cultured. But it can find ways to finance their schools, libraries, museums, and galleries." (*Economic Report of the President Together with the Annual Report of the Council of Economic Advisers* [Washington: Government Printing Office, 1965], p. 31.)

Chapter Five

Ecology—the Relentless Science

1. The process of interaction in the environment is traced and analyzed thoroughly in Part II of the monumental report of the International Symposium at Princeton entitled *Man's Role in Changing the Face of the Earth,* edited by William L. Thomas, Jr. (Chicago: University of Chicago Press, 1956). Among the major topics are such headings as the modifications of biotic communities, the alterations of climatic elements, and the ecology of wastes.

2. David Cushman Coyle, *The Ordeal of the Presidency* (Washington: Public Affairs Press, 1960), p. 208.

3. A descriptive discourse on ecological relationships is that of Philip L. Wagner, *The Human Use of the Earth* (Glencoe, Ill.: The Free Press, 1960), especially Chapter 3.

   Check Jack McCormick, *The Living Forest* (New York: Harper & Bros., 1959), for an analysis of the deciduous forest community.

   George K. Reid, *Ecology of Land Waters and Estuaries* (New York: Reinhold Publishing Corp., 1961), is a source that is rich.

   A highly informative text appropriate for the serious lay reader is that of Herbert C. Hanson and Ethan D. Churchill, *The Plant Community* (New York: Reinhold Publishing Corp., 1961.)

   Of a different sort and very thought-provoking is Joseph Harold Rush's *The Dawn of Life* (New York: Doubleday & Co., 1958), in which he suggests that man, by recklessly meddling with natural selection and natural processes, may have effectively checkmated his own evolution and mental and physical progress.

4. *Science,* Mar. 2, 1962, pp. 709ff.

5. A scholarly account through the "corridors of time" of

man's stewardship, or lack of it, is found on pages 115ff. of the report of the International Symposium, *Man's Role in Changing the Face of the Earth,* cited above.

6. Tom Gill, "Forest Pest Control," *Control and Wildlife Relationships: A Symposium,* Publication 897, National Academy of Sciences—National Research Council, Washington, D.C., 1961, p. 11.

7. *Science,* Mar. 2, 1962, p. 711.

8. Robert C. Cowen, "Why the Spider Waits in Vain," *Christian Science Monitor,* Dec. 1, 1964.

9. Marian Sorenson, "Hawks Help Man," *Christian Science Monitor,* May 2, 1964.

10. See R. MacDonald, "Death Road for the Condor," *Sports Illustrated,* Apr., 1964, pp. 39ff. Among a dozen such pleas for this raptor in recent popular journals.

11. Marshall T. Case, "Dead Trees—Vital Links in a Chain of Life," *Cornell Plantations,* XVIII, 2, Summer, 1962.

12. Report of a study by Dr. William A. Niering, Dr. R. H. Whittaker, and Dr. C. H. Lowe headlined "Extinction Perils Giant U.S. Cactus," in the *Christian Science Monitor,* Jan. 18, 1965, written by Ruby Zagoren.

13. "If We Slaughter a Bird . . . ," a review of *Our Animal Neighbors* by Alan Devoe with Mary Berry Devoe (New York: McGraw-Hill), in *National Humane Review,* June, 1963, p. 12.

14. Quoted by Malcolm Cowley in "The Writer As Craftsman," *Saturday Review,* June 27, 1964, p. 18.

15. *Sierra Club Bulletin,* Sept., 1965.

16. "Is Civilization Progress?" *Izaak Walton Magazine,* Nov., 1964.

17. Governor Rolvaag had the courage to veto 1965 bounty bills passed by the legislature. Minnesota has been practicing the wasteful system of paying bounties in the amount of $301,000 from fish and game funds each year. This money is now to be used by the counties for wildlife and habitat development—the positive rather than the negative approach in the "new conservation." Wisconsin's Conservation Department Director L. D. Voigt hails the state's recent elimination of the bounty system and declares that its yearly cost of $180,000 may now be put to-

ward "constructive fish and game projects—the most significant step forward . . . since the creation of public hunting and fishing grounds."

18. The Secretary of the Interior seeks an amendment to the Criminal Code to extend protective federal laws for the benefit of wildlife; among the benefactors would be the harassed Florida alligators, who "lose their hides" to poachers at the rate of $1 million a year. Women buying alligator bags and shoes unwittingly foster this racket.

19. *Man and Nature in America* (New York: Columbia University Press, 1965) gives a valuable picture incorporating a larger landscape.

Chapter Six

Space and Sprawl

1. Hans H. Landsberg, Leonard L. Fischman, and Joseph L. Fisher, *Resources in America's Future: Patterns of Requirements and Availabilities 1960–2000* (Baltimore: Johns Hopkins Press, 1963), p. 375.

2. *Ibid.*, p. 24.

3. "When the Century Clock Strikes Again," *Christian Science Monitor*, Sept. 22, 1960

4. See Hans Landsberg *et al.*, for tables of national park, monument, and recreation area visitors for the years 1960, 1980 (projected), and 2000 (projected), pp. 224ff. The editors comment:

> "the high level through 1980 simply projects past trends —specifically the period 1946–1960. If extended to 2000, this approach would yield what appear to be astronomically high figures; nearly 1 billion visits to the specified areas in the national park system by the year 2000 (over three visits each year by every man, woman, and child), and in the neighborhood of 9 billion visits each to the national forests and state parks (better than 2 visits per person each month." (p. 224.)

Those who question the acute need for a national redwood park might consider the "drive-to and walk-in" Muir Woods, which averages well over 1,000 visits *per acre* per year. Comment the editors. "The limits here seem to be set by the damage pedestrians may do to the ground by upsetting balances in the plant and ground-cover ecology." (p. 228.)

5. *Living Wilderness*, Summer, 1958, p. 5.

6. A description of our plight is depicted in Wilfred Owen's *Cities in the Motor Age* (New York: Viking, 1959), where in Chapter 2 he deals with "land pollution."

7. As quoted by George Alcorn: "Does California Need Agricultural Zoning?" an enlightening report on a new approach to agricultural space problems in the *Journal of the Commonwealth Club of California,* San Francisco, Mar. 17, 1958, p. 71.

8. "The Battle for Green Acres," Mar.–Apr., 1964, p. 81.

9. Latest reports from San Francisco, which has been desperately trying to avoid Los Angeles' fate, is that little "flea" cars are now in the first stages of development in an effort to decongest the highways leading into the city. These "fleas" will carry commuters from their homes to 36 peripheral stations where rapid transit trains will whizz them into the city's heart. The goal is a city devoid of cars and incoming highways that permit easy movement devoid of traffic snarls and halts.

10. "Esthetics or Economics?" *Sierra Club Bulletin,* Sept., 1965, pp. 3ff.

11. It is, however, the basis for a remarkable and well-illustrated handbook on the preservation of open space called *Stewardship: The Land, The Landowners, The Metropolis,* prepared by Charles E. Little and Robert L. Burnap for the Open Space Action Committee, 205 E. 42d Street, New York, N.Y. This is a "how to" manual, the outcome of experience and the inspiration for action.

12. *National Parks Magazine,* Mar., 1964, p. 5.

13. Write them, Washington, D.C. 20240, for Technical Publication I, *Federal Assistance to Outdoor Recreation, Available to States, Their Subdivisions, Organizations, Individuals.*

14. The "Wetlands Bill," so joyfully hailed when passed, has now reportedly "fizzled out" because a recalcitrant Congress failed to appropriate more than 15 per cent of the agreed funds.

15. Secretary Udall has reported with elation that sales of the Golden Eagle Passport in 1966 were up 400 per cent over 1965. For the Passport for the current year send $7.00 to the Bureau of Outdoor Recreation, Box 7763, Washington, D.C. 20044, and obtain access to 7,000 recreational areas.

Chapter Seven

The Great American Thirst

1. Report No. 29 of the Select Committee on National Water Resources, 87th Cong., 1st sess., Government Printing Office, Washington, D.C., Jan. 30, 1961. Also, *Water Resources Activities in the United States,* Select Committee Print No. 30, 86th Cong., 2d sess., Washington, D.C., 1960, pp. 48ff.

2. The concern is evidenced in the testimony on the Water Resources Planning Act before the Subcommittee on Irrigation and Reclamation of the Committee on Interior and Insular Affairs, 88th Cong., 2d sess., Mar. 23, 24, 26 and Apr. 20, 1964 (Serial No. 20).

3. See projected demands of 19 major drainage basins in the U.S. in *Has the United States Enough Water?* (Washington, D.C.: U.S. Government Printing Office), Cat. No. I 19.13:1797.

4. For other statistics, see Science Editor John Lear's "What Brought It On?" *Saturday Review,* Oct. 23, 1965, pp. 24ff.

5. The Science and Technology Office in the Executive Office of the President turned the high-powered talents of its Waters Resources Research Committee on the water problem recorded in *Federal Water Resources Program, Fiscal Year, 1966* (Washington, D.C.: Government Printing Office), Feb., 1965, Publication No. 3.

6. Wallace Stegner, "Myths of the Western Dam," *Saturday Review,* Oct. 23, 1965, pp. 29ff., offers thorough analysis.

7. But see Vincent Schaefer's "Artificially Induced Precipitation and Its Potentialities" in the Report of the International Symposium, *Man's Role in Changing the Face of*

the Earth, edited by William L. Thomas, Jr. (Chicago: University of Chicago Press, 1956), p. 607.

8. Glenn T. Seaborg of the Atomic Energy Commission predicts 500 million gallons of desalted water a day by 1980. *U.S. News & World Report,* Dec. 13, 1965, p. 100.

9. See "Desalinization Research Progressing at R.P.I.," Troy (N.Y.) *Record,* Feb. 5, 1966, p. B5.

10. "Boon to St. Thomas," *Christian Science Monitor,* Dec. 2, 1965.

11. *Bio-Technology: A New Approach to Our Water Problems,* pamphlet, Moraga (Calif.), 1964, p. 18.

12. *Ibid.,* p. 14.

13. For a contrast between an undisturbed river and an industrialized one—the Thelon in the Arctic and the Ohio —read the absorbing account of John E. Bardach, *Downstream: A Natural History of the River* (New York: Harper & Row, 1964).

14. See New York State Constitution Convention, 1894, revised record (Albany: Argus Co., 1900), 5 v.: *Report of the Special Committee on State Forest,* Vol. II, p. 201. Also see Richard F. Ward, "Catskills—Treasury of Water," *The Conservationist,* June–July, 1960, p. 20.

15. Michael Frome, *Whose Woods These Are* (New York: Doubleday & Co., 1962), pp. 14ff.

16. This is emphasized in the testimony before the Subcommittee on Irrigation and Reclamation of the 88th Cong., 2d sess., noted above.

17. *Crisis in Our Cities* (Englewood Cliffs, N.J.: Prentice-Hall, 1965).

18. John E. Bardach, *op. cit.*

Chapter Eight

Ravished Wonders

1. Stewart M. Brandborg, Executive Director of the Wilderness Society, *A Report*, Feb. 18, 1966, published by the Wilderness Society, 729 Fifteenth St., N.W., Washington, D.C.

2. See François Leydet, *Time and the River Flowing* (San Francisco: Sierra Club Press [Mills Tower], 1964).

3. For therapy of the soul one cannot do better than page back to John Muir, who in fresh and open terms relates the wilderness experience to civilized existence: *Our National Parks* (Boston: Houghton Mifflin, 1901).

4. "Grand Canyon: Reservoir of the Unknown," *Defenders of Wildlife News*, May, 1965, pp. 49ff.

5. Robert and Leona Rienow, "Chaos in the Redwoods," *Defenders of Wildlife News*, Dec., 1965, back cover; same authors, "Motive for Murder," *loc. cit.*, Jan.–Feb.–Mar., 1966, back cover; same authors, "The Betrayal," *loc. cit.*, June, 1966, back cover. See also "Anarchy Among the Redwoods," editorial, *National Parks Magazine*, Mar., 1964, inside front cover; "The Vanishing Redwoods: An Album" (a distinctive presentation), *Audubon Magazine*, Nov.–Dec., 1965, pp. 358ff.; Richard Sill, "Rumors Fly About Administration Plans for a Redwood Park," *Sierra Club Bulletin*, Mar., 1966, p. 18; Russell D. Butcher, "Redwoods Face a Race Against Time," *Audubon Magazine*, July–Aug., 1965, pp. 234ff. These are but samples of the many hundreds of articles embodying this critical subject. Probably one of the supreme photographic accomplishments of all time is Philip Hyde's and François Leydet's *The Last Redwoods*, published by the Sierra Club, Mills Tower, San Francisco, 1963.

6. "The Redwood Murder Case," California Redwood Association (mimeo), no date. The only living trees older

than the redwoods are some specimens of bristlecones (noted for their antiquity but not for their size or beauty). Borings had shown one 4,600 years old. Then in 1964 a scientist from the University of North Carolina was taking borings on what appeared to be a tremendously old tree. Having broken his borer he requested permission to cut down the tree with motives hardly distinguishable from the greed of a redwood lumberman. The U.S. Forest Service, under whose jurisdiction the tree was growing—even though it suspected that it was a record-breaker—to its eternal shame, acquiesced. And so a bristlecone, 4900 years old by ring count, poorly appreciated, succumbed to vandalistic curiosity, and the world was beggared for a statistic in a blue notebook.

7. Economist John Kenneth Deck has authored an impressive piece of research demonstrating how shortsighted the destruction of the coastal redwood would be. In *National Parks Magazine,* Feb., 1966, pp. 21ff., he considers the thousands of jobs made available in the development of a national park: the trails, access roads, and facilities, the maintenance, the large permanent park staff and general crews, as well as the unmatchable opportunities in tourism that national park status and publicity always bring. Because of the uniqueness and excitement of the redwoods he concludes that a national park making them accessible to the crowded millions of the future would assure the local citizenry of income more lucrative, and surely more secure, than any the lumbering industry might offer. However, the death of the big trees would mean the death of all hope of such a future. Especially interesting to the monetary-minded is the new survey by the American Society of Travel Agents, which discovered that states spend three times more for tourist promotion than for attracting industrial plants. There is a reason.

8. Marian Sorenson, "Florida Debates Everglades Project," *Christian Science Monitor,* Mar. 8, 1966.

9. "Many Shades of Confusion Riddle Everglades Problem," *The Miami Herald,* Jan. 31, 1966; "Let's Forget the Politics, Everglades Need Water," editorial, *The Miami News,* Jan. 25, 1966. Also, C. P. Idyll, "Freshwater Requirements of Everglades National Park," a study (unpublished), Institute of Marine Science, Univ. of Miami, Jan., 1965, obtainable from Superintendent, Everglades

National Park; William B. Robertson, Jr., "Inside the Everglades," *Audubon Magazine*, Sept.–Oct., 1965; reprints obtainable from the Society. C. P. Idyll, "Shrimp Need Fresh Water, Too," a paper presented at the Joint Convention of the Southeastern Fisheries Association and the Shrimp Association of the Americas, Miami Beach, June 22, 1956, Institute of Marine Science, Univ. of Miami.

10. *New York Times*, Aug. 10, 1960; Feb. 11, 1961; Nov. 12, 1961.

11. Marian Sorenson, "Conservation and the Corps," *Christian Science Monitor*, Nov. 30, 1964.

12. A valuable overall picture is that of Gladwin Hill, "The Great and Dirty Lakes," *Saturday Review*, Oct. 23, 1965, pp. 32ff.

13. "Lake Erie," Cleveland *Plain Dealer*, June 30, 1965.

Chapter Nine

Flight into Eternity

1. "The Economics of Rampart Dam," May, 1965, pp. 46ff.

2. *Izaak Walton Magazine* editorial, Oct., 1964.

3. *Christian Science Monitor,* Oct. 16, 1935.

4. Charles Hillinger, *Los Angeles Times,* June 13, 1965.

5. Professor Mario Girolami, authority in tropical and infectious diseases at the University of Rome, Italy. Interesting indeed in connection with the annual terror campaigns against this or that animal or bird are the recent findings of the Southern Medical Association that a human bite can be as dangerous as a snake bite or a dog bite. Even the accidental bite of a baby was found capable of producing a serious infection. ("Speaking of Your Health," Apr. 2, 1966, Hearst release, Lester L. Coleman, M.D., columnist.)

6. *National Parks Magazine,* Oct., 1965. From 16 kinds of American grizzly bears we have permitted only two kinds to survive and these on a very shaky footing. The sins are not only American but universal and the excuses for slaughter weak. Rhinoceroses are being exterminated in Africa by poachers because of the presumed value of their horns "ground and sold as an aphrodisiac." Giraffes are killed for their tails, used as fly swatters. To control the tsetse fly, vaccination of humans is overlooked in a Rhodesian campaign to exterminate all wildlife that might foster it.

7. News release, U.S. Department of the Interior, Nov. 27, 1964.

8. Fairfield Osborn notes that should priceless art treasures like the Taj Mahal and the Louvre be destroyed, man could reproduce much of their detail. "Not so the arts of

nature—the animals that adorn the earth. It has taken eons of evolution, not mere years, to create them, and their creation is far beyond the powers of man to duplicate. The destruction of an animal species is irrevocable." (From a speech given in New York City, as reported in the *New York Times,* Oct. 27, 1963, pp. 24ff.)

9. The roll call of the near extinct is sadly world-wide. A species of wild oxen called the kouprey and of which only 1,000 remain, are left to struggle in Cambodia. A primitive reptile, the tuatara, is in serious trouble. The orangutan of tropical Asia is down to 3,000 and dwindling. The great panda of northern China is on the critical list. The mountain gorilla of the Congo and western Uganda may not survive. The Survival Center of New York City, a special zoo, is looking for one of the last 56 wild horses (Mongolian Prjevalsky horse), a mountain zebra from the Cape Province (of which there are only 82), a Persian wild goat (if one can be found), and one of the last 30 or 40 Arabian oryxes. The list is tragically long.

10. *Mammals of North America,* (New York: Macmillan, 1958), treats the "wild dogs" most fascinatingly. These latest wolf estimates are contained in *Preliminary Study of the Distribution and Numbers of Cougar, Grizzly, and Wolf in North America* (New York: Zoological Society), Sept., 1964, p. 144.

11. The *coup de grâce* for a species can well come from the last frantic efforts of the zoo and museum keepers to preserve the specimen for science. The Noah's Ark movement (Wildlife Survival Centers) to save near extinct species, commendable in motive, is unfortunate because it salves the conscience of predatory man.

12. Address: 5502 Markland Drive, Los Angeles, California. Our last communication with the Committee and Mrs. Edmiston tells us that a movement is afoot to push the elk onto San Luis Island and thus make the proposed duck refuge serve double purpose as an elk habitat as well. "The manipulated swampland of the San Luis Island is a great place for ducks—not Tule Elk," says the Tule Elk Committee. The word "tule" is apparently a misnomer, leading many "well-meaning men into a proposal for an unnatural environment for the Tule Elk which is without scientific justification."

13. Allan Eckert, "The Vanishing Americans," *American Legion Magazine,* May, 1961, pp. 18.

14. D. J. Nelson, noted wildlife photographer, has produced probably the most remarkable film in existence of the last manatees in his "Inherit the Wild" (Audubon Lecture Series).

15. "U.S. Moves to Protect Rare Bird," special to the *New York Times,* June 25, 1964.

16. The character of the problem of wildlife survival has changed rather markedly. The nature of man's predation has altered. Today man with his increasing numbers elbows wildlife out of its habitat and contaminates its food supply with environmental pollution and poisoning.

Recognition of this fact was made by Secretary Stewart L. Udall, who appointed an Advisory Board of Wildlife Management consisting of five eminent conservationists headed by Aldo Starker Leopold of the University of California. Dr. Leopold's twenty-three-page report before the 28th North American Wildlife and Natural Resources Conference marked a milestone in the handling of our heritage and even in the organization of the Department of the Interior.

Basic to its philosophy was a recommendation to restore the natural communities of plants and animals in the national parks and the belief that policy goes beyond mere protection to recognition of enormous complexities. The committee asked for the controlled use of fire and the curtailed use of insecticides. (*New York Times,* Mar. 5, 1963, p. 16).

17. *The Red Book* of the World Wildlife Fund, which has been dubbed "The Doomsday Book," is a volume of 500 pages describing endangered species of mammals, fishes, birds, reptiles, amphibians, invertebrates, and plants.

18. Reprinted in the *Christian Science Monitor,* May 2, 1965.

19. In December of 1963 Dr. Ratcliffe flushed peregrines from their nests in Dumfriesshire Hills of Scotland. He suspected at least one of the pair was suffering from toxic chemicals and had previously destroyed her clutch.

Under license he took one of the bird's four eggs and found by analysis that it contained six identifiable kinds of agricultural pesticides: lindane, heptachlor, heptachlor epoxide, dieldrin, DDE, and DDT.

Returning to the nest some months later he found the peregrine stepmothering a brood of young kestrels (small falcons).

It is this same British scientist who blamed pesticides for recent cases of perversion, dementia, and self-destruction among British birds of prey. (*New York Times,* Dec. 29, 1963).

20. *The Lookout,* Oct., 1965.

21. Letters to the Editor, *New York Times,* June 15, 1964.

22. Dr. Alden H. Miller, Director, University of California's Museum of Vertebrate Zoology at Berkeley, aided by naturalist-ranchmen Eben and Ian McMillan, has presented a thoroughgoing study of the condor situation: "The Current Status and Welfare of the California Condor," a paper presented at the 60th annual convention of the National Audubon Society, Nov. 7, 1964.

23. Department of Interior release, Aug. 10, 1965.

24. Mar., 1964. Apparently ignoring the pleas of the naturalists, the Federal Communications Commission, it has just been announced, has on wholly technical grounds of interference and competition and relationship to air lanes authorized 2,000-foot towers. (*New York Times,* July 12, 1966, p. 87C.)

25. *National Parks Magazine,* Feb., 1966, p. 18.

Chapter Ten

The City Syndrome

1. Sergius Chermayeff and Christopher Alexander, "The Disappearance of Nature," *Current*, Oct., 1963, p. 59, extracted from their *Community and Privacy* (Garden City, N.Y.: Doubleday, 1963). In *Population Perspectives* Philip M. Hauser considers the immense cultural advantages of the city against the equally immense disadvantages. On the one hand, the individual is freed in great part from the constraints of tradition and convention imposed upon him by small-town living. New channels of self-expression and for the shaping of his destiny are open to him, thus promoting ingenuity and creativity. "The 'city mentality' has been characterized by objectivity, sophistication, utilitarianism, and rationalism. . . . But the same factors in the urban environment that are responsible for the great achievements . . . also produce social and personal disorganization." The restraints of the family, church, community, and school fade away, and frictions between man and the social order become overwhelming. (pp. 133–34.)

2. Chermayeff and Alexander, *loc. cit.*

3. But the world-famed Vienna Woods, valued as a natural air conditioner and recreational outlet, is a current victim of urban forces. The Woods are being hacked apart for summer homes by a newly mobile population now equipped with 300,000 automobiles. (*Christian Science Monitor*, Sept. 25, 1964.)

4. In connection with lack of humanness, Lewis Mumford (*The City in History: Its Origins, Its Transformations, and Its Prospects*, New York, 1961), takes the city apart in his daring and uncompromising manner. We have sacrificed all finer things, "our urban birthright, for a sorry mess of motorcars." But worse is the "deep contempt for organic processes that involve maintaining the complex partner-

ship of all organic forms." Man's relation to air, water, soil, and all his organic partners should not be constricted or effaced, but rather deepened and extended.

> "The popular technology of our time devotes itself to contriving means to displace autonomous organic forms with ingenious mechanical (controllable! profitable!) substitutes. . . . Their 'city of the future' is one levelled down to the lowest possibility of active, autonomous, fully sentient life: just so much life as will conform to the requirements of the machine. As we shall see, this would only carry the present forces at work in Megalopolis to their ultimate goal—total human annihilation." (p. 527.)

Elizabeth Green, editor of *Man and the Modern City* (University of Pittsburgh Press, 1963), in speaking of the pressured, "beat," overwhelmed cityite, says: "We have coined a scientific term for this desperate condition—information input overload." (p. 60.)

5. In contrast, back in 1939 Robert E. Park could write as he compared plant communities with human communities, "it is a comfort in these days of turmoil and strife to realize that society and human beings, when in repose, do retain and exhibit some of the dignity and serenity of plants." For pioneer thought in this field see his *Human Communities: The City and Human Ecology* (Glencoe, Ill.: The Free Press, 1952).

6. For the political and criminal implications of the megalopolis see Robert and Leona Train Rienow, *The Lonely Quest: The Evolution of Presidential Leadership*, Chapter 16, "In the Shadow of the Skyscrapers," pp. 235ff.

7. *U.S. News & World Report*, Mar. 2, 1966, p. 16.

8. Sally Carrighar, *Wild Heritage* (Boston: Houghton Mifflin, 1965), p. 174.

9. David E. Lilienthal notes how overpopulation, especially in the United States cities, has threatened the quality of life in a *New York Times Magazine* piece called "300,000,000 Americans Would Be Wrong," Jan. 9, 1966, p. 25.

10. Nor is Suburbia a solution. In the eyes of Mumford it suffers considerably in comparison with the city proper, for all the latter's woes. Not only is the suburbanite without restraining heritage, but he becomes "imprisoned by

the very separation that he has prized: he is fed through a narrow opening: a telephone line, a radio band, a television circuit." Elizabeth Green. editor of *Man and the Modern City* (cited above), adds that Suburbia, in robbing the self of a variety of experience and diversity, robs man of his powers of perception and discrimination in the area of making a choice. (p. 124.)

11. Michael E. Schiltz, "Social Action Must Adjust to the Demands of the New Age," *Social Order*, June, 1963.

12. Martin L. Gross, *The Doctors* (New York: Random House, 1966).

13. "The Jungle of Hugeness," *Saturday Review*, Mar. 1, 1958, p. 11.

14. René J. Dubos, "Beyond Traditional Medicine," *Harper's Magazine*, Oct., 1960, p. 167.

15. "Reducing the Hazards of Birth," *Harper's Magazine*, Jan., 1964, pp. 32–33.

Chapter Eleven

The Ultimate Horror—a Septic World

1. Hearings Before a Subcommittee of the Committee on Government Operations, 88th Cong., 2d sess., 8 vols., Feb.–May, 1964; Supt. of Documents, Government Printing Office, Washington 25, D.C. See also Robert and Leona Train Rienow, "Last Chance for the Nation's Waterways," *Saturday Review,* May 22, 1965, pp. 35ff.; and Gladwin Hall, "The Great and Dirty Lakes," *Saturday Review,* Oct. 23, 1965, pp. 32ff.; also, "The Crisis in Water, Regional Reports," *Saturday Review,* Oct. 23, 1965, pp. 35ff.

2. This graphic description was furnished by Dr. Evan R. Collins, President, State University of New York at Albany, following his 1965 sojourn in Afghanistan.

3. Long Islanders to whom aquifers mean their very lives run a risk of the contamination of underground waters because of interlaced cesspools and wells. This is a common hazard of both suburbia and exurbia. No wonder Suffolk County Executive Dennison was stunned by a State Supreme Court ruling that undid a county ordinance which provided for a minimum distance of 100 feet between wells and cesspools.

While we as a society become enmeshed in legal entrapments the pollution deepens. And a seminar sponsored by the American Institute of Physics at the Shoreham Hotel in Washington heard Dr. Richard Kassander of the University of Arizona admit, "We're really kind of losing the race" to grow food and increase water faster than the population grows. (Evert Clark, "Scientists Fear Nature May Win," *New York Times,* Mar. 15, 1966, p. 19.)

A conference on pollution held at Davis, California, in April, 1966, and sponsored by the Public Health Service, University of California, and California Water Agencies was called to assess the danger of underground seepage of nitrates, which are among the main elements in agricultural fertilizers, and their accumulation in wells.

4. A report of a survey, also in Suffolk County, of 120 launderettes indicated a combined waste discharge of over 150 million gallons a year. This and a load of 500,000 pounds of detergents is released without treatment to a subsurface leaching pool. From there it infiltrates the ground waters and "moves as a ribbon-like slug" in a southeasterly direction. There is almost no dilution, and the natural purification factors are virtually halted. For the whole story see John M. Flynn, "Launderette Waste Treatment System" *Water & Sewage Works,* Feb., 1963, CX, 2, pp. 83–84.

5. Pursuant to Senate Resolution 48, 86th Cong., Jan. 30, 1961, Supt. of Documents, Government Printing Office, Washington 25, D.C.

6. Even the sink garbage grinder adds to our peril as it enriches the sewers with food and creates optimum conditions for the multiplication of rats and the pestilence they carry.

7. The glittering and ever dramatic city of New York is under state orders to stop pouring raw sewage into the East and Hudson Rivers. It continues to plead poverty for its delinquency. We seem to have "progressed" beyond the point where ordinary and elemental disposal is feasible. Even the technicians pose the professional question, "How Do You Purify the Mississippi?" (*Engineering News,* Apr. 30, 1964, p. 15.)

8. *Izaak Walton Magazine,* Feb., 1964, p. 9. On the other hand, some advance is noted in the increased interest in organic polymeric flocculants for primary sewage treatment. Primary treatment, which is merely a settling process to reduce suspended solids, removes some 35 per cent of what is called the "biological oxygen demand"—that is, the amount of oxygen needed in a stream to counteract a certain amount of sewage. The polymers, costing about $7 per million gallons for use, will increase this 35 per cent to 60 per cent. Dow Chemical Company calls this "instant abatement." For a discussion of the potentials of the polymers see *Chemical and Engineering News,* Oct. 10, 1966, p. 40.

9. Dr. Ingraham gives his source as W. C. Heuper and W.

W. Payne, "Carcinogenic Effects of Adsorbates of Raw and Finished Water Supplies," *American Journal of Clinical Pathology*, XXXIX, May, 1963, p. 475.

10. Sept., 1965.

11. Belatedly, some action is being taken. The American Shipbuilding Corporation, it was announced in March, 1966, installed the first two of six Biogest marine sewage disposal units on U.S. Steel Corporation bulk carriers steaming the Great Lakes. The system uses aerobic bacteria to treat wastes.

12. John Allen Long, "Lake Michigan Accord Hailed," *Christian Science Monitor*, Feb. 16, 1966.

13. Discussion of eutrophic pollution is found in the *Interim Report: Pollution of Lake Erie, Lake Ontario, and the International Section of the St. Lawrence River*, U.S. & Canadian International Joint Commission, Dec., 1965.

14. Midwest Report, "Solid Waste," *Christian Science Monitor*, July 9, 1965.

15. Passed and signed into law, Oct., 1965.

16. The National Sciences Academy Pollution Committee under Dr. A. Sphihaus filed its so-called Sullivan report with the White House in the spring of 1966. The group of experts concluded that (1) man must find a way to cycle wastes back into the economy; (2) by 1980 the volume of sewage and other organic wastes will overwhelm twenty-two of our chief rivers purging them of oxygen in the low-stream flow; (3) there must be a bold federal program; (4) great complexes for processing sewage, purifying water, and doing other related work will dot the landscape.

17. Aug., 1956.

Chapter Twelve

38 Cigarettes a Day

1. Even pesticide residues have become a contaminant, according to A. W. Breidenbach, "Pesticide Residues in Air and Water," *Archives of Environmental Health,* June, 1965, pp. 827–30.

2. The technical literature is developing with articles such as M. B. Gardner's "Biological Effects of Air Pollution: Lung Tumors in Mice," *Archives of Environmental Health,* Mar., 1966, pp. 305–13; and R. B. W. Smith, "Tokyo-Yokohama Asthma: An Area Specific Air Pollution Disease," *Ibid.,* June, 1964, pp. 805–17. T. M. Gocke explores the field with a study called, "What Is the Role of Air Pollution as a Cause of Disease?" *American Journal of Public Health,* Jan., 1964, pp. 71–78.

3. C. W. Griffen, Jr., "America's Airborne Garbage," *Saturday Review,* May 22, 1965, pp. 32ff.

4. For a full discussion of the deadly qualities of ozone and other contaminants, see *The Breath of Life* by Donald E. Carr (New York: Norton, 1965), Chapter 7, p. 91.

5. John T. Middleton and Diana Clarkson, "Motor Vehicle Pollution Control," *Traffic Quarterly,* Apr., 1961, pp. 306–17. See also N. Kendall, "Atmospheric Pollution: Reducing Pollution from Motor Vehicles," *Automobile Engineer,* Nov., 1965, pp. 485–87.

6. Dr. Reid O. Bryson of the University of Wisconsin's Center for Climatic Research participating in a seminar on atmospheric physics speculates that man with his dust and pollution may have affected the climate. "Man is so industrialized, urbanized, mechanized that he has become as important as natural phenomena in the modification of weather," said this specialist. Then he added, "Every city

is putting out as much particulate matter as a volcano." (*New York Times,* Mar. 15, 1966, p. 19.)

7. Perhaps the most authoritative, objective, and yet understandable survey of contamination of the air—from fluorides to radioactivity—is the notable report of the Air Conservation Commission of the American Association for the Advancement of Science entitled *Air Conservation* and published by the Association, Washington, D.C., in 1965.

A report on what industry is doing to combat smog may be found in *Chemical and Engineering News* of Oct. 10, 1966, p. 33. Recognition of the importance of the nitrogen oxides and the highly reactive attributes of the olefins shows progress in analysis. Interesting also is the enigma of exactly what causes eye irritation. "Significant eye irritation occurs prior to and after the time of maximum nitrogen dioxide concentration, but is low or absent at maximum concentration. End products of the photochemical reactions are not sufficient to account for both periods of eye irritation, and the known end products do not account for the later period of eye irritation," said W. J. Hamming of the Los Angeles Air Pollution Control District. It also appears that the maximum rate of hydrocarbon disappearance "doesn't relate either to maximum formation of ozone and aldehydes or to eye irritation." It is evident that research in this field is just in its infancy.

8. *Science News Letter,* May 25, 1957, p. 325.

9. *Knickerbocker News* (Albany, New York), Nov. 19, 1958.

10. Lichty, "Grin and Bear It," New York *Journal-American,* Aug. 4, 1957.

11. The seventh annual air pollution research conference was held in Los Angeles, February 10–11, 1965, and the texts of its papers appeared in the *Archives of Environmental Health,* Feb., 1965, pp. 141–388. In Great Britain, where "smoke abatement" has long been acute, the National Society of Clean Air held its thirty-first conference October 20–23, 1965, reported in *Chemistry and Industry,* Nov. 21, 1964, p. 1947.

12. "Neglected Assets . . . Clean Air and Water," *Current Municipal Problems,* Nov., 1963, pp. 103–09.

13. Walter Sullivan's "Polluted Air Said to Raise Death

Rates," (*New York Times,* Nov. 13, 1963), capsuling report by Division of Air Pollution of U.S. Public Health Service and Vanderbilt University School of Medicine covering a twelve-year period ending in 1960, is recommended. Consult L. D. Neidberg, J. J. Schueneman, P. A. Humphrey, and R. A. Prindle, "Air Pollution and Health: General Description of a Study in Nashville, Tenn.," *Journal, Air Pollution Control Assn.,* June, 1961, pp. 289–97.

14. A thoroughgoing study by Dr. Malcolm L. Peterson called "Environmental Contamination from Nuclear Reactors" appears in *Scientist and Citizen,* Nov., 1965, a publication of the St. Louis Citizens' Committee for Nuclear Information. With scientific precision it details the sources of pollutants and the areas of ignorance in which we are operating.

15. U.S. Senate Air Pollution Study under Ron M. Linton, staff director of the Senate Public Works Committee, as reported in the *New York Times,* Oct. 25, 1963, p. 62.

16. Lung cancer, once almost unknown, reached a new high of 4,000 deaths in 1935. Since then, it has literally skyrocketed. Today about 43,000 Americans die each year from this one cause, reported the U.S. Public Health Service in 1966.

17. Mr. Duval speaking to George R. Reiss in an exclusive interview for the *Christian Science Monitor,* June 22, 1964.

18. Dr. James P. Lodge of the National Center for Atmospheric Research is reported to have observed that what man does to pollute the air and similar problems can only be met by population control. (*New York Times,* Mar. 15, 1966, p. 19.)

19. Donald E. Carr (*op. cit.*) presents the case for and against the gas turbine engine (Chapter 11, p. 139), as well as much more enlightenment on the comparative values of the fuel cell and electric storage battery as replacements for the internal combustion engine.

Chapter Thirteen

Crisis in Beauty

1. John A. Fenton, special to the *New York Times*, July 21, 1957.

2. Copyrighted interview, *U.S. News & World Report*, Nov. 30, 1964, p. 84.

3. Joseph W. Penfold in the *Izaak Walton Magazine*, Feb., 1965, p. 20.

4. A CBS Documentary Report on Sept. 14, 1965.

5. There is a full-scale attack on the national parks with Exhibit "A"—what is obviously a "timber-grab by the lumber interests"—the proposed cutting of 69,000 acres of virgin forest from the Olympic National Park See "Report from the Executive Director," The Wilderness Society, Feb. 18, 1966.

6. Remarks of President Lyndon B. Johnson to the White House Conference on Natural Beauty, White House release, May 25, 1965.

7. H. L. Mencken once said he had spent his life watching the growth of the roadside jungles in our nation and had been forced to the gloomy conclusion that the American people do not merely tolerate ugliness, but have a positive passion for it.

8. Mrs. Lyndon B. Johnson gives the beauty program primary social relevance. She says: "When I go into the poorest neighborhoods, I look for the flash of color—a geranium in a coffee can, a window box against the scaling side of a tenement, a border of roses struggling in a tiny patch of open ground. Where flowers bloom, so does hope —and hope is the precious, indispensable ingredient without which the war on poverty can never be won." (Address before the Luncheon at the Annual Convention of

the Associated Press Managing Editors Association, White House release, Oct. 1, 1965.)

9. There is a symbolism in the story from Germany that the air, polluted by sulphuric acid from the industrial Ruhr, is corroding the exterior of the Cologne Cathedral. The contention of these forces is universal, but the driving culture of the new world has aggravated the corrosion.

10. Brochure published by the Izaak Walton League of America (1326 Waukegan Rd., Glenview, Ill.), entitled *The Boundary Waters Canoe Area* (no date), presents all factual information and maps.

11. Quoted by Walter Boardman, "What Is the Forest Preserve?" Speech before the Constitutional Council for the Forest Preserve, Schenectady, N.Y., Mar. 12, 1965.

12. Dr. Fay Welch, special lecturer at the School of Forestry, Syracuse University, N.Y., has authored an interesting paper on the subject titled "Deer Management in the Forest Preserve Within the Provisions of Our State Constitution," which he read at the 30th annual convention of the New York State Conservation Council at Monticello, N.Y., on October 4, 1963. David L. Newhouse of the Adirondack Mountain Club incorporated it into an article for the May–June issue of the organization's magazine, *Adirondack*, pp. 45ff.

13. The historian Vernon Parrington called the exploitation the "great barbecue" of resources.

14. Remarks by Mrs. Lyndon B. Johnson at the 12th annual meeting of Keep America Beautiful, Inc., Oct. 7, 1965.

15. Some of the story is told gracefully and worshipfully by Stewart L. Udall in his *The Quiet Crisis* (New York: Holt, Rinehart & Winston, 1963), Chapters 4, 6, 7, 8, 9, and 10.

Chapter Fourteen

The Redemption of Beauty

1. How well and effectively this new emphasis on beauty permeates the bureaucracy is in doubt. Perfunctorily each agency produces a five-page pamphlet of platitudes on beauty that it may have a toehold in the door to the President's favor. There is solace in the knowledge that ensconced in each agency is a small phalanx of supporters of beauty who now have standing, and perhaps even status, in promoting programs with an aesthetic emphasis.

2. Statement by the President, Office of the White House Press Secretary, release, Oct. 3, 1965. For a detailed statement see remarks of Edward C. Crafts, Director, Bureau of Outdoor Recreation, Department of Interior, before the Outdoor Recreation congress for the Greater Pacific Northwest, Wanatchee, Washington, Department of Interior release, Apr. 1, 1965.

3. Even a study that focuses on material sufficiency provides us with this observation:

> "Thus policymakers must weigh *ecological and esthetic considerations in the balance along with economic and technological factors,* as a matter of promoting the public welfare in a broad sense. Further efforts to bring these considerations sensibly within the ambit of economic analysis, perhaps under the heading of welfare economics, are worth making." *

4. President Johnson's Message on Natural Beauty to the Congress of the United States, Feb. 8, 1965, pp. 1, 2.

5. Remarks of Stewart L. Udall, "Conservation and the

---

* Landsberg *el al., Resources in America's Future: Patterns of Requirements and Availabilities 1960–2000* (Baltimore: Johns Hopkins Press, 1963), p. 51.

Good Life," at the New Hampshire Governor's Conference on Outdoor Recreation, Concord, N.H., Apr. 20, 1965, Department of Interior release, Apr. 21, 1965.

6. Remarks by Mrs. Lyndon B. Johnson to National Council of State Garden Clubs and American Forestry Association, Jackson Hole, Wyoming; release, Sept. 7, 1965.

7. Launched to give community emphasis to the natural beauty movement is the America the Beautiful Fund. The executive director, Paul Bruce Dowling, writes us:

> "The America the Beautiful Fund of the Natural Area Council makes *incentive grants* to individual or group programs starting unique projects for the preservation of land and its natural beauty. Eighteen such grants were made in its first year of operations. Write them at 219 Shoreham Building, Washington, D.C., 20005, for informative leaflets on the work of the Fund."

8. Remarks before the Greater Vermont Association at Stowe, Vermont, Department of Interior release, Oct. 22, 1965.

Anthony Wayne Smith, President of the National Parks Association, asks for a national commission "composed of policy-minded persons outside the government." It would

> "re-examine the place and functions of the Army Engineers and the Bureau of Reclamation in the Federal Government power structure; a spotlight might be turned on the combinations of construction contractors, building and machinery supply manufacturers, municipal and agricultural land speculators, which are part of the vicious circle which perpetuates these agencies, to say nothing of the self-perpetuational propensities of the bureaucracies themselves, military and civilian. The result might be the abolition of these agencies or their firm subordination in a purely operational function to some such national policy agency as the new Water Resources Council."

Many other concerned persons are asking why technicians, such as engineers, should be makers of public policy? Why single-drive technology experts in any line should be considered competent to judge what is best for the public weal and to utter ultimatums and make decisions that will affect the whole of the society and the environment for all time to come? On the other hand, what we also need, according to Dr. James Rhyne Killian, Jr., Chairman of the Board of the Corporation of Massachusetts Institute of Technology, is a new breed of engineers, a revoltionary new engineering philosophy: "Simon Ramo has called it 'the greater engineering'—deeply committed and sensitively attuned to the humanistic goals of our society. This kind of engineering, as a tie between science and the humanities, stands for a technology shaped, disciplined, and controlled first and last to enhance, not to corrode, humanity." (*Saturday Review*, May 1, 1965, p. 60.) It becomes increasingly obvious that if technology is to retrieve its image with the public it is going to have to work on it.

9. *Report to the President and the President's Response: Statement by the Chairman an Summation by the Fifteen Panel Charimen of the White House Conference on Natural Beauty*, May 24, 25, 1965, Washington, D.C.

10. Hugo Fisher, "Esthetics and Economics," *Sierra Club Bulletin*, Sept., 1965, pp. 3ff.

11. Department of Interior release, Oct. 5, 1965.

12. The famous cartoonist Herblock, of the *Washington Post*, has struck devastatingly at the dallying of congressional leadership under the influence of the timber lobby. His cartoon depicts the lumbermen buzz-sawing redwoods so furiously they cannot hear the cry of "Save the Redwoods." The *Washington Post* has given powerful editorial support not only to the redwood campaign but to the cause of conservation in its growing impact.

13. That our heritage of widerness is dissipated was evidenced when a search was made for unspoiled and natural streams to include in a "wild rivers" system. Only six immediately qualified candidates for such status could be found. Nine others were slated for study. Under pending legislation they would be catalogued as scenic, if not wild, and offered some guarantee against further abuse.

14. Of indispensable value to conservationists and study groups are the *Reports* as well as the magazine *The Living Wilderness* issued by the Wilderness Society (729 Fifteenth St., Washington, D.C. 20005). For example, the *Executive Director's Report* (III, 1, Feb. 18, 1966) concisely lists and analyzes the current threats to the nation where loss of wilderness is involved, from Minnesota's canoe country to the Northern Cascades, Olympic Park, the Redwoods, Wild Missouri, Grand Canyon, Upper Sell-

way, and others. It also discusses highway beauty, the Hudson River Highlands, Appalachia, the Great Smokies, the Potomac River study, implementation to the Wilderness Act, and the Wild Rivers bill. *Audubon Magazine* (1130 Fifth Avenue, New York, N.Y.) performs a similar service, concisely alerting readers to what is happening to open space and natural beauty as well as to animal species over the country. *Izaak Walton Magazine*'s conservation news has the fresh-water smell of the Midwestern canoe country (its address is 1326 Waukegan Rd., Glenview, Ill.). The *Sierra Club Bulletin* (Mills Tower, San Francisco) redolent of high country campfires and adventure among the Western peaks, has a conservation news and a Washington news section, and *National Parks Magazine* (1300 New Hampshire Ave., N.W., Washington D.C. 20036) is unexcelled by any other park magazine in the world, both in beauty and in helpful information. All of these magazines plus a few others not here mentioned devote themselves on a non-profit basis to a public service for protection of the land and its natural beauty and should find the support of every American of good will.

Chapter Fifteen

Noise, Nerves, and Neurotics

1. By definition, say the technical experts, "noise is unwanted sound." The door you slam is not nearly so upsetting as your neighbors'. From an unsigned article, "When Sound Becomes Noise," *Engineering,* Dec. 11, 1964, p. 742, we extract this table on audibility. An increase of 10 decibels in intensity is roughly comparable to doubling the loudness.

a whisper—3 ft. from the meter	40 db
conversation	60–70 db
machine shop noise	80–100 db
forging hammer	110 db
drop forge	130 db
a jet engine	130 db upwards

"For steady noise accompanying daily routine, 85 db is considered the safe level. . . ."

2. *Christian Science Monitor,* Sept. 13, 1965.

3. A study of industrial noise in the shops of federal penitentiaries between 1953 and 1959 sought to establish its relationship to hearing acuity. They confirmed the hearing conservation standards set up by the Subcommittee on Noise of the American Academy of Ophthalmology and Otolaryngology and of the Air Force. (Charles O. Yaffe and Herbert H. Jones, *Noise and Hearing,* Government Printing Office, 1961, Public Health Service Publication No. 850.)

4. *New York Times,* July 12, 1964.

5. By far the most readable analysis of the noise problem is the final report of the Committee on the Problem of Noise, entitled simply *Noise* (London: Her Majesty's Stationery Office, 1963). Chapter 2, "The General Effects of Noise," makes special note of what airports do to the sleep of their unfortunate neighbors.

6. Former Senator Kenneth B. Keating, speech before the Senate, *Congressional Record*, 88th Cong., 1st sess., July 10, 1963, pp. 11,703–06.

7. The complaints are universal. Even the Council of Europe through its Committee of Experts on Public Health and Dr. L. Molitos of the Grand Duchy of Luxembourg prepared a report called *Noise Abatement* (Strasbourg, 1964), which deals at some length with real or alleged "noise neurosis." They gave short shrift to the report on thirteen attempted suicides in one and the same new block that asserted: "They were all simply emotional short-circuit reactions resulting from unbearable noise stress." There were, after all, epidemics of suicide in other and quieter places, too. (p. 12.)

8. Interesting tables of noise sources can be found in Arnold P. G. Peterson and Ervin E. Gross, *Handbook of Noise Measurement* (West Concord, Mass.: General Radio Co., 1963), pp. 4, 6.

9. Noise abatement, however, has become a prominent item on the reading agenda of industrial engineers, architects, and technologists as evidenced by this sampling of the literature:

J. J. Martiner, "Does Noise in Your Plant Endanger Hearing?" *Plant Engineering*, Mar., 1964, pp. 122–24.

"F. H. A. Joins the Tenants' War Against Noise," *Architectural Forum*, Mar., 1964, pp. 96–97.

E. F. Feldman, "Frequency Analysis of Noise," *Electro-Technology*, June, 1964, pp. 36–42.

J. A. Jensen, "Audible Noise and Vibration Measurement," *Electro-Technology*, Oct., 1964, pp. 101ff.

10. Memphis, Tennessee, is claiming the title of the "quiet please" city by enforcement of the law against horn-blowing and defective mufflers with substantial fines. See *Today's Health*, Feb., 1963, pp. 42–43.

11. "Background Noise Levels in Suburban Communities," *New York Times*, May 16, 1963.

12. Wallace Turner, *New York Times*, Jan. 15, 1963.

13. Joseph Kaselow, New York *Herald Tribune*, Apr. 25, 1964.

14. Albany (N.Y.) *Times-Union*, May 11, 1965. The political authorities on the crowded island of Great Britain are sensitive to the protests. R. J. Stephenson recently

wrote a summary of action called "Noise in the City: Research and Legislation in Britain," *Local Government Throughout the World*, Mar. 9, 1964 (a bimonthly sponsored by the Union of Local Authorities).

15. *National Parks Magazine*, Jan., 1965, p. 21.

16. "The Era of Supersonic Mortality," June 6, 1964, p. 49.

17. The very title of the Federal Aviation Agency's publication is so soothing: "Sounds of the Twentieth Century" (Washington: Government Printing Office, 1961), 16 pp. It deals with airport noise problems but in the spirit of the Pepsi generation.

18. A special investigating subcommittee of the House Committee on Science and Astronautics held hearings on missile and spacecraft noise problems in 1960 (86th Cong., 2d sess., No. 13). A subcommittee of the Interstate and Foreign Commerce Committee conducted hearings from 1959 to 1962 (86th and 87th Cong.), recorded in Committee Print No. 43 and House Report No. 36 (88th Cong., 1st sess., 1963).

19. *New York Times*, July 2, 1964.

20. Report of the World Health Organization, Geneva, July 20, 1964.

21. James C. Turner, *Wall Street Journal*, May 15, 1963, CLXI, 99.

22. *Ibid.*

23. *Newsweek*, Sept. 7. 1964.

24. John Hughes, staff correspondent in Hong Kong; *Christian Science Monitor*, Dec. 8, 1962.

25. Dec. 8, 1962.

Chapter Sixteen

Our Rising Standard of Poisons

1. Rachel Carson, it must be emphasized, is not without champions in high places. When on May 12, 1964, President Lyndon B. Johnson was signing a pesticides bill, he expressed sorrow that

> "one voice which spoke so often and so eloquently for measures like this is still today—the voice of Rachel Carson. She would have been proud of this bill and of this moment. We owe much to her and to those who still work for the cause of a safer and healthier America." *

This bill ended the privilege of a manufacturer of pesticides to market his product while protesting the refusal of the Department of Agriculture ro register it.

2. Emphasis has most generally been on the accumulation of DDT in the fat and muscles of warm-blooded animals; actually, insecticides of every classfication lodge, according to the preference of each, in the vital organs as well. For tables detailing the amounts of various poisons found in birds, see U.S. Department of Interior's Circular 167, *Pesticide-Wildlife Studies: A Review of Fish and Wildlife Service Investigations During 1961 and 1962*, especially charts on pp. 48, 49, 51, 68, 73. Toxicity of various insecticides and herbicides to vertebrates and invertebrates is recorded, as well as residues found in dead specimens from both agricultural field application and from controlled tests.

Also found in this bulletin are dozens of references of experiments in the field and laboratory, ranging from Sprunt's and Cunningham's Bald Eagle Projects to Hunt and Bischoff's *Inimical Effects on Wildlife of Periodic*

---

* *New York Times*, May 13, 1964.

DDD Applications to Clear Lake (California Fish and Game Commission), Frear's *Pesticide Handbook*, a consideration of heptachlor epoxide residues in the organs of living creatures, and many others.

Official defense of pesticide use has shifted sharply from insistence that residues did not exist in any important degree to the insistence on their harmlessness in the quantities now present.

3. A resolution adopted by 2,000 biologists at the final sessions of the 12th International Congress of Entomology (1964) at London predicted that the indiscriminate methods of spraying would cause "drastic reconstructions of local insect faunas," would bring about "the elimination of many species," and result in "vast reservoirs of insect pests."

Yet the commercial sign over the poison counter at our garden store ignorantly proclaims: "The only good bug is a dead bug."

4. A report on agricultural conditions in *Agway Cooperator,* a farmers' supply house organ (Apr., 1966, p. 7), deplores the resistant strains of rootworms that have developed in response to the intensive use of aldrin, dieldrin, heptachlor, and the like, in the great Midwestern corn belt, which has been "committed to chemical control for years." Northeastern dairy farmers are warned to take heed of the plight of the farmer of the Midwest and "avoid these persistent insecticides which may contaminate forage and milk." Something new has indeed been added in advertising circles.

5. *Chemicals in Your Food,* New York, 1960, pp. 66ff. Of interest in this post-Carson age is the pontifical attitude displayed by agricultural agents as recently as 1958 and displayed with succinct perfection in Dr. David B. Hand's explanatory piece "Chemical Additives in Foods" in *Farm Research,* Dec., 1958, a quarterly bulletin of the New York State Agricultural Experiment Station at Geneva and the Cornell University Agricultural Experiment Station at Ithaca.

6. "Some food labels show all the ingredients while others do not because the 1938 Federal Food, Drug, and Cosmetic Act does not require a complete statement of ingredients on foods which are *standardized*." Sec. 401 states that "in prescribing a definition and standard of identity

for any food or class of food in which optional ingredients are permitted, the Secretary shall, for the purpose of promoting honesty and fair dealing in the interest of consumers, designate the optional ingredients which shall be named on the label." Regardless of whether a standard of identity has been established for a food, the Act requires that if it contains any artificial flavoring, artificial coloring, or chemical preservative, it must bear labeling stating that fact, "except that colors used in butter, cheese, and ice cream do not have to be declared." Until the Food Additives Amendment of 1958, says the statement, "Little interest was expressed by consumers in having all optional ingredients listed" on the labels. More recently there has been a public clamor to have labels bear lists of all ingredients. At the same time, industry has set up a clamor for more and a bigger variety of additives. In other words the most common foods, which include bread, butter, and ice cream, may contain a standardized list of additives of all sorts that do not need to be mentioned on the label; only when some adventuresome manufacturer improvises with some new pet chemicals must he declare them on the label. Continues the statement, "From time to time, as the older standards are reviewed, FDA will take into consideration the desire of consumers to have ingredients declared." In other words, we get what we deserve and demand. So long as we accept the "secret ingredients" of bread and ice cream, etc., without listing, we shall get them. (*Statement Concerning Declaration of Ingredients on Labels for Standardized Foods,* Department of Health, Education, and Welfare, FDA, Aug. 18, 1965.)

A lengthy article in *Chemical Engineering News* (Oct. 10, 1966) pp. 100ff., deals with "intentional additives" and gives industry's side of the story. Arthur D. Little, Inc., which estimated that 661 million pounds of additives were used in 1965, predicts 852 million pounds will be used in 1970 and 1.03 billion pounds in 1975, not including the ordinary additives of sugar, salt, starch, pepper, cinnamon, citric acid, monosodium glutamate, mono- and diglycerides, and about 575 other such materials exempt from federal control. The additives business has leaped from \$172 million at the manufacturers' level in 1955 to \$285 million in 1965. "By 1970 these sales are expected to reach about \$400 million and by 1975 are likely to exceed \$500 million" and many chemical companies are working diligently to develop new chemicals to add to new foods. Years ago chemical companies merely filled orders for chemical additives; today they are eagerly pursuing the additive business as an unlimited bonanza.

7. Fish and Wildlife Service. Department of Interior news release. Sept. 7, 1965. On the subject of toxicity Massachusetts Audubon Society published a special report, *Pesticide Applications and the Public Welfare*, by William H. Drury, Jr. (reprint from the Sept.—Oct., 1961, magazine), with valuable charts comparing the various toxicities of most-used pesticides Some of the charts ranged in order of lethal qualities for both fish and birds. Also given were effects of normal field use of pesticides on survival ratio of different species of birds, along with plentiful references of experiments.

8. For effect of pesticide spraying on the salmon of the Miramichi River in New Brunswick, see Ira N. Gabrielson's report in *Pest Control and Wildlife Relationships: A Symposium* Wildlife Management Institute ("Wildlife—Pesticides Research Needs." pp 19–25, especially p. 23). This is a publication of the National Academy of Sciences —National Research Council, Washington, D.C., 1961.

9. Gleason, Gosselin, and Hodge *Clinical Toxicity of Commercial Products* (Baltimore: Williams and Wilkins, 1963), 2d ed., lists Sevin with a toxicity rating of 4, the same rating as given DDT *Science* (Apr. 12, 1963, No. 140: pp. 170–71) explains discovery of earlier unsuspected residues as due to more sensitive methods of chemical analysis Effects of Sevin on wildlife are apparently, as yet, in the balance. An agricultural agent friend of ours who originally was a strong advocate of Sevin has recently reversed his opinion in an equally strong manner.

10. *Pesticides, Their Use and Effect* Proceedings of a symposium sponsored by the New York State Joint Legislative Committee on Natural Resources Albany N.Y., Sept. 23, 1963, Senator R. Watson Pomeroy. Chairman. This symposium by no means maintains that we can dispense with our poisoning program, but voices pleading for restraint are heard.

11. U.S. Department of Interior press release, Sept. 7, 1965.

12. *Pesticides and the Living Landscape* (Madison: University of Wisconsin Press, 1964), pp. 162ff.

13. *Rural New Yorker,* Mar. 1, 1958, p. 9.

14. Dr. Theron G. Randolph in his incisive study supported by clinical notes entitled *Human Ecology and Susceptibility to the Chemical Environment* (Springfield, Ill.: Charles Thomas, 1962), points out that toxicity studies on animals are quite remote from the medical problem. The medical problem is not concerned with the middle of the distribution curve, he says, but with the far end. In other words man is more vulnerable than his animal experiments indicate.

15. One wonders if he might not gain insight by paying special heed to the rabbits who were given DDT by stomach tube when they refused to eat it on food. The two females gave birth to two live rabbits each and killed them on day of birth to escape the punishment. (Fish and Wildlife Service, *Pesticide-Wildlife Studies,* Circular 167 [Washington, D.C.: Government Printing Office, 1963] p. 48.)

16. For detailed charts of tolerances of all major and many minor pesticides as established under the Food Additives Amendment to the Federal Food, Drug, and Cosmetic Act, complete through Dec. 31, 1965, see *N.A.C. News and Pesticide Review* of the National Agricultural Chemicals Association (1155 Fifteenth St., N.W., Washington, D.C.), dated Feb., 1966. The variation in a poison's permissible residue from food to food leads to the suspicion that the tolerance is based not so much on a scientific evaluation of how much the human body can absorb without undue effects as it is on a realistic bow to expediency: how little can the producer promise while still sustaining his production? For instance, why was but 0.1 ppm. (parts per million) of aldrin permitted on cherries, while 0.25 ppm. of the same poison was permitted on apricots? (Aldrin has since been largely discredited anyway.) If the poison tolerances are person-oriented, as claimed, why is Carbaryl, for example, twice as poisonous on beets (tolerance, 5 ppm.) as on apples (tolerance, 10 ppm.)?

17. Robert L. Rudd, *Pesticides and the Living Landscape* (Madison: University of Wisconsin Press, 1964), p. 170.

18. P. A. Clifford, "Pesticide Residues in Fluid Milk Market," *Public Health Report,* LXXII, No. 8, pp. 729ff.

19. See the Senate Governmental Operations Subcommittee's Hearings, July, 1963.

20. *Christian Science Monitor,* May 18, 1964.

21. Senator Abraham A. Ribicoff, "Pesticides and Public Policy," *Sierra Club Bulletin,* Apr., 1965, pp. 12ff.

22. Some support for Dr. Bicknell's worry is found in preliminary report of a study made by four specialists of the University of Miami School of Medicine and Dade County agencies. They discovered traces of pesticides in unborn babies in excess of those in children in the age group from infancy to five years and resembling the burden of the adult population. There is transmission of pesticides from mother to unborn child. (*New York Times,* Jan. 30, 1966, p. 72, and *Industrial Medicine and Surgery.*)

23. Ira N. Gabrielson, *loc. cit.,* describes a mosquito-control project in Florida where water-level manipulation obviated the need of spraying for salt-marsh mosquitoes (p. 24). In the same publication Tom Gill of the Charles Lathrop Pack Forestry Foundation ("Forest Pest Control") instances the protective value of mixed versus pure timber stands in forest management, a new emphasis on planting techniques that can eliminate much wholesale spraying of commercial timber lands (pp. 8–13).

Chapter Seventeen

The Death of Dignity

1. See the report of Population and Economic Planning, *World Population and Resources,* London, relating population pressure to personal abasement (fn. 6 in Chapter IV).

The literature on the population explosion is replete with dark forebodings in the way it hastens the Orwellian year of 1984. But there is little attempt to give these asserted consequences some measure of specificity. It is comparable to the widespread and official worry that population pressures abroad will affect our foreign policy and undermine its effectiveness. Yet save for the obvious impact of increased numbers of people on the terms of foreign aid there is almost no careful appraisal. There are black hints about the instability that accompanies population pressure, but except for references to Hitler's drive for *Lebensraum* the documentation is lacking, and even the speculation has little substantive support. It is a proposition, however, that seems self-evident even as the observation that dignity is lost in a sea of elbows seems obvious.

2. Dec. 8, 1956, p. 3.

3. The final insult to man's dignity may yet come from the "intelligent" machine. Dr. Norbert Wiener observes, for instance, that the checker-playing machine can defeat the man who programed it.

"Again and again," he states in the second edition of his book *Cybernetics* (Cambridge: MIT Press, 1961),

"I have heard the statement that learning machines cannot subject us to any new dangers, because we can turn them off when we feel like it.

But can we? To turn a machine off effectively, we must be in possession of information as to whether the danger point has come. The mere fact that we have made the machine does not guarantee that we shall have the proper information to do this." *

4. *Harper's Magazine,* January, 1964, pp. 63ff, adapted from *An African Student in China,* Emmanuel John Hevi (New York: Praeger, 1963).

5. The political philosopher Henry B. Mayo notes with what strain democracy contends with rapid technological change. Population pressures, he suggests, are of the same order and effect. (*An Introduction to Democratic Theory* [New York: Oxford University Press, 1960], p. 220.)

6. Actually, where population presses there is little room for the exercise of the ethics of excellence as Hooker described it and a commensurate, and perhaps even expanding, insistence on a minimal level of moral virtue—the necessary duties for social survival. See Robert K. Faulkner, "Reason and Revelation in Hooker's Ethics," *American Political Science Review,* Sept., 1965, pp. 680ff.

7. Marguerite Angelo Smelzer, "Uncontrollable 'Control'," reprinted from *Nature Magazine,* Jan., 1959, for Defenders of Furbearers, Washington, D.C.

8. AP release, Washington, Mar. 16, 1966, as reported in the Albany (N.Y.) *Times-Union* (not further pursued). Dr. Proctor, chief of the Department of Behavioral and Neurological Sciences at the Edsel B. Ford Institute, made these pedictions at a symposium on the space age before the American Astronautical Society.

9. Paul Sears, *Science Digest,* Aug., 1960, pp. 14–20.

William H. Draper, Jr., who has served three American Presidents in the study of military and population problems, overseas, has some thought-provoking observations to make on the effect of family size on undesirable citizenry. Selective Service Boards show that 47 per cent of army rejects for low mentality come from families with six or more children, even though these families contain only 11 per cent of all children in the nation. Quoting Sheldon and Eleanor Glueck's class study "Unravelling Juvenile Delinquency," he notes that even in families closely matched in income, ethnic background, intelligence, and community living conditions, "the average number of children in the families of the delinquents [is] 6.8 and in those

---

* *Christian Science Monitor,* May 15, 1961.

of the non-delinquents, 5.9." Competition, crowding, emotional strain, tensions, friction, and loss of privacy were cited as causes of large family delinquencies. (*National Parks Magazine,* Apr., 1966, pp. 10ff.)

Chapter Eighteen

Growth, Greed, and Gung Ho

1. Put the other way around, should the rest of the world attempt to match American consumptive standards the effort would call for a *hundredfold* increase in the production of basic raw materials.

2. To aid us on our way and to blueprint the pitfalls and possibilities, the 88th Congress had authorized the formation of the National Commission on Technology, Automation and Economic Progress. Its 115-page report, called *Technology and the American Economy* (Washington: Government Printing Office, 1966), showed how to shore up landslides and washouts on the path of progress. (It also marked the termination of the agency's life.)

3. The uneven participation in this advance, the by-passed pockets of what has been officially classified as "hardship," has invited governmental correction. The Economic Development Administration in the Commerce Department has been created with a mission of swishing the mop of progress in neglected corners.

4. Arnold B. Barach, *U.S.A. and Its Economic Future* (New York: Macmillan, 1964).

5. The emphasis of the members of the economic Joint Committee is unwavering on the side of economic growth. See its latest report, *Improved Statistics for Economic Growth, Comments by Government Agencies on Views Submitted to Subcommittee on Economic Statistics* (Joint Committee print, 89th Cong., 2d sess.).

6. Don Robinson in *Phi Delta Kappan*.

7. See the emphasis by the contributors to "Recent Thinking on Economic Growth and Fluctuations," *Annals of the American Academy of Political & Social Science*, Mar., 1966, pp. 8–68.

8. Albany (N.Y.) *Times-Union,* Oct. 14, 1965.

9. As quoted by James Reston, *ibid.*

10. There is a growing literature on the corporate role and the relationship of the corporation to government and public purposes. In this respect see A. Shonfield, *Modern Capitalism, the Changing Balance of Public and Private Power,* Royal Institute (Oxford: Oxford University Press, 1965).

11. The Great Power confrontation inspired a professional seminar at the Center of International Studies at Princeton on this matter of economic growth patterns. The findings are presented in a paperback volume, Klaus Knorr and William J. Baumol, eds., *What Price Economic Growth?* (Englewood Cliffs, N.J.: Prentice-Hall, 1961).

12. Quoted by Dr. E. H. Smith in *Pesticides, Their Use and Effect: Proceedings of a Symposium,* New York State Joint Legislative Committee on Natural Resources, Sept. 23, 1963. Dr. Smith was speaking specifically of the proportionate amount of time spent producing food as contrasted to all other needs of mankind.

13. *U.S. News & World Report,* Nov. 15, 1965, p. 93.

14. Paul B. Sears, "Ecology—a Subversive Subject," *Bioscience,* July, 1964, p. 13.

15. *Top Soil and Civilization* (University of Oklahoma Press, 1955).

16. *Soil: The Yearbook of Agriculture,* 1957, U.S. Dept. of Agriculture (WAshington, D.C.: Government Printing Office), p. 26.

Chapter Nineteen

To the Rescue: The Seas!

1. See Robert Rienow, "The Troubled Seas," *Rotarian Magazine*, Apr., 1962, where the author called attention to the fact that the jurisdictional problems of the sea were a direct outcome of the shift in the emphasis on use to which the sea is subjected. It is now a potential source of food as well as an artery of commerce. Rapidly it is assuming a major disposal function even for spent missiles.

2. Much serious research in oceanography centers on man's adjustment. See, for instance, G. F. Bond, "Effects of New and Artificial Environment on Human Physiology," *Archives of Environmental Health*, Jan., 1966, pp. 85–90.

The symposium, Man's Extension Into the Sea, held in Washington, Jan. 11–12, 1966, is reported in *Marine Engineering Log*, Mar., 1966, pp. 51–53.

"Trends in Marine Technology" by O. H. Oakley appears in *Astronautics and Aeronautics*, Apr., 1966, pp. 50–61.

3. Remarks of Secretary of the Interior Stewart L. Udall before the World Food Congress, Washington, D.C., June 6, 1963, as released to the afternoon newspapers.

4. A recent issue of *Resources* (May, 1966) highlights the destructibility of the resources of the sea unless we settle our jurisdictional problems (published by Resources for the Future), pp. 22.

A worthwhile volume is S. Oda, *International Control of Sea Resources* (Dobbs Ferry, N.Y.: Oceana, 1963).

5. Robert C. Cowen, "Food for Hungry Peoples," *Christian Science Monitor*, Sept. 21, 1961.

6. The military aspects of the dispute over the seas is reported in *Current*, July, 1966, pp. 22ff., quoting extensively from Frank B. Case, "The Free Sea," *Military Re-*

view, U.S. Army Command and General Staff College, Ft. Leavenworth, Mar., 1966, pp. 22ff.

7. There is little doubt but that the seas will produce new deposits of minerals. The black nodules strewn on the sea floor—cobalt, nickel, copper—invite a technological breakthrough in the sweeping department. As yet the sea is inhospitable to its exploiters. See such serious studies as "Aluminant May Open Wealth of Sea," *Steel,* Sept. 7, 1964, p. 28; "Ocean Mining Looks Practical," *Chemical and Engineering News,* Apr. 15, 1963, pp. 41–42; J. Keene, "Under-sea Mining: New Research Aimed at Tapping Nature's Biggest Resource," *Engineering & Mining Journal,* June, 1964, pp. 114–17.

8. *New York Times,* Feb. 3, 1964.

9. *Hearings: Water Pollution Control and Abatement,* before a Subcommittee of the Committee on Government Operations, House of Representatives, 88th Cong., 2d sess., Feb. 21, 1964 (Washington, D.C., 1965), Part 7, p. 3718.

10. Address by Robert M. Paul, special assistant to Assistant Secretary of the Interior for Fish and Wildlife before the Audubon Society, Nov. 10, 1962, Department of Interior release; and U.S. Department of the Interior, *Pesticide-Wildlife Studies: A Review of Fish and Wildlife Service Investigations During 1961 and 1962,* Circular 167, Washington, D.C., June, 1963.

Chapter Twenty

To the Rescue—The Sciences!

1. This adulation is more a product of ignorance than scientific egocentrism. It afflicts the scientific outlanders and in that sense can be regarded as a consequence of the failure of communication between the cultures—the social and the scientific. The classic expression of scientific isolation and distortion is that of C. P. Snow, whose celebrated lecture "The Two Cultures" now has been published as *The Two Cultures and a Second Look* (Cambridge: University Press, 1965). Professor Snow not only sees danger in the alienation of the scientific from the traditional culture. It is the animosity in the cultural divide that disturbs him. What we note here is a new paganistic idolatry.

2. A symposium "devoted to the role of agricultural science and technology in the acceleration of economic progress in newly developing nations" was sponsored by the American Association for the Advancement of Science and published under the editorship of Albert H. Moseman under the title *Agricultural Science for the Developing Nations* in Washington, D.C. in 1964. The opening essay by Ervin J. Long weighs in brilliant fashion the obstacles to progress imposed by social institutions.

3. Copyrighted interview, *U.S. News & World Report*, Feb. 22, 1960.

4. *Science Digest*, Aug., 1960.

5. "Billions for Science: Is It Worth the Price?" *U.S. News & World Report*, Dec. 6, 1965, p. 79.

6. *Pest Control and Wildlife Relationships: Part III: Research Needs: A Report by the Subcommittee on Pest Control and Wildlife Relationships, Division of Biology and Agriculture, National Academy of Sciences—National Research Council.* Publication 920-C: National Academy

of Sciences—National Research Council, Washington, D.C., 1963.

7. "How Pure Is Your City Water?" *U.S. News & World Report*, Feb. 29, 1960, p. 53.

8. Before the League of Women Voters in Atlanta, July 26, 1965, *Izaak Walton Magazine*, Nov., 1965, pp. 14–15.

9. *Journal of the Canadian Medical Association*, July 20, 1963.

10. Albany (N.Y.) *Times-Union*, July 10, 1963.

11. On an intellectual level an exchange is growing over the impact of science on values and social goals. Alvin M. Weinberg, Director of Oak Ridge National Laboratory, has a fascinating piece called "Science, Choice and Human Values," in *Bulletin of Atomic Scientists*, Apr., 1966, pp. 8–13. J. Bronowski took his lead in the dialogue on the relationship of science to the humanities in a volume called *Science and Human Values*, 2d ed. (New York: Harper & Row, 1965).

12. R. H. Wright, "Chemical Control of Chosen Insects," *New Scientists*, Dec. 5, 1963.

13. Representative Henry S. Reuss of Wisconsin launched an investigation of the lack of direction in our national research program. See two articles in *Bulletin of Atomic Scientists*, May, 1966: Gerard Pill, "Federal Funds and Science Education," pp. 10–15 (the writer is also author of *Science in the Cause of Man*, New York, 1961); and Lee A. DuBridge, "The Government Role in Science Education," pp. 16–20. Dr. DuBridge is President of the California Institute of Technology.

14. National Academy of Sciences, *op. cit.*, p. 6.

15. See Howard James, "Flood Ally: Apathy Plus . . . ," *Christian Science Monitor*, Apr., 23, 1965.

16. Medical science has carried us so far in the cannibalization of organs from the newly dead that it has come face to face with the ethics of perpetuating a human vegetable. Dr. George Pickering, Regius Professor of Medicine at Oxford, points out that the transplanting of the brain because of its intricate connections is quite unlikely. "Medicine," he says, "strives toward the indefinite extension of life, perhaps in the end with somebody else's arteries, but not with somebody else's brain. Should medi-

cine succeed in such transplantations, 'those with senile brains and senile behavior will form an ever increasing fraction of the inhabitants of the earth. . . . I find this a terrifying prospect.' " From an address to the Columbia University College of Physicians and Surgeons, New York, May 26, 1966, entitled "Degenerative Diseases: Past, Present and Future," reproduced in *Current*, July, 1966, p. 59.

Chapter Twenty-One

Prolonging Our Moment in the Sun

1. When Philip M. Hauser figures out that "one hundred persons multiplying at 1 per cent per year, not over the period of 200,000 to 1 million years of man's occupancy of this globe, but merely for the 5,000 years of human history, would have produced a contemporary population of 2.7 billion persons per square foot of land surface of the earth!" he admits such "dramatic" and "propagandistic" arithmetic is valued for only one reason. It is "a conclusive way of demonstrating that a 1 per cent per year increase in world population could not have taken place for very long in the past; nor can it continue for very long into the future." (*Population Perspectives*, Rutgers, 1960, p. 5)

But it demonstrates another hard fact. The pretense of feeding the multiplying billions is shown up as a self-deception beyond the realm of comment. It is a trap. On May 28, 1963, Dr. Sture C. Linner, former head of United Nations operations in the Congo, told a Stockholm audience that more people are starving to death today than at any time in world history. The statement is true, he said, "whether we think in relative or absolute figures," and no one has since come forth to refute him. In that same year, the Entomological Society of America was told in conference by Dr. Edward A. Steinhaus of the University of California that "the use of processed insects as food has assumed a new importance because of the growing human population. . . . Insects are one of the best remaining untapped sources of animal protein." With the population increasing prodigiously in the years since these statements were made, we have as yet found no customers for mass insect-feeding.

2. "Why I Am Not Going to the Moon," *Saturday Review*, Nov. 20, 1965.

3. That a crisis is upon us is getting belated congressional recognition, as evidenced by the hearings on the population crisis before the Senate Committee on Government Operations, Subcommittee on Foreign Aid Expenditures, 89th Cong., 1st sess, 1965.

4. (Boston: Houghton Mifflin, 1940.)

5. *Ibid.*, p. 474.

6. As the Aswan High Dam rises in Egypt the hungry *fellahs*, eagerly anticipating new harvests of sugar cane and beans, have added 800,000 new babies a year to the nation's intolerable burden, promising now that Egypt's 30-million-plus will double in less than fifteen years. A report by Patrick Seale, Middle East correspondent for the London *Observer*, and Irene Beeson, Cairo correspondent, in an article entitled "Babies Along the Nile" in *The New Republic*, May 7, 1966, pp. 10ff., observes that while it took Nasser fourteen years of power to have the terrible urgency of population control borne in upon him, now that he has recognized it, he has acted drastically. In February of 1966 he launched, within the jurisdiction of the Combined Service Units (social center clinics), a massive nationwide network of birth-control centers—2,000 of them, in fact. Intrauterine loops are provided and pills sold at about twenty cents for a month's supply—all government issue, of course. The Egyptian government's substantial budget for this purpose has been bolstered by an initial $440,000 from the Ford Foundation with more to follow. Loops are "strictly home manufacture" with an assist from the Population Council of New York, which controls the patent. Can mass propaganda overcome age-old social patterns and save Egypt?

7. *U.S. News & World Report,* Nov. 22, 1965.

8. Sylvia Porter, syndicated column of Sept. 9, 1965.

9. There is a sensitivity born of race and privilege that bristles at the study of one nation's procreation by another. "What are you trying to do, foster national suicide?" complain the underprivileged, especially in Latin America. That is why American *example* is so important and why, domestically, personal riches ought not to be used to justify ten or a dozen kids. For this same reason the United Nations may be in the most strategic position to work on the population issue. It has shown some inter-

est but mostly in feeding the world's population. See, however, *Provisional Report on World Population Prospects As Assessed in 1963,* Department of Economic and Social Affairs, the United Nations, 1964.

10. "Too Many People in the World?" A copyrighted interview with *U.S. News & World Report,* July 13, 1956.

11. Emile Capuya, *Saturday Review,* Dec. 19, 1964, p. 33. We are now told that by May, 1966, Red China was also curtailing food for children over three in number.

12. *The Meaning of the Twentieth Century* (New York: Harper & Row, 1964).

13. *U.S. News & World Report,* June 8, 1964.

In connection with pills to regularize the fertility cycle, Dr. Robert L. Friedlander, assistant professor of obstetrics and gynecology at Albany, New York, Medical Center, stated on October 14, 1966, that intensive research is now under way seeking a method of "entrainment," which means "the fairly precise effecting of ovulation at a determined time of the women's monthly cycle." Such control of ovulation—or even the perfection of a reliable method for determining the precise time of ovulation, might be the ideal method of contraception "since it would appear to permit effective use of the rhythm system." Some compounds for such entrainment are now in study, but are not yet ready for field trials in humans.

14. The graduate research of Neil Furst and Inez Gifford at the State University of New York at Albany dates the turning point in American policy in December, 1962, when, almost unreported, the United Nations voted a resolution affirming awareness of the world's population problems and the American delegate Richard Gardner, although abstaining for technical reasons, announced: "While we will not advocate any specific policy regarding population growth to another country, we can help other countries, upon request, to find potential sources of information and assistance on ways and means of dealing with population problems." (*Department of State Bulletin,* Jan. 7, 1963, p. 18.)

15. "A scientific, educational organization, founded in 1929 by a group of biologists, sociologists and economists. To make the facts of population change readily and usefully available to all, it gathers, coordinates, interprets

and distributes demographic data," reads the Bureau's brochure. Non-profit and tax-deductible, the Bureau offers the *Population Bulletin,* published eight times a year, each issue dealing with a country or region; "Population Profiles," brief supplementary releases at a minimum cost; and an information service answering demographic queries from citizens, students, teachers, groups, press, and industry. List of brochures is available by writing the Population Reference Bureau, 1755 Massachusetts Ave., N.W., Washington, D.C. 20036. At the forefront of the movement to mobilize Americans to the need for countermeasures to a booming population is the Hugh Moore Fund, 51 East 42nd St., New York, N.Y. They invite correspondence and solicit action.

16. Perhaps a cold-blooded computation of what it costs a couple to raise one child and put him through college might dampen the big-family ardor. James Moran, who is currently engaged in writing a book for single persons, estimates the cost per child at $88,000 (reports Jerome Beatty in his *Saturday Review* column), an eye-bulging figure indeed.

17. There will soon be dozens of oral contraceptives of varying formulae and physiological approach, all with their professional partisans. The contention that young people should not be encouraged in immorality by easy means of evasion of consequences certainly has validity. On the other hand how can any society that not only exuberantly condones sex experimentation but immerses young people in an atmosphere of sex and sex worship from birth decently refuse its victims contraceptives? Such an attitude is not only appallingly hypocritical but socially reckless. A most illuminating article on "the pill" as far as laymen are concerned is Lawrence Lader's thorough and meticulous discussion, "Three Men Who Made a Revolution," in the *New York Times Magazine,* Apr. 10, 1966, pp. 8ff. Devout Catholic Dr. John Rock, one of the "three fathers of the birth control pill," ridicules the charge that the pill has had an influence on morality. "After all, any high school kid knows about Saranwrap from the kitchen," he says. He does not believe morality can be enforced by prohibitions or legislation. "It must come from within."

18. Marion Clawson of Resources for the Future, Inc.,

points out that economic growth is intimately related to availability of natural resources and that the issue of international development is connected to the natural resource base. See Marion Clawson, ed., *Natural Resources and International Development* (Baltimore: Johns Hopkins Press, 1964).

About the Authors

Robert Rienow, Ph.D., Litt.D., is professor of Political Science at the Graduate School of Public Affairs, State University of New York at Albany. He is a past president of the New York State Political Science Association and consultant to the New York State Board of Regents. Through long association with conservation movements, he has brought an ecological orientation to his writing and teaching in the fields of government and public affairs. He has served Nature Conservancy for many years, both as chairman of its Eastern New York Chapter and as a member of its national Board of Governors. Currently he is on its Committee on Ecology, and he is also a member of the National Board of Trustees of Defenders of Wildlife.

Leona Train Rienow, his wife, has collaborated with him on several books and is an author in her own right. The Rienows live in a remodeled 200 year old colonial farmhouse near Selkirk, N.Y., which they bought in 1941. When they took over the 138-acre farm it had been exploited almost beyond repair. Since then the Rienows' conscientious reclamation program has restored the land and renewed its wildlife so that the farm is today an ecological showplace.

Index

Index